T3-BIF-458

Prepared Tests for

Elementary Algebra

with Diagnostic Test

Virginia Hamilton
Shawnee State University

James Braswell
Educational Testing Service

SAUNDERS COLLEGE PUBLISHING
Philadelphia Fort Worth Chicago
San Francisco Montreal Toronto
London Sydney Tokyo

Printed in the United States of America.

Mugridge: Prepared Tests for ELEMENTARY ALGEBRA

ISBN # 0-03-032714-8

012 095 987654321

PREFACE

PREPARED TESTS AND DIAGNOSTIC TEST has been prepared to accompany Mugridge's ELEMENTARY ALGEBRA. This supplement contains six tests (Forms A - F) for each chapter in the text; three of the tests are multiple choice format, and three are open-ended in format. There are also Midterm Examinations (Forms A and B) and six Final Examinations (Forms A - F). The number of tests for each chapter will allow you to give make-up exams easily, or to use each test at variable times. This flexibility is particularly useful in a lab setting in which re-tests are given frequently and you want to "protect the answers." You may also want to use several forms of the test at once to discourage copying.

The tests are designed so that they can be torn out of the book, photocopied, and given directly to the student. We have provided space for the student's name, score, and the answers that are to be filled in.

The answers to the tests are provided at the end of each chapter. They are in a column format so you can easily compare them to the individual test forms for faster grading.

Each test is based on the exercises appearing in Mugridge's ELEMENTARY ALGEBRA. If you would like to add your own questions (for example, to place greater emphasis on one of the topics), the following suggestions may help:

1. Photocopy questions from previous, unused chapter test items from ELEMENTARY ALGEBRA. Then cut and paste them at the end of a test before you begin the duplication.

2. Use items from the accompanying Test Bank or Computerized Test Bank.

This book also contains a Diagnostic Test to pinpoint strengths and weaknesses; it can facilitate placement of the student in the appropriate course. The Diagnostic Test, with suggestions for its use, is in the back of this text.

TABLE OF CONTENTS

Name ______________________ Chapter 1 Form A Score ______

1. Write $\frac{18}{42}$ in lowest terms. 1. ______

2. Find the product of $8 \cdot \frac{12}{35} \cdot \frac{56}{64}$ and reduce to lowest terms. 2. ______

3. Write as a single fraction in lowest terms 3. ______

$$\left(\frac{15}{16} \cdot \frac{8}{9}\right) \div \frac{25}{36}$$

4. Write as a single fraction in lowest terms 4. ______

$$\frac{5}{8} + \frac{7}{8} - \frac{2}{8} =$$

5. Johny ate $\frac{1}{5}$ of a cherry pie and Joseph ate $\frac{1}{4}$ of the same pie. How much of the cherry pie was left? 5. ______

6. Simplify the expression: $18 - 2^2 \cdot 3 + 12 \div 3$ 6. ______

7. Write the expression in words: $3x - 1$ 7. ______

8. Simplify: $\frac{41 - 7 \cdot 2}{2^3 \cdot 3}$ 8. ____________

9. Draw a number line, then graph the numbers from the set $\{-4, 0.75, -2\frac{1}{2}, 5\}$ 9. ____________

10. If 89 means 89 miles north, what does -89 mean? 10. ____________

11. Find the absolute value of -2.45. 11. ____________

12. Determine which number is larger: 12. ____________

$-\frac{5}{6}$ or $-\frac{4}{5}$

13. Simplify the expression: $5 + 4[-2 + (-7)]$ 13. ____________

14. Find the additive inverse of -0.8 14. ____________

15. Simplify: $14 - [11 - (7 - 12)]$ 15. ____________

16. The temperature at 10 a.m. was $-2°$ and by 5 o'clock it had dropped 6 degrees. What is the temperature at 5 o'clock?

16. ____________

17. Simplify: $\left(\frac{2}{3}\right)\left(-\frac{9}{14}\right) \div \frac{21}{14}$

17. ____________

18. Joey bought hamburgers for the boys on the little league team. If each hamburger cost 69¢ and he bought 22 hamburgers, how much did the sandwiches cost?

18. ____________

19. Evaluate $x^2 - (2 - y) - 8$ if $x = -3$ and $y = -4$.

19. ____________

20. Write the word phrase as an algebraic expression "four less than the square of a number"

20. ____________

21. Check for solutions of the equation
$2 + |x| = 3x$ from the set $\{-1, 0, 1, 2\}$

21. ____________

22. Write as an equation using x as a variable and check for solutions from the set $\{0, 1, 2, 3, 4\}$: "the square of a number is the difference of four times the number and three."

22. ____________

23. Simplify: $-(1 - x) + 6(-0.2)$

23. ____________

24. State the property of real numbers illustrated by: $(6 + 0) + 3x = 6 + 3x$

24. ____________

25. Use the associative property of multiplication to complete the following statement correctly:

25. ____________

$$\left(\frac{1}{4} \cdot 4\right)w = \_\_\_\_\_\_\_\_\_\_.$$

Name ______________________ Chapter 1 Form B Score ________

1. Write $\frac{35}{56}$ in lowest terms. 1. ________

2. Find the product of $6 \cdot \frac{15}{16} \cdot \frac{56}{72}$ and reduce to lowest terms. 2. ________

3. Write as a single fraction in lowest terms 3. ________

$$\left(\frac{8}{9} \cdot \frac{14}{24}\right) \div \frac{28}{27}$$

4. Write as a single fraction in lowest terms 4. ________

$$\frac{4}{9} - \frac{2}{9} + \frac{5}{9} =$$

5. Joey ate $\frac{1}{5}$ of a cherry pie and Kathy ate $\frac{1}{6}$ of the same pie. How much of the cherry pie was left? 5. ________

6. Simplify the expression: $14 + 3^2(-1) + 6 \div 2$ 6. ________

7. Write the expression in words: $5x + 2$ 7. ________

8. Simplify: $\dfrac{29 - 3 \cdot 7}{3^2 \cdot 2}$

8. ____________

9. Draw a number line, then graph the numbers from the set $\{-3, -1\frac{1}{4}, 0.5, 2\}$

9. ____________

10. If -63 means 63 miles south, what does 63 mean?

10. ____________

11. Find the absolute value of 3.8 .

11. ____________

12. Determine which number is larger:

$\dfrac{9}{7}$ or $\dfrac{10}{8}$

12. ____________

13. Simplify the expression: $8 + 3[-5 + 9]$

13. ____________

14. Find the additive inverse of -2.5

14. ____________

15. Simplify: $18 - [13 - (9 - 4)]$

15. ____________

16. The temperature at 2 a.m. was $-5°$ and by noon it had raised 12 degrees. What is the temperature at noon?

16. ______________

17. Simplify: $\left(-\frac{3}{8}\right)\left(-\frac{20}{21}\right) \div \frac{14}{35}$

17. ______________

18. Tom bought 15 bottles of pop at 55 ¢ a bottle. How much change did Tom get from a ten dollar bill?

18. ______________

19. Evaluate $x^2 - (3 - y) + 2$ if $x = -4$ and $y = -2$.

19. ______________

20. Write the word phrase as an algebraic expression "three more than the square of a number".

20. ______________

21. Check for solutions of the equation
$x(x-3) = 4$ from the set $\{-1, 0, 1, 2\}$

21. ______________

22. Write as an equation using x as a variable and check for solutions from the set $\{0, 1, 2, 3, 4\}$: "the sum of a number and thirteen is sixteen".

22. ______________

23. Simplify: $-0.5(10w) - 3w$

23. ____________

24. State the property of real numbers illustrated by: $\frac{2}{5}\left(\frac{5}{2}\right) = 1$

24. ____________

25. Use the additive identity property to complete the following statement correctly: $(2w - x) + 0 =$ ______

25. ____________

Name ______________________ Chapter 1 Form C Score ______

1. Write $\frac{48}{90}$ in lowest terms.

1. ______

2. Find the product of $12 \cdot \frac{9}{28} \cdot \frac{42}{48}$ and reduce to lowest terms.

2. ______

3. Write as a single fraction in lowest terms

$$\left(\frac{9}{15} \cdot \frac{25}{36}\right) \div \frac{4}{5}$$

3. ______

4. Write as a single fraction in lowest terms

$$\frac{5}{12} + \frac{11}{12} - \frac{7}{12}$$

4. ______

5. Joella ate $\frac{1}{7}$ of a cake and Suzi ate $\frac{1}{5}$ of the same cake. How much of the cake was left?

5. ______

6. Simplify the expression: $20 - 2^3(-1) - 18 \div 3$

6. ______

7. Write the expression in words: $2x - 7$

7. ______

8. Simplify: $\frac{48 - 6 \cdot 2}{3^3 \cdot 2}$ 8. ______

9. Draw a number line, then graph the numbers from the set $\{-1, 2.5, -3\frac{1}{2}, 6\}$ 9. ______

10. If 59 means 59 miles east, what does -59 mean? 10. ______

11. Find the absolute value of -0.354 11. ______

12. Determine which number is larger: 12. ______

$\frac{9}{11}$ or $\frac{10}{13}$

13. Simplify the expression: $-4 + 5[6 - (-2)]$ 13. ______

14. Find the additive inverse of 0.69 14. ______

15. Simplify: $24 - [18 - (4 - 7)]$ 15. ______

16. The temperature at 4 p.m. was $-18°$ and by midnight it had dropped 25 degrees. What is the temperature at midnight?

16. ____________

17. Simplify: $\left(-\frac{4}{9}\right)\left(\frac{15}{26}\right) \div \frac{25}{26}$

17. ____________

18. There are 12 cans of soda in a case. Each case costs $2.24. How much would it cost to buy 108 cans?

18. ____________

19. Evaluate $y^2 - (x - 4) - 3$ if $x = -5$ and $y = -2$.

19. ____________

20. Write the word phrase as an algebraic expression "four less the square of a number".

20. ____________

21. Check for solutions of the equation $x(x - 2) = 3$ from the set $\{-1, 0, 1, 2, 3\}$

21. ____________

22. Write as an equation using x as a variable and check for solutions from the set $\{0, 1, 2, 3, 4\}$: "the sum of the square of a number and six is five times the number."

22. ____________

23. Simplify: $(9z - 6) - 14$

23. ____________

24. State the property of real numbers illustrated by: $3 \cdot (6 \cdot 1) = 3 \cdot 6$

24. ____________

25. Use the multiplication inverse property to complete the following statement correctly:

$$\left(\frac{4}{9} \cdot \frac{9}{4}\right)z = \underline{\qquad\qquad}.$$

25. ____________

Name ____________________ Chapter 1 Form D Score ________

1. Write $\frac{32}{72}$ in lowest terms. 1. ____________

a. $\frac{3}{7}$

b. $\frac{8}{18}$

c. $\frac{4}{9}$

d. $\frac{1}{3}$

e. none of these

2. Find the product of $12 \cdot \frac{8}{78} \cdot \frac{52}{72}$ and reduce to lowest terms. 2. ____________

a. $\frac{8}{9}$

b. $\frac{60}{49}$

c. $\frac{104}{117}$

d. $\frac{2}{27}$

e. none of these

3. Write as a single fraction in lowest terms 3. ____________

$$\left(\frac{9}{15} \cdot \frac{16}{27}\right) \div \frac{36}{45}$$

a. $\frac{64}{225}$

b. $\frac{1}{3}$

c. $\frac{4}{3}$

d. $\frac{4}{9}$

e. none of these

4. Write as a single fraction in lowest terms

4. ________

$$\frac{8}{15} + \frac{9}{15} - \frac{7}{15}$$

a. $\frac{8}{5}$

b. $\frac{5}{3}$

c. $\frac{2}{3}$

d. $\frac{2}{5}$

e. none of these

5. Johny ate $\frac{1}{3}$ of his Halloween candy. His sister ate $\frac{1}{6}$ of his candy. How much of his candy is left?

5. ________

a. $\frac{7}{9}$

b. $\frac{1}{2}$

c. $\frac{1}{6}$

d. $\frac{5}{6}$

e. none of these

6. Simplify the expression: $15 - 2(4) + 21 \div 7$

6. ________

a. 14
b. 4
c. 55
d. 26
e. none of these

7. Write the expression in words: $5 - 3x$

7. ________

a. The difference of five and three times a number.
b. The sum of five and three times a number.
c. The difference of three times a number and five.
d. Three times a number less five.
e. none of these

8. Simplify: $\dfrac{26 - 3 \cdot 2}{2^3 \cdot 5}$

8. ______________

a. $\dfrac{23}{20}$

b. $\dfrac{1}{20}$

c. $\dfrac{1}{2}$

d. $\dfrac{2}{3}$

e. none of these

9. On the number line, identify the set of numbers graphed.

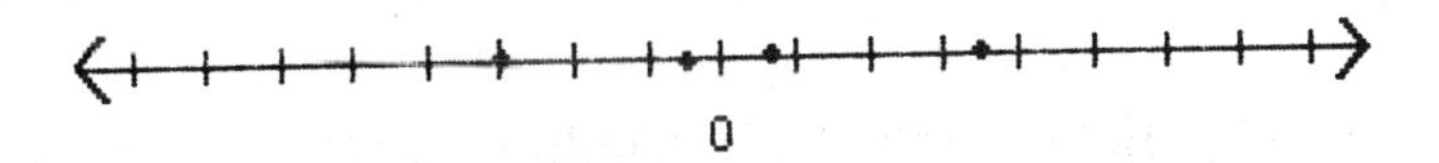

a. $\{\frac{3}{4}, 5, -\frac{1}{4}, -4\}$

b. $\{-4, 1, -\frac{1}{4}, 3\}$

c. $\{-3, -1, \frac{3}{4}, 3\frac{1}{2}\}$

d. $\{-3, \frac{3}{4}, 3\frac{1}{2}, -\frac{1}{4}\}$

e. none of these

10. If -16 means 16 miles west, what does 16 mean?

a. 16 miles east
b. 16 miles south
c. 16 miles north
d. 16 miles west
e. none of these

11. Find the absolute value of $-6 - 3$.

11. ______________

a. 3
b. 9
c. -9
d. -3
e. none of these

12. Which of the following statements is the true statement relating $-1\frac{3}{7}$ and $-1\frac{2}{5}$.

12. ____________

a. $-1\frac{3}{7} > -1\frac{2}{5}$

b. $-1\frac{3}{7} = -1\frac{2}{5}$

c. $-1\frac{2}{5} < -1\frac{3}{7}$

d. $-1\frac{2}{5} > -1\frac{3}{7}$

e. none of these

13. Simplify the expression: $7 + 4[3 + (-9)]$

13. ____________

a. 10
b. -66
c. 31
d. -41
e. none of these

14. Find the additive inverse of $-\frac{2}{5}$

14. ____________

a. $-\frac{5}{2}$

b. $\frac{5}{2}$

c. $\frac{2}{5}$

d. 0

e. none of these

15. Simplify: $16 - [14 - (5 - 9)]$

15. ____________

a. 16
b. -2
c. -12
d. 6
e. none of these

16. The temperature at 3 p.m. was 35°. By 11 p.m. it had dropped 27 degrees. What is the temperature at 11 p.m.?

16. ______________

a. 8°
b. 62°
c. -8°
d. 12°
e. none of these

17. Simplify: $\left(-\frac{8}{15}\right)\left(\frac{21}{40}\right) \div \left(-\frac{14}{15}\right)$

17. ______________

a. $\frac{3}{7}$
b. $\frac{3}{35}$
c. $\frac{98}{225}$
d. $-\frac{3}{10}$
e. none of these

18. Catherine bought hot dogs for her eight children. Each child got two hot dogs. The hot dogs cost 39¢ each. How much was Catherine's bill?

18. ______________

a. $5.64
b. $6.24
c. $4.84
d. $3.12
e. none of these

19. Evaluate $x^2 - (6 - y) - 7$ if $x = -6$ and $y = 8$.

19. ______________

a. -17
b. 31
c. 27
d. 15
e. none of these

20. Write the word phrase as an algebraic expression "two less the square of a number".

20. ______________

a. $(2 - x)^2$
b. $x^2 - 2$
c. $(x - 2)^2$
d. $2 - x^2$
e. none of these

21. Check for solutions of the equation $\frac{n^2 + n}{n + 1} = 1$ from the set {-1, 0, 1, 2, 3} 21. ____________

a. 0
b. -1 and 1
c. 1
d. -1
e. none of these

22. Write as an equation using x as a variable and check for solutions from the set {0, 1, 2, 3, 4}: 22. ____________
"the difference of nine and three times a number is three ".

a. $9 - 3x = 3$, 2
b. $3x - 9 = 3$, 4
c. $9 - 3x = 3$, no solution from the set
d. $3x - 9 = 3$, no solution from the set
e. none of these

23. Simplify: $6(4 - x) -3(-2)$ 23. ____________

a. $30 - x$
b. $18 - 6x$
c. $18 - x$
d. $30 - 6x$
e. none of these

24. State the property of real numbers illustrated by $(-3 + 3) + 6 = -3 + (3 + 6)$ 24. ____________

a. Commutative property of addition.
b. Associative property of addition.
c. Additive inverse property.
d. Distributive property.
e. None of these

25. Use the commutative property of addition to complete the following statement correctly: 25. ____________

$(8 + -3) + 6 =$ ____________

a. $(8 + 6) + -3$
b. $8 + (-3 + 6)$
c. $6 + (8 + -3)$
d. $5 + 6$
e. none of these

Name ______________________ Chapter 1 Form E Score ________

1. Write $\frac{56}{72}$ in lowest terms.

1. ____________

a. $\frac{7}{9}$

b. $\frac{1}{2}$

c. $\frac{23}{36}$

d. $\frac{7}{8}$

e. none of these

2. Find the product of $9 \cdot \frac{36}{45} \cdot \frac{30}{63}$ and reduce to lowest terms.

2. ____________

a. $\frac{2}{21}$

b. $\frac{6}{5}$

c. $\frac{24}{7}$

d. $\frac{10}{7}$

e. none of these

3. Write as a single fraction in lowest terms

3. ____________

$$\left(\frac{6}{7} \cdot \frac{21}{27}\right) \div \frac{12}{15}$$

a. $\frac{15}{49}$

b. $\frac{5}{6}$

c. $\frac{8}{15}$

d. $\frac{5}{8}$

e. none of these

4. Write as a single fraction in lowest terms

4. ____________

$$\frac{6}{15} + \frac{11}{15} - \frac{5}{15}$$

a. $\frac{4}{15}$

b. $\frac{22}{15}$

c. $\frac{3}{5}$

d. $\frac{4}{5}$

e. none of these

5. Joseph ate $\frac{3}{8}$ of his Halloween candy. His sister ate $\frac{1}{4}$ of his candy. How much of his candy is left?

5. ____________

a. $\frac{3}{8}$

b. $\frac{2}{3}$

c. $\frac{5}{8}$

d. $\frac{7}{8}$

e. none of these

6. Simplify the expression: $24 - 4(2)^2 + 15 \div 3$

6. ____________

a. 85

b. $\frac{23}{3}$

c. 17

d. 13

e. none of these

7. Write the expression in words: $9x - 5$.

7. ____________

a. The difference of five and nine times a number.

b. The sum of nine times a number and five.

c. The difference of nine times a number and five.

d. Five less nine times a number .

e. none of these

8. Simplify: $\frac{18 - 4 \cdot 3}{3^3 \cdot 2}$

8. ____________

a. $\frac{2}{5}$

b. $\frac{1}{2}$

c. $\frac{7}{9}$

d. $\frac{1}{3}$

e. none of these

9. On the number line, identify the set of numbers graphed.

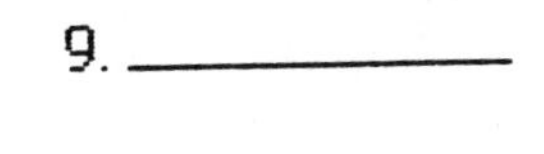

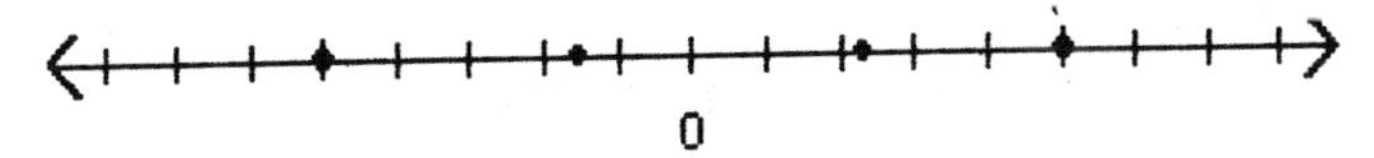

a. $\{-6, 3, -2, 5\}$

b. $\{-5, 2\frac{1}{4}, 4, -1\frac{1}{2}\}$

c. $\{-1\frac{1}{2}, 2\frac{1}{4}, 5, -5\}$

d. $\{-1\frac{1}{2}, 2\frac{1}{4}, 5, -6\}$

e. none of these

10. If 35 means 35 meters south, what does -35 mean?

10. ____________

a. 35 meters west

b. 35 meters south

c. 35 meters north

d. 35 meters east

e. none of these

11. Find the absolute value of $-9 + 2$.

11. ____________

a. 7

b. -7

c. 11

d. -11

e. none of these

12. Which of the following statements is the true statement relating $-2\frac{1}{9}$ and $-2\frac{1}{8}$.

12. ____________

a. $-2\frac{1}{9} = -2\frac{1}{8}$

b. $-2\frac{1}{9} > -2\frac{1}{8}$

c. $-2\frac{1}{8} > -2\frac{1}{9}$

d. No relationship can be determined

e. none of these

13. Simplify the expression: $-7 + 9[-3 + (-4)]$

13. ____________

a. -70

b. -14

c. -38

d. 56

e. none of these

14. Find the additive inverse of 2.6 .

14. ____________

a. $-\frac{5}{13}$

b. $\frac{5}{13}$

c. 2.6

d. -2.6

e. none of these

15. Simplify: $15 - [11 - (10 - 4)]$

15. ____________

a. -10

b. -45

c. 10

d. 18

e. none of these

16. The temperature at 1 a.m. was 12°. By 7 a.m. a cold front came through and the temperature dropped 19 degrees. What was the temperature at 7 a.m.?

16. ____________

a. 5°

b. 7°

c. 31°

d. -7°

e. none of these

17. Simplify: $\left(-\frac{9}{12}\right)\left(-\frac{18}{21}\right) \div \left(-\frac{9}{14}\right)$ 17. ________

a. $-\frac{1}{3}$

b. -1

c. $-\frac{81}{196}$

d. $-\frac{9}{2}$

e. none of these

18. There are 24 cans in a case of soda. Each case costs \$5.12 . How much does 120 cans of soda cost? 18. ________

a. \$20.48

b. \$25.50

c. \$25.20

d. \$25.40

e. none of these

19. Evaluate $y^2 - (x - 3) + 4$ if $x = -3$ and $y = -5$. 19. ________

a. 0

b. 21

c. 35

d. 29

e. none of these

20. Write the word phrase as an algebraic expression "seven less than five times a number". 20. ________

a. $5x - 7$

b. $7 - 5x$

c. $5(x - 7)$

d. $x^5 - 7$

e. none of these

21. Check for solutions of the equation 21. ________

$\frac{n^2 + 2n}{n + 2} = 2$ from the set $\{-2, -1, 0, 1, 2\}$

a. -2

b. 0

c. -2 and 2

d. 2

e. none of these

22. Write as an equation using x as a variable and check for solutions from the set {0, 1, 2, 3, 4}: "the difference of twice the square of a number and eight times the number is 0 ".

22. ____________

a. $8x - 2x^2 = 0$, 4 and 0
b. $2x^2 - 8x = 0$, 0 and 4
c. $8x - 2x^2 = 0$, 2 and 4
d. $2x^2 - 8x = 0$, 2 and 4
e. none of these

23. Simplify: $\frac{2}{3} - \frac{4}{9}(y - \frac{3}{8}) + 1$

23. ____________

a. $\frac{31}{24} - \frac{4}{9}y$
b. $\frac{3}{2} - \frac{4}{9}y$
c. $\frac{7}{4} - \frac{4}{9}y$
d. $\frac{2}{9}y - \frac{11}{12}$
e. none of these

24. State the property of real numbers illustrated by $\left(\frac{3}{4} \cdot \frac{4}{3}\right) \cdot \frac{9}{16} = \left(\frac{4}{3} \cdot \frac{3}{4}\right) \cdot \frac{9}{16}$

24. ____________

a. Associative property of multiplication.
b. Multiplicative inverse property.
c. Multiplicative identity property.
d. Commutative property of multiplication.
e. None of these

25. Use the distributive property to complete the following statement correctly:

25. ____________

$$(\frac{1}{5} - x)(-5) = \_\_\_\_\_\_\_\_$$

a. $\frac{1}{5}(-5) - x(-5)$
b. $-1 + 5x$
c. $\frac{1}{5} - x(-5)$
d. $(-5)(\frac{1}{5} - x)$
e. none of these

Name ______________________ Chapter 1 Form F Score ______

1. Write $\frac{30}{72}$ in lowest terms.

1. ______________

a. $\frac{5}{13}$

b. $\frac{15}{36}$

c. $\frac{15}{31}$

d. $\frac{5}{12}$

e. none of these

2. Find the product of $8 \cdot \frac{18}{28} \cdot \frac{35}{45}$ and reduce to lowest terms.

2. ______________

a. 3

b. 4

c. 8

d. $\frac{1}{2}$

e. none of these

3. Write as a single fraction in lowest terms

3. ______________

$$\left(\frac{7}{8} \cdot \frac{16}{28}\right) \div \frac{9}{10}$$

a. $\frac{5}{9}$

b. $\frac{9}{20}$

c. $\frac{20}{9}$

d. $\frac{9}{5}$

e. none of these

4. Write as a single fraction in lowest terms 4. ____________

$$\frac{17}{24} + \frac{9}{24} - \frac{5}{24}$$

a. $\frac{1}{4}$

b. $\frac{7}{8}$

c. $\frac{23}{24}$

d. $\frac{31}{24}$

e. none of these

5. Cynthia ate $\frac{4}{9}$ of her box of Christmas cookies. 5. ____________

Her sister ate $\frac{1}{3}$ of the box. How much of the box

of cookies was left?

a. $\frac{7}{12}$

b. $\frac{1}{9}$

c. $\frac{1}{3}$

d. $\frac{4}{9}$

e. none of these

6. Simplify the expression: $27 - 2^2(4) + 16 \div 8$ 6. ____________

a. 13
b. 94
c. 19
d. -35
e. none of these

7. Write the expression in words: $7 - 6x$. 7. ____________

a. The difference of six times a number and seven.
b. Six times a number less seven.
c. The sum of seven and six times a number.
d. The difference of seven and six times a number .
e. none of these

8. Simplify: $\dfrac{42 - 9 \cdot 3}{2^3 \cdot 3}$

8. ________

a. $\dfrac{25}{24}$

b. $\dfrac{5}{6}$

c. $\dfrac{33}{8}$

d. $\dfrac{5}{8}$

e. none of these

9. On the number line, identify the set of numbers graphed.

a. $\{-6, 2, 6, -1\}$

b. $\{-\frac{3}{4}, 2, 6, -4\frac{1}{2}\}$

c. $\{-\frac{3}{4}, 2, 5\frac{1}{2}, -4\frac{1}{2}\}$

d. $\{-4\frac{1}{4}, 2, -1, 5\frac{1}{2}\}$

e. none of these

10. If -$25 means withdraw $25, what does $25 mean?

10. ________

a. Write a check for $25
b. Deposit $25
c. Subtract $25
d. Balance is $25
e. None of these

11. Find the absolute value of $-8 - 4$.

11. ________

a. 4
b. -12
c. 12
d. -4
e. none of these

12. Which of the following statements is the true statement relating $3\frac{1}{12}$ and $3\frac{1}{13}$. 12. ____________

a. $3\frac{1}{12} > 3\frac{1}{13}$

b. $3\frac{1}{13} > 3\frac{1}{12}$

c. $3\frac{1}{12} = 3\frac{1}{13}$

d. No relationship can be determined

e. none of these

13. Simplify the expression: $6 - 2[-9 + 2]$ 13. ____________

a. 26
b. -28
c. 20
d. -34
e. none of these

14. Find the additive inverse of $-\frac{1}{5}$. 14. ____________

a. 5
b. $\frac{1}{5}$
c. -5
d. $-\frac{1}{5}$
e. none of these

15. Simplify: $22 - [19 - (4 - (-3))]$ 15. ____________

a. 2
b. 4
c. -4
d. -2
e. none of these

16. The temperature at 3 a.m. was 11° below zero. By noon, it had raised 24 degrees. What was the temperature at noon? 16. ____________

a. 35°
b. 13°
c. -13°
d. 8°
e. none of these

17. Simplify: $\left(\frac{5}{6}\right)\left(-\frac{16}{27}\right) \div \left(\frac{25}{36}\right)$

17. ____________

a. $-\frac{32}{45}$

b. $-\frac{250}{729}$

c. $-\frac{6}{5}$

d. $-\frac{4}{45}$

e. none of these

18. Jonathon bought a hamburger and french fries for each of his six nephews. If hamburgers cost 69¢ and french fries cost 52¢, how much was Jonathon's bill?

18. ____________

a. $7.16
b. $6.76
c. $6.66
d. $7.26
e. none of these

19. Evaluate $x^2 - (1 - y) - 7$ if $x = -4$ and $y = -6$.

19. ____________

a. 14
b. -30
c. -22
d. 4
e. none of these

20. Write the word phrase as an algebraic expression "The difference of seven times a number and the number squared".

20. ____________

a. $x^2 - 7x$
b. $7x^2 - x$
c. $7x - x^2$
d. $7x + x^2$
e. none of these

21. Check for solutions of the equation

$y + y^2 = 2y + 6$ from the set {-2, - 1, 0, 1, 2}

21. ____________

a. 2
b. -2
c. 0 and 2
d. 0 and -2
e. none of these

22. Write as an equation using x as a variable and check for solutions from the set {0, 1, 2, 3, 4}: "the square of a number is the difference of five times the number and four".

22. ____________

a. $x^2 = 5x - 4$, no solution from set
b. $x^2 = 4 - 5x$, 1 and 4
c. $x^2 = 4 - 5x$, no solution from set
d. $x^2 = 5x - 4$, 1 and 4
e. none of these

23. Simplify: $2.4 + (0.6 - t)(-5)$

23. ____________

a. $-0.6 + 5t$
b. $3 + 5t$
c. $3 - 5t$
d. $2.1 + 5t$
e. none of these

24. State the property of real numbers illustrated by $2 + [3.5 + (-3.5)] = 2 + 0$

24 ____________

a. Associative property of addition.
b. Additive identity property.
c. Additive inverse property.
d. distributive property.
e. None of these

25. Use the commutative property of multiplication to complete the following statement correctly:

25. ____________

$$4 \cdot (7x + \frac{1}{4}) = \underline{\qquad\qquad}$$

a. $4 \cdot (\frac{1}{4} + 7x)$

b. $4(7x) + 4(\frac{1}{4})$

c. $4 \cdot 7x + \frac{1}{4}$

d. $(7x + \frac{1}{4}) \cdot 4$

e. none of these

CHAPTER # 1 TEST KEYS

Form A

1. $\frac{3}{7}$
2. $\frac{12}{5}$
3. $\frac{6}{5}$
4. $\frac{5}{4}$
5. $\frac{11}{20}$
6. 10
7. The difference of three times a number and 1.
8. $\frac{9}{8}$
9. 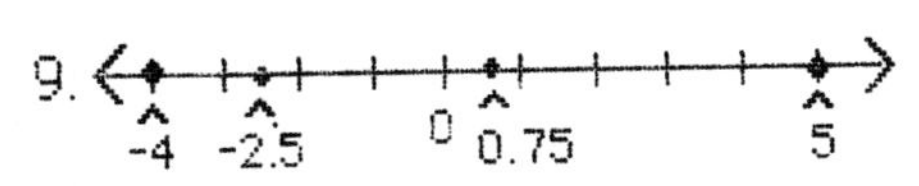

10. 89 miles south
11. 2.45
12. $-\frac{4}{5}$
13. -31
14. 0.8
15. -2
16. -8°
17. $-\frac{2}{7}$
18. $15.18
19. -5
20. $x^2 - 4$
21. 1
22. $x^2 = 4x - 3$, 1,3
23. $x - 2.2$
24. Additive identity
25. $\frac{1}{4} \cdot (4 \cdot w)$

Form B

1. $\frac{5}{8}$
2. $\frac{35}{8}$
3. $\frac{1}{2}$
4. $\frac{7}{9}$
5. $\frac{19}{30}$
6. 8
7. The sum of five times a number and two.
8. $\frac{4}{9}$
9. 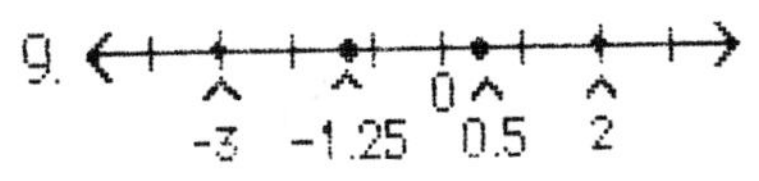

10. 63 miles north
11. 3.8
12. $\frac{9}{7}$
13. 20
14. 2.5
15. 10
16. 7°
17. $\frac{25}{28}$
18. $1.75
19. 13
20. $x^2 + 3$
21. -1
22. $x + 13 = 16$, 3
23. $-8w$
24. Multiplicative inverse
25. $2w - x$

CHAPTER # 1 TEST KEYS

Form C

1. $\frac{8}{15}$
2. $\frac{27}{8}$
3. $\frac{25}{48}$
4. $\frac{3}{4}$
5. $\frac{23}{35}$
6. 22
7. The difference of twice a number and seven.
8. $\frac{2}{3}$
9. 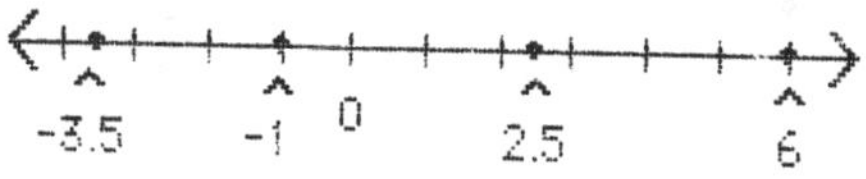

10. 59 miles west
11. .354
12. $\frac{9}{11}$
13. 36
14. -0.69
15. 3
16. -7°
17. $-\frac{4}{15}$
18. $20.16
19. 10
20. $4 - x^2$
21. -1, 3
22. $x^2 + 6 = 5x$, 2, 3
23. $9z - 20$
24. Multiplicative identity
25. 1z

Form D

1. c) $\frac{4}{9}$
2. a) $\frac{8}{9}$
3. d) $\frac{4}{9}$
4. c) $\frac{2}{3}$
5. b) $\frac{1}{2}$
6. e) None of these
7. a) The difference of five and three times a number.
8. c) $\frac{1}{2}$
9. d) $\{-3, \frac{3}{4}, 3\frac{1}{2}, -\frac{1}{4}\}$
10. a) 16 miles east
11. b) 9
12. d) $-1\frac{2}{5} > -1\frac{3}{7}$
13. e) None of these
14. c) $\frac{2}{5}$
15. b) -2
16. a) 8°
17. e) None of these
18. b) $6.24
19. b) 31
20. d) $2 - x^2$
21. c) 1
22. a) $9 - 3x = 3$, 2
23. d) $30 - 6x$
24. b) Associative property of Addition
25. c) $6 + (8 + -3)$

CHAPTER # 1 TEST KEYS

Form E

1. a) $\frac{7}{9}$
2. c) $\frac{24}{7}$
3. b) $\frac{5}{6}$
4. d) $\frac{4}{5}$
5. a) $\frac{3}{8}$
6. d) 13
7. c) The difference of nine times a number and five.
8. e) none of these
9. b) $\{-5, 2\frac{1}{4}, 4, -1\frac{1}{2}\}$
10. c) 35 meters north
11. a) 7
12. b) $-2\frac{1}{9} > -2\frac{1}{8}$
13. a) -70
14. d) - 2.6
15. c) 10
16. d) -7°
17. b) -1
18. e) none of these
19. c) 35
20. a) $5x - 7$
21. d) 2
22. b) $2x^2 - 8x = 0$ 0 and 4
23. e) none of these
24. d) commutative property of multiplication
25. a) $\frac{1}{5}(-5) - x(-5)$

Form F

1. d) $\frac{5}{12}$
2. b) 4
3. a) $\frac{5}{9}$
4. b) $\frac{7}{8}$
5. c) $\frac{1}{3}$
6. a) 13
7. d) The difference of seven and six times a number.
8. d) $\frac{5}{8}$
9. c) $\{-\frac{3}{4}, 2, 5\frac{1}{2}, -4\frac{1}{2}\}$
10. b) deposit $25
11. c) 12
12. a) $3\frac{1}{12} > 3\frac{1}{13}$
13. c) 20
14. b) $\frac{1}{5}$
15. e) none of these
16. b) 13°
17. a) $-\frac{32}{45}$
18. d) $7.26
19. e) none of these
20. c) $7x - x^2$
21. b) -2
22. d) $x^2 = 5x - 4$ 1 and 4
23. a) $-0.6 + 5t$
24. c) additive inverse property
25. d) $(7x + \frac{1}{4}) \cdot 4$

Name ______________________ Chapter 2 Form A Score ________

1. Determine the coefficients of the like terms in the expresssion: $5x^3 - 6x^2 - 3x + 12x^2 + 1$

2. Simplify by combining like terms:
   $6a - 3b - 8a + 12b - 3$

   2. ____________

3. Remove parentheses using the distributive property, then simplify: $2(4y - 6) - 3(8 + 2y)$

   3. ____________

4. Solve the equation: $1\frac{3}{8} = 4\frac{5}{12} + x$

   4. ____________

5. Solve the equation: $3(2 + 5y) = 16y - 3$

   5. ____________

6. Write an equation and solve: The sum of twice a number and seven is three less than the number.

   6. ____________

7. Solve the equation: $-\frac{21}{25} = \frac{7}{15}t$

   7. ____________

8. Solve the equation: $18 - 5x = 4x - 6$

   8. ____________

9. Solve the equation: $9 - 4x = -3$ 9. ____________

10. Solve the equation: $5t - 8t - 3 = 12t - 15$ 10. ____________

11. Solve the equation: $18 - 3(9y - 8) = 3y - 8$ 11. ____________

12. Write an equation and solve: The sum of twice a number and $\frac{2}{3}$ is 8 12. ____________

13. Convert the word phrase "$\frac{5}{6}$ of the sum of twice a number and twelve" into a mathematical expression using n as the variable. 13. ____________

14. Find the number described by "6 fewer than a number is four times the number". 14. ____________

15. Find the number described by "The quotient of four times a number and five is 40 more than 30% of the number". 15. ____________

16. John is four times as old as his son, Chris. Four years ago, Chris was $\frac{1}{8}$ as old as his Dad. How old is John now?

16. ____________

17. Rena has $1.95 in nickels and dimes. If she has 6 more dimes than nickels, how many coins of each type does she have?

17. ____________

18. A solution containing 16% acid is to be mixed with a solution containing 24% acid to obtain a 50 liter mixture of 18% acid. How many liters of each solution should be used?

18. ____________

19. Solve the inequality $x - 6 < 9$ and graph the solution.

19. ____________

20. Solve the inequality $-1.5 < x + 3 < 2.5$ and graph the solution.

20. ____________

21. Solve the inequality: $-5x \leq -\frac{15}{28}$

21. ____________

22. Solve the inequality: $-7 < 3 - 4x < -1$

22. ____________

23. Allen received grades of 82, 78, and 88 on his first three mathematics tests. What possible scores on the fourth test will give a final average of at least 80% ?

23. ____________

24. Two trains leave a station at the same time traveling in opposite directions. One is traveling at 40 mph and the other at 50 mph. How long will it take for them to be 60 miles apart ?

24. ____________

25. Solve: $\frac{x}{4} - \frac{y}{3} = 1$ for y.

25. ____________

Name ______________________ Chapter 2 Form B Score ______

1. Determine the coefficients of the like terms in the expresssion: $7y^4 - 8y^2 - 4y + 9y^2 + 3$

1. ______

2. Simplify by combining like terms:
$11x - 9y - 15x + 3y - 5$

2. ______

3. Remove parentheses using the distributive property, then simplify: $7(2x - 3) - 4(6 - 5x)$

3. ______

4. Solve the equation: $\frac{5}{6} = \frac{7}{9} + x$

4. ______

5. Solve the equation: $4(5 + 3x) = 13x - 7$

5. ______

6. Write an equation and solve: The sum of twice a number and eight is four more than the number.

6. ______

7. Solve the equation: $\frac{x}{15} = -\frac{14}{21}$

7. ______

8. Solve the equation: $-9.56 + 3.8 = 4.7x - 8.3x$ 8. ____________

9. Solve the equation: $\frac{8}{5} - \frac{4}{5}t = 2$ 9. ____________

10. Solve the equation: $5.6n - 0.5 - 1.2n = -5.44 + 2.3$ 10. ____________

11. Solve the equation: $9 - (x - 5) = 4(6 - 2x)$ 11. ____________

12. Write an equation and solve: The sum of eight times a number and four is sixteen. 12. ____________

13. Convert the word phrase "$\frac{3}{4}$ of the difference of twice a number and 5" into a mathematical expression using n as the variable. 13. ____________

14. Find the number described by "5 fewer than a number is six times the number". 14. ____________

15. Find the number described by "The quotient of three times a number and five is 30 more than 30% of the number". 15. ____________

16. Alex is three times as old as his daughter, Judy. Six years ago, Judy was $\frac{1}{6}$ as old as her Dad. How old is Alex now?

16. ____________

17. Jeremy has $3.55 in dimes and quarters. If he has three more quarters than dimes, how many coins of each type does he have?

17. ____________

18. A solution containing 12% acid is to be mixed with a solution containing 20% acid to obtain a 40 liter mixture of 14% acid. How many liters of each solution should be used?

18. ____________

19. Solve the inequality $x + \frac{1}{4} \geq \frac{3}{4}$ and graph the solution.

19. ____________

20. Solve the inequality $-2.4 < x + 2.1 < 3.6$ and graph the solution.

20. ____________

21. Solve the inequality: $3 - 4x > -13$

21. ____________

22. Solve the inequality: $-7 < 5 - 3x < -2$

22. ____________

23. Rochelle received grades of 65, 93, and 84 on her first three mathematics tests. What possible scores on the fourth test will give a final average of at least 80% ?

23. ____________

24. Two cars leave a town at the same time traveling in the same direction. One is traveling at 50 mph and the other at 60 mph. How long will it take for the two cars to be 15 miles apart ?

24. ____________

25. Solve: $y = \frac{6 - 4x}{3}$ for x.

25. ____________

Name ____________________________ Chapter 2 Form C Score ______

1. Determine the coefficients of the like terms in the expresssion: $8x^5 - 9x^3 + 3x + 6x^3 - 4$

2. Simplify by combining like terms: $\frac{1}{3}x^2 - \frac{3}{4}y + \frac{5}{6} - \frac{2}{3}y + \frac{1}{2}x^2$

2. ____________

3. Remove parentheses using the distributive property, then simplify: $9(4w - 1) - 5(2 + 4w)$

4. Solve the equation: $x + 3.8 = -6.42$

4. ____________

5. Solve the equation: $8x + 7 = 9x - 4$

5. ____________

6. Write an equation and solve: Ten minus four times a number is the difference of 9 and five times the number.

6. ____________

7. Solve the equation: $-9 = \frac{t}{3.24}$

7. ____________

8. Solve the equation: $11\frac{3}{8}t - 9\frac{1}{2}t = 5\frac{1}{3} + 2\frac{1}{6}$ 8. ____________

9. Solve the equation: $-21.65 - 7.6w = 4.95$ 9. ____________

10. Solve the equation: $15x + x - 28 + 2 = 4x - x$ 10. ____________

11. Solve the equation: $\frac{1}{6}(9 - 3y) - 2 = \frac{2}{3}(6 - 3y)$ 11. ____________

12. Write an equation and solve: The sum of ten and three and three fourths times a number is negative one half. 12. ____________

13. Convert the word phrase " Thirty-seven percent of the sum of 625 and a number" into a mathematical expression using x as the variable. 13. ____________

14. Find the number described by "The sum of seven times a number and eight is negative six". 14. ____________

15. Find the number described by "The difference of six times a number and four is divided by two. The resut is the sum of five times the number and three". 15. ____________

16. Max must cut a thirteen-foot board into two pieces The length of the longer piece must be three times the length of the shorter piece. Find the length of the longer piece. 16. ____________

17. Joseph has $220 in $10 and $20 bills. If he has a total of 15 bills, how many of each kind does he have? 17. ____________

18. A candy shop mixes chocolate covered peanuts at $2.25 a pound with chocolate covered raisins that normally sell for $1.75 a pound to make a special mix of chocolates. If 14 pounds of the mixture is sold at $1.95 per pound, how many pounds of raisins were in the mixture if the store lost no money? 18. ____________

19. Solve the inequality $-3 + 7x \leq 6x + 1$ and graph the solution. 19. ____________

20. Solve the inequality $-4 \leq x - 1 < 2$ and graph the solution. 20. ____________

21. Solve the inequality: $5 + 2(x - 3) \geq 3 - 2x$ 21. ____________

22. Solve the inequality: $-3 < \frac{1 - 2x}{5} < 2$ 22. ____________

23. Solve the word problem: The sum of six times a number and 0.3 is not less than the sum of 1.9 and twice the number. 23. ____________

24. How much interest is made on $3800 at $9\frac{1}{2}$% for two years? 24. ____________

25. Solve: $y + 8 = -4(x - 6)$ for x 25. ____________

Name ______________________________ Chapter 2 Form D Score ________

1. Determine the coefficients of the like terms in the expresssion: 1. ____________

$$4.2m^2n - 8.1\ mn^2 + 6.1mn - 3.1\ mn^2 + 3$$

a. 8.1 and 3.1
b. 4.2, -8.1, and -3.1
c. -8.1 and -3.1
d. 4.2, -8.1, 6.1, and -3.1
e. none of these

2. Simplify by combining like terms: 2. ____________

$$1.4w - 2.35w^2 + w + 3.6 + 1.8w^2$$

a. $1.4w - 0.55w^2 + 3.6$
b. $2.4w - 0.55w^2 + 3.6$
c. $2.4w - 4.15w^2 + 3.6$
d. $5.45w^2$
e. none of these

3. Remove parentheses using the distributive property, then simplify: $8 - 7(2 - x) + 3x$ 3. ____________

a. $2x - 6$
b. $2 + 2x$
c. $-6 - 4x$
d. $10x - 6$
e. none of these

4. Solve the equation: $\frac{3}{8} = \frac{5}{12} + x$ 4. ____________

a. $x = -\frac{1}{24}$
b. $x = \frac{19}{24}$
c. $x = -\frac{1}{2}$
d. $x = \frac{2}{5}$
e. none of these

5. Solve the equation: $4 - 13x = 15 - 14x$ 5. 

a. $x = 8$
b. $x = 19$
c. $x = 11$
d. $x = -\frac{19}{27}$
e. none of these

6. Write an equation and solve: The sum of a number and five is four less than twice a number. 6. ____________

a. 3
b. 1
c. $\frac{1}{3}$
d. 9
e. none of these

7. Solve the equation: $\frac{y}{14} = -\frac{6}{21}$ 7. ____________

a. $y = -49$
b. $y = -4$
c. $y = 4$
d. $y = 49$
e. none of these

8. Solve the equation: $12 + 3y = 7 - 4y$ 8. ____________

a. $y = -\frac{7}{5}$
b. $y = -19$
c. $y = 12$
d. $y = 5$
e. none of these

9. Solve the equation: $8 - 5x = -2$ 9. ____________

a. $x = 2$
b. $x = -\frac{2}{3}$
c. $x = 5$
d. $x = -\frac{6}{5}$
e. none of these

10. Solve the equation: $7s - 11s - 4 = 8s - 6$ 10. ____________

a. $s = -\frac{2}{3}$
b. $s = -\frac{5}{2}$
c. $s = -6$
d. $s = -\frac{3}{5}$
e. none of these

11. Solve the equation: $12 - 4(6x - 5) = 2 - 4x$ 11. ________

a. $x = \frac{1}{4}$

b. $x = \frac{2}{3}$

c. $x = \frac{3}{2}$

d. $x = \frac{21}{26}$

e. none of these

12. Write an equation and solve: The sum of twice a number and $\frac{4}{5}$ is 6. 12. ________

a. $x = 2\frac{3}{5}$

b. $x = 2\frac{1}{5}$

c. $x = 3\frac{4}{5}$

d. $x = 3\frac{2}{5}$

e. none of these

13. Convert the word phrase " sixty-five percent of the sum of 350 and twice a number" into a mathematical expression using n as the variable. 13. ________

a. $0.65(350 - 2n)$
b. $0.65(350) + 2n$
c. $0.65(350 + 2n)$
d. $65(350 + 2n)$
e. none of these

14. Find the number described by "12 fewer than a number is three times the number". 14. ________

a. 3
b. -3
c. 6
d. -8
e. none of these

15. Find the number described by "The sum of three times a number and one is divided by four. The resut is the sum of twice the number and four". 15. ____________

a. $3\frac{3}{4}$
b. -3
c. $-\frac{3}{5}$
d. 5
e. none of these

16. Marvin must cut a sixteen-foot board into two pieces. The length of the longer piece must be twice as long as the length of the shorter piece. Find the length of the longer piece. 16. ____________

a. $5\frac{1}{3}$ ft.
b. $10\frac{2}{3}$ ft.
c. 13 ft.
d. 12 ft.
e. none of these

17. Joan has $300 in $10 and $20 bills. If she has a total of 21 bills, how many $20 bills does she have? 17. ____________

a. 9
b. 12
c. 11
d. 10
e. none of these

18. How many ounces of an alloy containing 30% gold must be melted with an alloy containing 40% gold to obtain100 ounces of an alloy containing 36% gold? 18. ____________

a. 51 ounces
b. 60 ounces
c. 42 ounces
d. 40 ounces
e. none of these

19. Solve the inequality $x - 3 \leq 8$ and graph the solution.

a) $x \leq 5$

b) $x \leq 11$

c) $x \leq \frac{8}{3}$

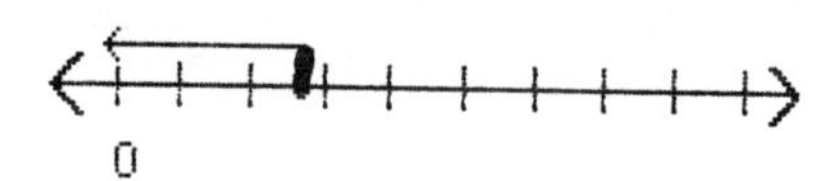

d) $x \leq \frac{3}{8}$

e) none of these

20. Solve the inequality $-5 < x - 2 \leq 0$ and graph the solution.

a) $-7 < x \leq -2$

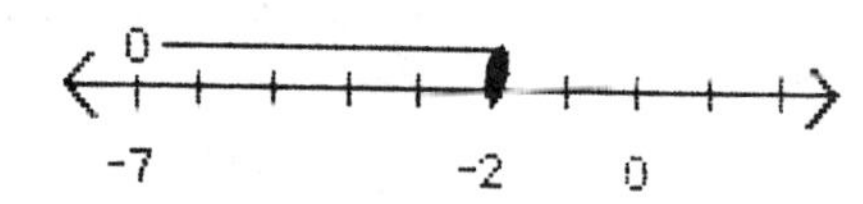

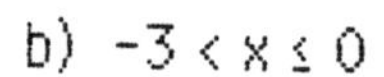

b) $-3 < x \leq 0$

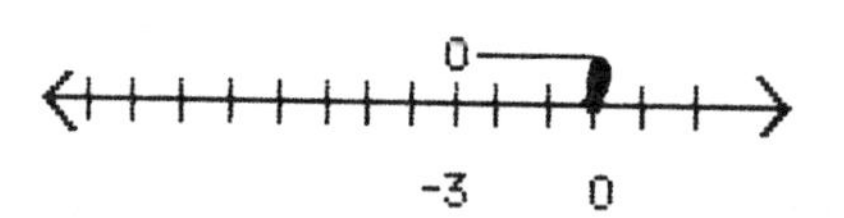

c) $-3 < x \leq 2$

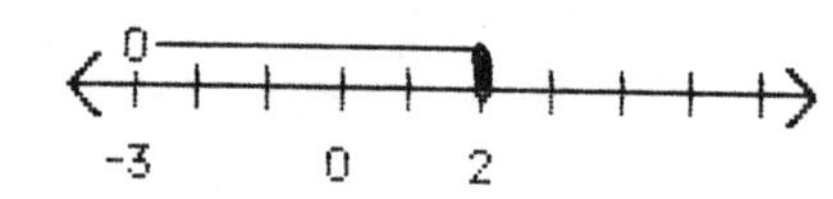

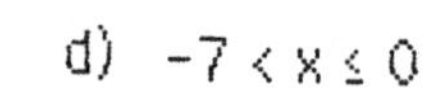

d) $-7 < x \leq 0$

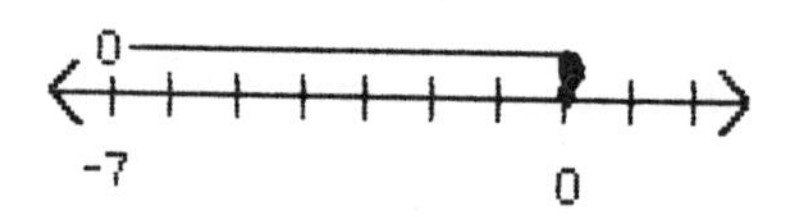

e) none of these

21. Solve the inequality: $-\frac{2}{9}y \geq -\frac{1}{36}$

21. ____________

a. $y > \frac{1}{8}$

b. $y > \frac{1}{162}$

c. $y < -\frac{1}{8}$

d. $y < \frac{1}{8}$

e. none of these

22. Solve the inequality: $-8 \le 4 - 3x < 5$ 22. ______

a. $\frac{4}{3} \ge x > -3$

b. $4 \ge x > -\frac{1}{3}$

c. $-9 \le x < -2$

d. $4 \ge x > -3$

e. none of these

23. Solve the word problem: The sum of five times a number and 0.8 is not less than the sum of 3.2 and twice the number. 23. ______

a. $x \ge -0.26$

b. $x \le 0.8$

c. $x > 0.8$

d. $x \ge \frac{4}{7}$

e. none of these

24. How much interest is made on $5200 invested at $7\frac{1}{2}$% for 6 months? 24. ______

a. $195

b. $390

c. $189.50

d. $1950

e. none of these

25. Solve: $\frac{x}{3} - \frac{y}{4} = 1$ for y 25. ______

a. $y = \frac{4x - 1}{3}$

b. $y = \frac{4x - 12}{3}$

c. $y = \frac{4x}{3} - 1$

d. $y = \frac{4x + 12}{3}$

e. none of these

Name ____________________ Chapter 2 Form E Score ______

1. Determine the coefficients of the like terms in the expresssion: 1. __________

$$-25t - 5s^2t + 3st^2 - s^2t + 4s^2t^2$$

a. 5 and 1
b. -5 and -1
c. -2, -5, 3, -1, and 4
d. -5, -1, and 4
e. none of these

2. Simplify by combining like terms: 2. __________

$$\frac{4}{9}a^2 + \frac{1}{6}b - \frac{1}{3} + \frac{5}{6}a^2 - \frac{2}{3}b + 3$$

a. $\frac{3}{5}a^2 - \frac{1}{3}b + \frac{8}{3}$
b. $\frac{31}{9}a^2b$
c. $\frac{23}{18}a^2 - \frac{5}{6}b + \frac{10}{3}$
d. $\frac{23}{18}a^2 - \frac{1}{2}b + \frac{8}{3}$
e. none of these

3. Remove parentheses using the distributive property, then simplify: $1.5(6 - t^2) - 0.7(4 + 5t^2)$ 3. __________

a. $-1.9 - 5t^2$
b. $6.2 + 4t^2$
c. $6.8 - 5t^2$
d. $6.2 + 3.5t^2$
e. none of these

4. Solve the equation: $3\frac{1}{5} = 5\frac{3}{10} + x$ 4. __________

a. $x = 8\frac{4}{15}$
b. $x = -2\frac{2}{5}$
c. $x = -2\frac{1}{10}$
d. $x = 8\frac{1}{2}$
e. none of these

5. Solve the equation: $8(4 + 3y) = 25y - 2$ 5. ________

a. $y = 34$
b. $y = 12$
c. $y = \frac{17}{11}$
d. $y = 30$
e. none of these

6. Write an equation and solve: The sum of eighteen and eight times a number is fifteen more than seven times the number. 6. ________

a. 18
b. 3
c. 33
d. 5
e. none of these

7. Solve the equation: $\frac{27}{28} = -\frac{3}{7}t$ 7. ________

a. $t = -\frac{9}{4}$
b. $t = -\frac{81}{196}$
c. $t = -\frac{4}{9}$
d. $t = -\frac{49}{24}$
e. none of these

8. Solve the equation: $7.1 - 18.6 = 3.2x - 7.8x$ 8. ________

a. $x = -2.5$
b. $x = -6.9$
c. $x = 6.9$
d. $x = 2.5$
e. none of these

9. Solve the equation: $\frac{5}{8} - \frac{15}{8}y = -1$ 9. ________

a. $y = -\frac{4}{5}$
b. $y = \frac{13}{15}$
c. $y = \frac{1}{5}$
d. $y = \frac{1}{4}$
c. none of these

10. Solve the equation: $3.8x + 2.1 + 2.9x = -14.3 + 4.34$ 10. ____________

a. $x = -1.7$

b. $x = -1.17$

c. $x = -1.8$

d. $x = -2.12$

e. none of these

11. Solve the equation: $10 - (3 - 2x) = 6(2 - x)$ 11. ____________

a. $x = \frac{7}{4}$

b. $x = \frac{5}{8}$

c. $x = \frac{5}{3}$

d. $x = -5$

e. none of these

12. Write an equation and solve: The sum of seven and four fifths of a number is fifteen. 12. ____________

a. $6\frac{2}{5}$

b. 10

c. $27\frac{1}{2}$

d. $1\frac{12}{13}$

e. none of these

13. Convert the word phrase " The reciprocal of the sum of a number and 10" into a mathematical expression using x as the variable. 13. ____________

a. $\frac{1}{x} + 10$

b. $-(x + 10)$

c. $\frac{1}{x} + \frac{1}{10}$

d. $\frac{1}{x + 10}$

e. none of these

14. Find the number described by "Six times the sum of a number and negative four is negative three".

a. $\frac{1}{6}$

b. $-4\frac{1}{2}$

c. $3\frac{1}{2}$

d. -14

e. none of these

14. ____________

15. Find the number described by "The difference of twice a number and 7.5 is 80% of the number ".

a. 2.6

b. 2.7

c. 3

d. $6\frac{7}{8}$

e. none of these

15. ____________

16. Jolene is paid $315 a week plus a commission of 7% on sales. Find the sales, in dollars, needed to give her a weekly total of $496.02.

a. $11786

b. $1267.14

c. $4500

d. $2586

e. none of these

16. ____________

17. Maria has $4.95 in dimes and quarters. If she has twice as many dimes as quarters, how many dimes does she have?

a. 11

b. 16

c. 22

d. 24

e. none of these

17. ____________

18. Twenty-four gallons of chocolate ice cream that contains 25% butterfat is mixed with vanilla ice cream that contains 15% butterfat to make chocolate ripple ice cream that contains 21% butterfat. How much vanilla ice cream is used?

18. 

a. 16 gal.
b. $30\frac{2}{3}$ gal.
c. 11 gal.
d. 17 gal.
e. none of these

19. Solve the inequality $x + 0.7 > \frac{1}{5}$ and graph the solution.

19. 

a) $x > -\frac{1}{2}$

b) $x > 0.9$

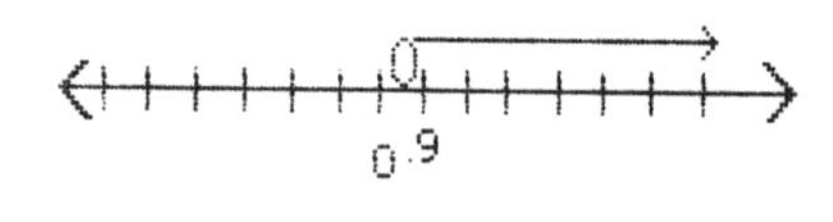

c) $x > 0.9$

d) $x > -\frac{1}{2}$

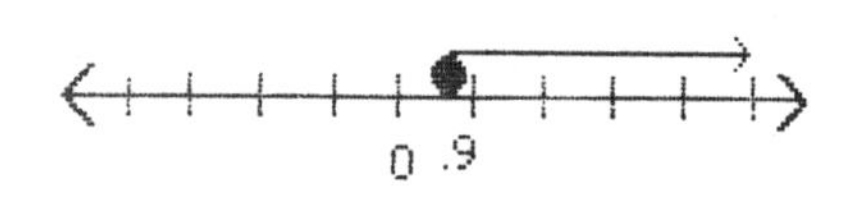

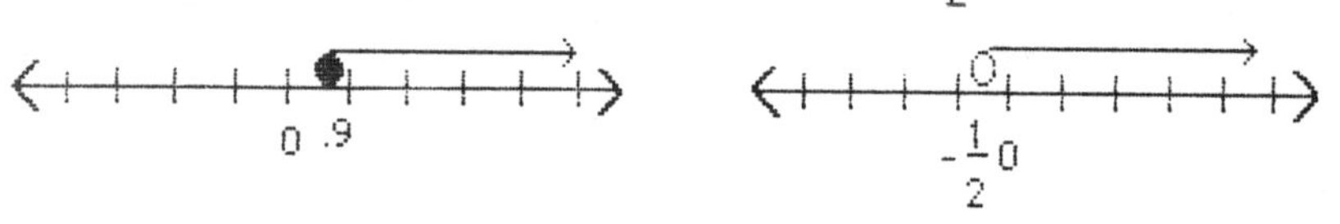

e) none of these

20. Solve the inequality $\frac{1}{8} < x + \frac{5}{8} < 2\frac{1}{8}$ and graph the solution.

20. ____________

a) $\frac{3}{4} < x < 2\frac{3}{4}$

b) $-\frac{1}{2} < x < 1\frac{1}{2}$

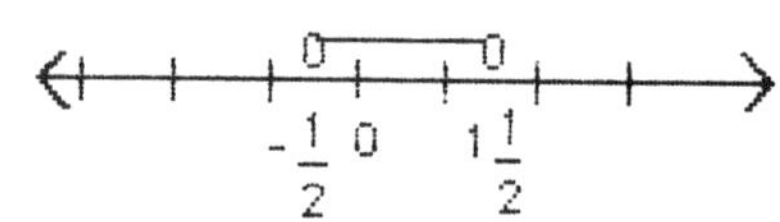

c) $\frac{1}{8} < x < 1\frac{1}{2}$

d) $-\frac{1}{2} < x < 2\frac{1}{8}$

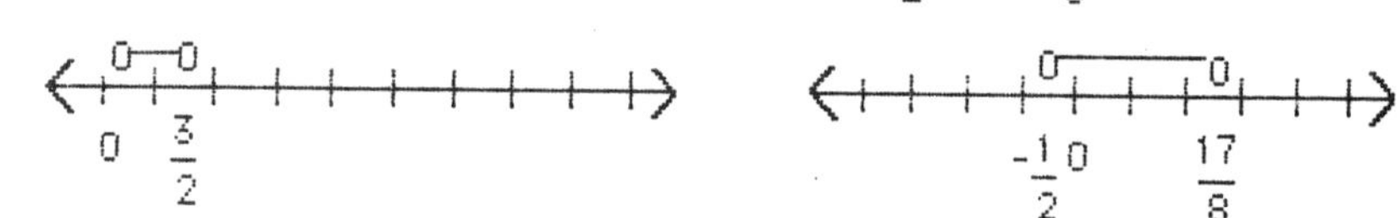

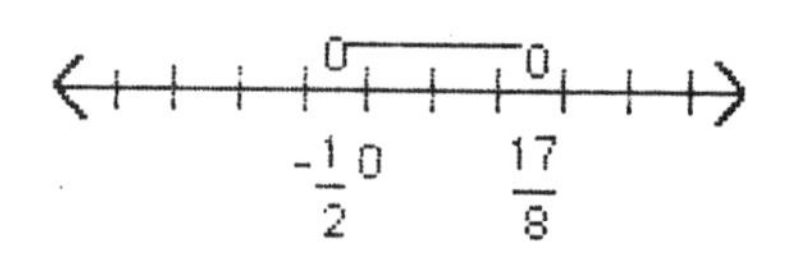

e) none of these

21. Solve the inequality: $4 - 6x > -12$. 21. ________

a. $x < \frac{8}{3}$

b. $x > -10$

c. $x < \frac{4}{3}$

d. $x < 6$

e. none of these

22. Solve the inequality: $-9 \le 3 - 4x < -1$ 22. ________

a. $\frac{3}{2} \ge x > -\frac{1}{2}$

b. $-3 \le x \le 1$

c. $3 \ge x > 1$

d. $-16 \le x < 0$

e. none of these

23. The local school P.T.A. makes 65¢ on each birthday calendar it sells in the community. How many calendars must it sell to make a profit of at least $7800? 23. ________

a. at least 120 calendars

b. at least 1200 calendars

c. at least 120,000 calendars

d. at least 12,000 calendars

e. none of these

24. A rectangular garden, 62 feet by 48 feet, is to be enclosed by fencing costing $1.50 per foot. What is the total cost of the fence? 24. ________

a. $436.40

b. $300.00

c. $461.40

d. $320.00

e. none of these

25. Solve: $y = \frac{9 - 2x}{5}$ for x 25. ________

a. $x = \frac{5y - 9}{2}$

b. $x = 5y - 7$

c. $x = \frac{9 - 5y}{2}$

d. $x = \frac{4 - y}{2}$

e. none of these

Name ____________________ Chapter 2 Form F Score ______

1. Determine the coefficients of the like terms in the expresssion: 1. ________

$$12x^2y - 6xy^2 - x^2y^2 + xy + 4x^2y^2$$

a. 12, -1, and 4
b. 4 and 1
c. 12, -6, -1, 1, and 4
d. 4 and -1
e. none of these

2. Simplify by combining like terms: 2. ________

$$8x - 11 - 2y - 15x - 6y + y - 3$$

a. $-7x - 7y - 14$
b. $-28xy$
c. $23x - 7y - 14$
d. $-7x - 9y - 14$
e. none of these

3. Remove parentheses using the distributive property, then simplify: $\frac{4}{9}\left(\frac{3}{2} - \frac{3}{4}p^2\right) - \frac{4}{5}\left(\frac{25}{12}p^2 + 10\right)$ 3. ________

a. $-7\frac{1}{3} - \frac{2}{3}p^2$
b. $-\frac{4}{3}p^2 - 8$
c. $-7\frac{1}{3} - 2p^2$
d. $10\frac{2}{3}p^2 - 2$
e. none of these

4. Solve the equation: $x - 6.21 = -3.9$ 4. ________

a. $x = -10.11$
b. $x = 2.31$
c. $x = 3.31$
d. $x = 3.71$
e. none of these

5. Solve the equation: $9(2 + x) = 4 + 10x$ 5. ________

a. $x = 2$
b. $x = \frac{14}{9}$
c. $x = 22$
d. $x = \frac{22}{19}$
e. none of these

6. Write an equation and solve: The sum of three fourths a number and four is the difference of six and one fourth the number. 6. ____________

a. 10
b. -2
c. 2
d. -20
e. none of these

7. Solve the equation: $-3.4 = \frac{x}{2.5}$ 7. ____________

a. $x = -1.36$
b. $x = -0.9$
c. $x = -8.3$
d. $x = -8.5$
e. none of these

8. Solve the equation: $2\frac{5}{9} - 6\frac{2}{3} = 4\frac{2}{3}y - 8\frac{5}{6}y$ 8. ____________

a. $y = \frac{9}{10}$
b. $y = \frac{74}{75}$
c. $y = 1\frac{2}{3}$
d. $y = \frac{13}{15}$
e. none of these

9. Solve the equation: $23.35 - 4.9m = -8.5$ 9. ____________

a. $m = 9.95$
b. $m = -26.95$
c. $m = 6.5$
d. $m = -3.02$
e. none of these

10. Solve the equation: $19y - 2y - 35 + 7 = 5y + 4y$ 10. ____________

a. $y = \frac{7}{2}$
b. $y = -2$
c. $y = 2$
d. $y = \frac{2}{7}$
e. none of these

11. Solve the equation: $\frac{5}{8}(8 - 3w) - 3 = \frac{1}{4}(6 - 5w)$ 11. ________

a. $w = 2$
b. $w = \frac{5}{4}$
c. $w = -\frac{1}{4}$
d. $w = -\frac{28}{25}$
e. none of these

12. Write an equation and solve: The sum of two and one and three eighths times a number is negative five eighths. 12. ________

a. $-\frac{7}{11}$
b. 1
c. $-\frac{5}{27}$
d. $-1\frac{10}{11}$
e. none of these

13. Convert the word phrase "Twenty-four times the sum of a number and 18, reduced by 21" into a mathematical expression using n as the variable. 13. ________

a. $24n + 18 - 21$
b. $24(n + 18) - 21$
c. $24(n + 18 - 21)$
d. $\frac{24(n + 18)}{21}$
e. none of these

14. Find the number described by "Negative five times the difference of two and a number is four". 14. ________

a. $2\frac{4}{5}$
b. -14
c. $1\frac{1}{5}$
d. 22
e. none of these

15. Find the number described by "The difference of twice a number and 23.4 is 5% of the number ".

15. ____________

a. -7.8
b. 11.4
c. 18
d. 12
e. none of these

16. The sum of two numbers is 21. The larger of the two numbers is 5 times the smaller. Find the larger number.

16. ____________

a. 5.25
b. 3.5
c. 17.5
d. 15
e. none of these

17. Susan has $4.15 in nickels and quarters. If she has five more nickels than quarters, how many nickels does she have?

17. ____________

a. 13
b. 18
c. 10
d. 19
e. none of these

18. A grocer mixes 6 pounds of coffee that is 60% Colombian with one that is 80% Colombian. How much of the second type should be used to obtain a mixture that is 78% Colombian?

18. ____________

a. 18 pounds
b. 54 pounds
c. 120 pounds
d. 52 pounds
e. none of these

19. Solve the inequality $6 + 4x > 5x + 8$ and graph the solution. 19. ____________

a) $2 > x$

0 2

b) $-2 > x$

-2 0

c) $x < -2$

d) $x > 2$

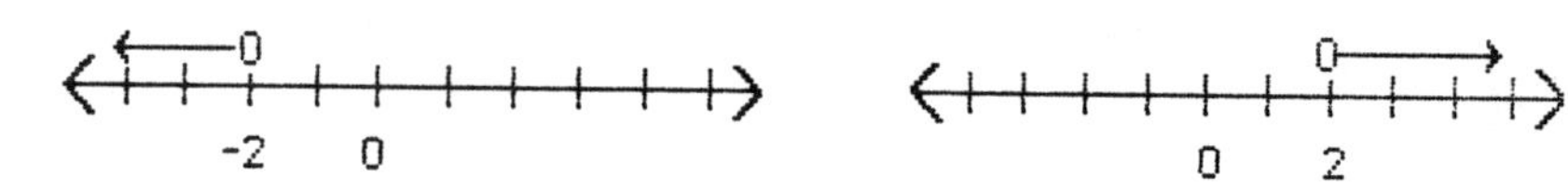
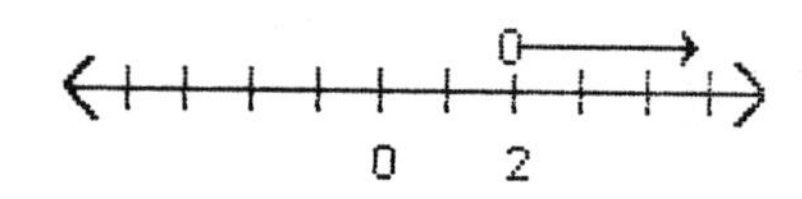

e) none of these

20. Solve the inequality $-\frac{1}{2} \le x + \frac{3}{10} < \frac{4}{5}$ and graph the solution. 20. ____________

a) $-\frac{4}{5} \le x < \frac{1}{2}$

b) $-\frac{1}{5} \le x < \frac{11}{10}$

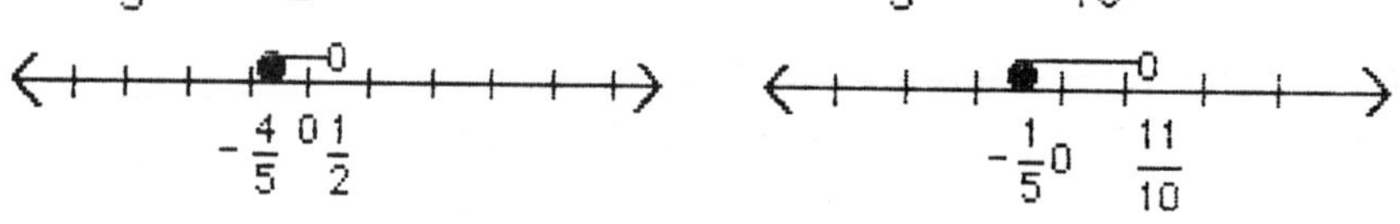
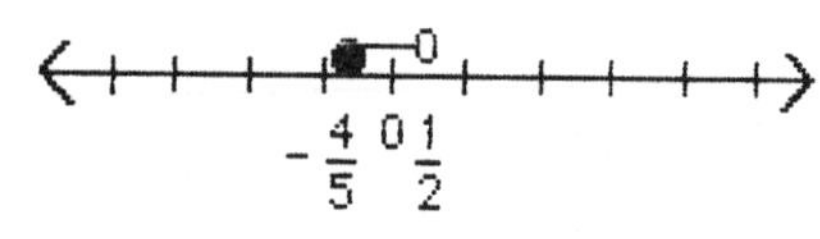

c) $-\frac{4}{5} \le x < \frac{4}{5}$

d) $-\frac{1}{2} \le x < \frac{1}{2}$

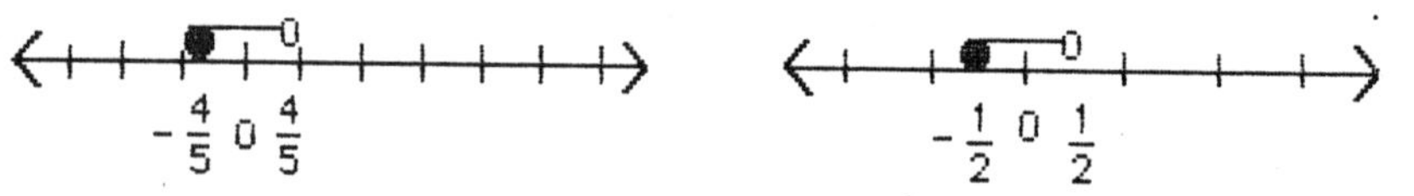
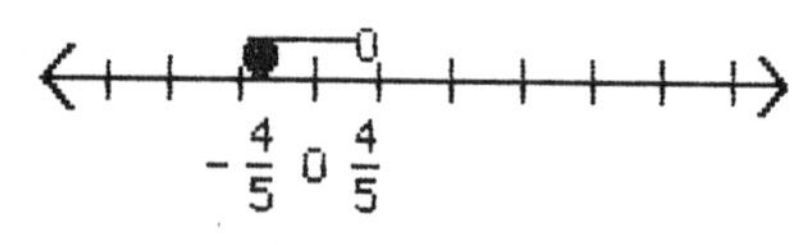

e) none of these

21. Solve the inequality: $3 + 3(x - 5) < 6 - 7x$ 21. ____________

a. $x < \frac{4}{5}$

b. $x < \frac{9}{5}$

c. $\frac{3}{2} > x$

d. $\frac{36}{13} > x$

e. none of these

22. Solve the inequality: $-4 < \frac{4 - 6x}{6} < 2$ 22. ________

a. $\frac{10}{3} > x > -\frac{8}{3}$

b. $-22 < x < 14$

c. $-\frac{14}{3} < x < \frac{8}{3}$

d. $\frac{1}{3} > x > -\frac{2}{3}$

e. none of these

23. A company that makes light bulbs makes 12¢ profit on each 4-pack they sell. How many 4-packs must they sell to have a profit of at least $900? 23. 

a. at least 7500 packs

b. at least 750 packs

c. at least 75 packs

d. at least 75000 packs

e. none of these

24. The measure of the first angle of a triangle is three fourths the measure of a second angle. The measure of a third angle is twice the second angle. Find the measure of the largest angle. 24. ________

a. 48°

b. 110°

c. 90°

d. 96°

e. none of these

25. Solve: $w + 3 = 4 - 2(x + 1)$ for x 25. ________

a. $x = \frac{w + 1}{2}$

b. $x = \frac{2 - w}{2}$

c. $x = \frac{w + 5}{-2}$

d. $x = \frac{-1 - w}{2}$

e. none of these

CHAPTER # 2 TEST KEYS

Form A

1. -6 and 12
2. $-2a + 9b - 3$
3. $2y - 36$
4. $x = -3\frac{1}{24}$
5. $y = 9$
6. -10
7. $t = -\frac{9}{5}$
8. $x = \frac{8}{3}$
9. $x = 3$
10. $t = \frac{4}{5}$
11. $y = \frac{5}{3}$
12. $x = 3\frac{2}{3}$
13. $\frac{5}{6}(2n + 12)$
14. -2
15. 80
16. 28 years old
17. 9 nickles, 15 dimes
18. 37.5 ℓ of 16%, 12.5 ℓ of 24%
19. $x < 15$
20. $-4.5 < x < -0.5$
21. $x \geq \frac{3}{28}$
22. $\frac{5}{2} > x > 1$

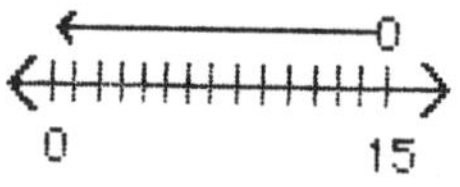

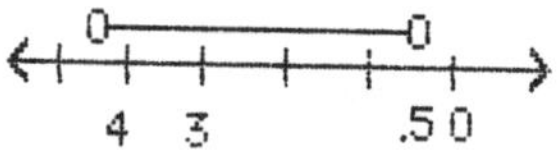

Form B

1. -8 and 9
2. $-4x - 6y - 5$
3. $34x - 45$
4. $x = \frac{1}{18}$
5. $x = 27$
6. -4
7. $x = -10$
8. $x = 1.6$
9. $t = -\frac{1}{2}$
10. $n = -0.6$
11. $x = \frac{10}{7}$
12. $x = \frac{3}{2}$
13. $\frac{3}{4}(2n - 5)$
14. 11
15. 100
16. 30 years old
17. 8 dimes, 11 quarters
18. 30 ℓ of 12%, 10 ℓ of 20%
19. $x \geq \frac{1}{2}$

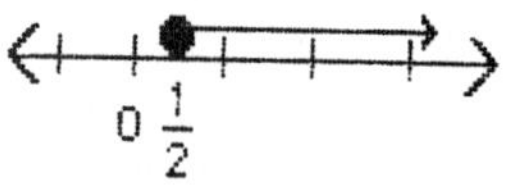

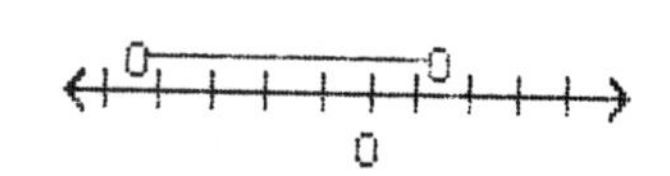

20. $-4.5 < x < 1.5$
21. $x < 4$
22. $4 > x > \frac{7}{3}$

CHAPTER # 2 TEST KEYS

Form A

23. score $\geq$ 72%
24. 40 minutes
25. $y = \frac{3x - 12}{4}$

Form B

23. score $\geq$ 78%
24. $1\frac{1}{2}$ hours
25. $x = \frac{6 - 3y}{4}$

CHAPTER # 2 TEST KEYS

Form C

1. -9 and 6
2. $\frac{5}{6}x^2 - \frac{17}{12}y + \frac{5}{6}$
3. $16w - 19$
4. $x = -10.22$
5. $x = 11$
6. $x = -1$
7. $t = -29.16$
8. $t = 4$
9. $w = -3.5$
10. $x = 2$
11. $y = 3$
12. $x = -2\frac{4}{5}$
13. $.37(625 + x)$
14. -2
15. $-2\frac{1}{2}$
16. $9\frac{3}{4}$ ft.
17. 8 10's and 7 20's
18. 8.4 pounds
19. $x \le 4$

20. $-3 \le x < 3$

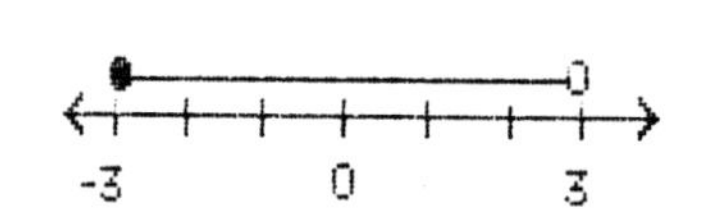

21. $x \ge 1$
22. $7 > x > -\frac{9}{2}$
23. $x \ge .4$
24. \$722
25. $x = \frac{16 - y}{4}$

Form D

1. c) -8.1 and -3.1
2. b) $2.4w - 0.55w^2 + 3.6$
3. d) $10x - 6$
4. a) $x = -\frac{1}{24}$
5. c) $x = 11$
6. d) 9
7. b) $y = -4$
8. e) none of these
9. a) $x = 2$
10. d) $s = -\frac{3}{5}$
11. c) $x = \frac{3}{2}$
12. a) $x = 2\frac{3}{5}$
13. c) $0.65(350 + 2n)$
14. e) none of these
15. b) -3
16. b) $10\frac{2}{3}$ ft.
17. a) 9
18. d) 40 ounces
19. b) $x \le 11$
20. c) $-3 < x \le 2$
21. d) $y < \frac{1}{8}$
22. b) $4 \ge x > -\frac{1}{3}$
23. e) none of these
24. a) \$195
25. b) $y = \frac{4x - 12}{3}$

CHAPTER # 2 TEST KEYS

Form E

1. b) -5 and -1
2. d) $\frac{23}{18}a^2 - \frac{1}{2}b + \frac{8}{3}$
3. a) $-1.9 - 5t^2$
4. c) $x = -2\frac{1}{10}$
5. a) $y = 34$
6. e) none of these
7. a) $t = -\frac{9}{4}$
8. d) $x = 2.5$
9. b) $y = \frac{13}{15}$
10. c) $x = -1.8$
11. b) $x = \frac{5}{8}$
12. b) 10
13. d) $\frac{1}{x + 10}$
14. c) $3\frac{1}{2}$
15. e) none of these
16. d) \$2586
17. c) 22
18. a) 16 gal.
19. d) $x > -\frac{1}{2}$
20. b) $-\frac{1}{2} < x < 1\frac{1}{2}$
21. a) $x < \frac{8}{3}$
22. c) $3 \geq x > 1$
23. d) at least 12000 calendars
24. e) none of these
25. c) $x = \frac{9 - 5y}{2}$

Form F

1. d) 4 and -1
2. a) $-7x - 7y - 14$
3. c) $-7\frac{1}{3} - 2p^2$
4. b) $x = 2.31$
5. e) none of these
6. c) 2
7. d) $x = -8.5$
8. b) $y = \frac{74}{75}$
9. c) $m = 6.5$
10. a) $y = \frac{7}{2}$
11. e) none of these
12. d) $-1\frac{10}{11}$
13. b) $24(n + 18) - 21$
14. a) $2\frac{4}{5}$
15. d) 12
16. c) 17.5
17. b) 18
18. b) 54 pounds
19. c) $x < -2$
20. a) $-\frac{4}{5} \leq x < \frac{1}{2}$
21. b) $x < \frac{9}{5}$
22. e) none of these
23. a) at least 7500 packs
24. d) 96°
25. $x = \frac{-1 - w}{2}$

Name ________________ Chapter 3 Form A Score ______

1. Find the value of 8^4 1. ________

2. Simplify: $(xy)^0$ 2. ________

3. Simplify: $x^5(x^2)^8$ 3. ________

4. Write the expression 8^{-1} without negative exponents. 4. ________

5. Simplify and write your answer without negative exponents: $\frac{28m^2}{7m^5}$ 5. ________

6. Write 8×10^{-4} in standard notation. 6. ________

7. Evaluate using scientific notation and write your answer in standard form. $\frac{800}{0.025}$ 7. ________

8. Multiply $\frac{6}{7}mn^5$ by $\frac{35}{36}m^3n$. 8. ________

9. Simplify the expression: $(3ab^2c^3)(-2ac^2)(a^2bc^3)$ 9. ______________

10. Simplify the expression writing your answer without negative exponents: $\frac{-6xy^3}{21x^5y}$ 10. ______________

11. Find the degree of the polynomial $7x^2 - 12x^5 + 3$ 11. ______________

12. Simplify the polynomial and write your answer in descending order of the exponents: 12. ______________

$$9 - y^4 + 8y^3 + y^3 - 7y^4 - 3$$

13. Evaluate $2x^3 - x^4 - 1$ for $x = -2$ 13. ______________

14. Add the polynomials: 14. ______________

$$(12x^4 - 6x^2 + 6) + (x^4 - 3x^2 - x)$$

15. Subtract: $(-6x^4 + 8x^2 - 5x) - (-x^2 - 7x^4 - 12)$ 15. ______________

16. Simplify. Write your answer in descending order of exponents.

$$(5z^2 - z - 2) - (6 - 3z + z^2) + (9z^2 - 6 - 11z)$$

17. The sides of a triangle are $8x^2 + x - 3$, $4x + 1$, and $x^2 + 6x$. Express the perimeter as a polynomial in x.

17. ____________

18. Simplify: $18 - [6x^2 + 3 - (x^2 - 5)]$

18. ____________

19. Simplify: $(5x - 3)(x^2 - 6x - 9)$

19. ____________

20. Simplify: $(x - 3y)(x + 4y) - (2x - y)(5x + 2y)$

20. ____________

21. Find the product: $(x - 12)^2$

21. ____________

22. Find the product: $\left(a + \frac{7}{8}\right)\left(a - \frac{7}{8}\right)$

22. ____________

23. The difference of the square of a number and three is equal to the square of the sum of the number and one. Find the number.

23. ____________

24. Divide and simplify: $\dfrac{7.2m^6 - 4.8m^4 + 12m^2}{2.4m^3}$

24. ____________

25. Divide: $\dfrac{3 - 8y + y^3}{y + 3}$

25. ____________

Name ______________________ Chapter 3 Form B Score ________

1. Find the value of $\left(\frac{5}{9}\right)^3$ 1. ______________

2. Simplify: $y^5 \cdot y^8$ 2. ______________

3. Simplify: $(x^3)^4(y^7)^3$ 3. ______________

4. Write the expression y^{-12} without negative exponents. 4. ______________

5. Simplify and write your answer without negative exponents: $\left(\frac{3y}{z}\right)^{-4}$ 5. ______________

6. Write 2.35×10^3 in standard notation. 6. ______________

7. Evaluate using scientific notation and write your answer in standard form. (0.00006)(18400) 7. ______________

8. Multiply $-\frac{3}{4}(w^2y^5)^3$ by $(4wy^2)^2$ 8. ______________

9. Simplify the expression:

$$\frac{7}{10}(20m^2n^3p)(mnp^5)(m^3p^2)$$

9. ____________

10. Simplify the expression writing your answer without negative exponents:

$$\frac{6xy^2w^3(-4)xyw^4}{3x^5yw^6}$$

10. ____________

11. Find the degree of the polynomial $\frac{2}{3}y^4 - 8y + \frac{1}{3}y^2$

11. ____________

12. Simplify the polynomial and write your answer in descending order of the exponents:

$$\frac{3}{5}w^2 - \frac{1}{2}w - \frac{7}{10}w + \frac{3}{2}w^2 - \frac{1}{10}w^2$$

12. ____________

13. Evaluate $\frac{1}{3}y^3 + \frac{1}{4}y^2 - 5$ for $y = -3$

13. ____________

14. Add the polynomials:

$$(m^5 - 7m^3 - m + 1) + (3m^3 - m^4 + 2m - 6)$$

14. ____________

15. Subtract:

$$(3.4d^5 + 8.1d^3 - d + 7) - (3.6d^3 + 6.1d^5 + 3d)$$

15. ____________

16. Simplify. Write your answer in descending order of exponents.

$$(-4y^3 + 8y^2) - (-6y^4 - 2y^3) - (y^4 + 7y^3 - y^2)$$

16. __________

17. Subtract the sum of $(-3x^2 - x + 6)$ and $(4x^4 - x^2)$ from $(7x^4 + 8x^2 - 3)$

17. __________

18. Simplify: $7x + [9x - (3 - x)]$

18. __________

19. Simplify: $(3x + 1)(4x^2 - 6x - 3)$

19. __________

20. Simplify: $(6m + 4)(2m - 5) + 12(3 - m)$

20. __________

21. Find the product: $(7w - t)^2$

21. __________

22. Find the product: $\left(\frac{3}{7} + \frac{1}{3}k\right)\left(\frac{3}{7} - \frac{1}{3}k\right)$

22. __________

23. Find two consecutive odd integers so that the difference of their squares is 120.

23. __________

24. Divide and simplify: $\dfrac{15y^4 - 12y^2 + 6y}{3y^4}$

24. ____________

25. Divide: $(9 - 3y^4 + y^6 + 3y^2) \div (y^2 + 3)$

25. ____________

Name ____________________ Chapter 3 Form C Score ________

1. Find the value of -9^2 1. ____________

2. Simplify: $a^{15}a^2b^{14}b$ 2. ____________

3. Simplify: $(-\frac{3}{5}mt^2)^3$ 3. ____________

4. Write the expression $(3p^2t)^{-4}$ without negative exponents. 4. ____________

5. Simplify and write your answer without negative exponents: $(a^{-3}b)^{-2}(ab^3)^{-1}$ 5. ____________

6. Write 0.00483 in scientific notation. 6. ____________

7. Evaluate using scientific notation and write your answer in standard form. $\frac{(65{,}000)(0.000009)}{(0.006)(.3000)}$ 7. ____________

8. Divide: $\frac{1}{8}xy^5$ by $\frac{1}{2}x^3$. 8. ____________

9. Simplify the expression: $\left(-6m^4n^5\right)^2\left(-\frac{1}{3}mn\right)^4$ 9. ______

10. Simplify the expression writing your answer without negative exponents: $\dfrac{45\,(g^2h^3m^4)^3}{15(gm^2)^5(gh^2)}$ 10. ______

11. Find the degree of the polynomial 11. ______

$$a^3 - 3a^4 + 4a^5 + a^7 - 1$$

12. Simplify the polynomial and write your answer in descending order of the exponents: 12. ______

$$12\left(d^4 - d^2 + \frac{1}{3}d\right) - \frac{1}{2}\left(8d^2 - 4d^4\right)$$

13. The daily cost C (in dollars) of making x refrigerators is given by $C = 160x - 3x^2 + \frac{1}{4}x^3 + 400$. 13. ______

Find the cost if 8 refrigerators are made in a day.

14. Add the polynomials: 14. ______

$$(9 - 3w + 6w^3 + 4w^2) + (8w^4 - 5w^2 - 6w + 6)$$

15. Subtract: $\left(\frac{3}{4}t^4 - \frac{1}{6}t + \frac{1}{3}\right) - \left(\frac{5}{6}t^3 - \frac{1}{2}t - \frac{5}{12}\right)$ 15. ____________

16. Simplify. Write your answer in descending order of exponents. 16. ____________

$$12x^3 - 7x^2 - [x^2 - (3x^3 - 9x^2)]$$

17. Find the sum of 17. ____________

$$(3x^2 + xy - 8y^2) \text{ and } (15y^2 - 9xy - 11x^2)$$

18. Simplify: $-2m - \{5m - [8 - (12 - 7m)]\}$ 18. ____________

19. Simplify: $(x + 8)(x^2 + 3x + 1)$ 19. ____________

20. Simplify: $(2y + 7)(3y - 2) - (6y - 1)(y + 1)$ 20. ____________

21. Find the product: $(x^2 + 9y^2)^2$ 21. ____________

22. Find the product: $(p^3 - q)(p^3 + q)$ 22. ____________

23. The square of the difference of three times a number and two is equal to nine times the sum of the square of the number and four. Find the number.

23. ______________

24. Divide and simplify: $\dfrac{56b^9 - 28b^6 - 14b^3}{14b^3}$

24. ______________

25. Divide: $\dfrac{2x^4 + 2x^3 - 12x^2 + x + 3}{x + 3}$

25. ______________

Name ______________________ Chapter 3 Form D Score ______

1. Find the value of 4^3 1. ________

   a. 12
   b. 81
   c. 64
   d. 256
   e. none of these

2. Simplify: $(mnt)^0$ 2. ________

   a. 1
   b. mnt
   c. 0
   d. mn
   e. none of these

3. Simplify: $m^7(m^3)^5$ 3. ________

   a. m^{105}
   b. m^{26}
   c. m^{15}
   d. m^{22}
   e. none of these

4. Write the expression 6^{-1} without negative exponents. 4. ________

   a. -6
   b. $\frac{1}{6}$
   c. $-\frac{1}{6}$
   d. 6
   e. none of these

5. Simplify and write your answer without negative exponents: $\frac{33x^5}{44x^9}$ 5. ________

   a. $\frac{3}{4x^4}$
   b. $\frac{3}{4}x^4$
   c. $\frac{3}{4}x$
   d. $\frac{3x}{4}$
   e. none of these

6. Write 6×10^{-3} in standard notation. 6. ____________

a. 6000

b. 0.006

c. 0.0006

d. 0.06

e. none of these

7. Evaluate using scientific notation and write your answer in standard form. $\frac{0.0387}{900}$ 7. ____________

a. 0.000403

b. 0.00043

c. 0.043

d. 0.43

e. none of these

8. Multiply $\frac{15}{28}p^3q$ by $\frac{42}{45}pq^5$. 8. ____________

a. $\frac{1}{2}p^3q^5$

b. $\frac{3}{14}p^3q^5$

c. $\frac{3}{14}p^4q^6$

d. $\frac{1}{2}p^4q^6$

e. none of these

9. Simplify the expression: $(4x^2yz)(-3xy^4)(-xyz^3)$ 9. ____________

a. $-12x^4y^6z^4$

b. $-12x^2y^4z^3$

c. $12x^4y^6z^4$

d. $12x^2y^4z^3$

e. none of these

10. Simplify the expression writing your answer without negative exponents: $\frac{-12m^2n^2}{28mn^6}$ 10. ____________

a. $-\frac{m}{8n^4}$

b. $-\frac{3m^2}{7n^4}$

c. $-\frac{3m}{7n^4}$

d. $-\frac{3m}{7n^3}$

e. none of these

11. Find the degree of the polynomial $-\frac{2}{3}x^3 - 8x^7 - 1$ 11. ____________

a. 3
b. 7
c. 0
d. 10
e. none of these

12. Simplify the polynomial and write your answer in descending order of the exponents: 12. ____________

$$11 - z^2 - 6z^4 + 3z^2 + 12 - z^4$$

a. $18z^{12}$
b. $23 - 2z^2 - 7z^4$
c. $-7z^4 + 4z^2 + 23$
d. $-7z^4 + 2z^2 + 23$
e. none of these

13. Evaluate $5x^2 - x^4 - 3$ for $x = -3$ 13. ____________

a. 123
b. 303
c. -93
d. 54
e. none of these

14. Add the polynomials: 14. ____________

$$(6y^3 - 3y^5 + 2) + (4y^5 - 2y^3 - 6)$$

a. $10y^3 - 5y^5 - 4$
b. $y^5 + 4y^3 - 4$
c. $y^5 + 8y^3 - 4$
d. $y^5 + 4y^3 - 8$
e. none of these

15. Subtract: $(-12y^3 + 7y^2 - 3) - (5y^2 - 2y^3 - y)$ 15. ____________

a. $-10y^3 + 2y^2 - y - 3$

b. $-10y^3 + 2y^2 - 3y$

c. $-10y^3 + 2y^2 + y - 3$

d. $-14y^3 + 2y^2 - y - 3$

e. none of these

16. Simplify. Write your answer in descending order of exponents. 16. ________

$$(7m + m^2 - 3) + (8m^2 - 4m - 6) - (2 - 7m - 3m^2)$$

a. $12m^2 + 10m - 11$
b. $6m^2 - 4m - 9$
c. $6m^2 + 10m - 11$
d. $11m^2 + 10m - 11$
e. none of these

17. The sides of a triangle are $9t^2 - 6$, $8t^2 + t - 1$, and $t^2 - 3t$. Express the perimeter as a polynomial in t. 17. ________

a. $18t^2 - 2t + 6$
b. $18t^2 - 4t - 7$
c. $18t^2 - 2t - 7$
d. $16t^2 - 7$
e. none of these

18. Simplify: $26 - [12y^2 + 9 - 4(3 - x^2)]$ 18. ________

a. $11 - 12y^2 + 5x^2$
b. $12y^2 - 4x^2 + 29$
c. $23 - 12y^2 - x^2$
d. $29 - 12y^2 + 4x^2$
e. none of these

19. Simplify: $(8x - 5)(x^2 - 2x - 7)$ 19. ________

a. $8x^3 - 21x^2 - 46x + 35$
b. $8x^3 - 2x + 35$
c. $8x^3 - 21x^2 - 66x + 35$
d. $8x^3 - 21x^2 + 10x + 35$
e. none of these

20. Simplify: $(a - 4b)(a + 2b) - (5a - b)(a + 3b)$ 20. ________

a. $-4a^2 - 5b^2$
b. $-4a^2 + 12ab - 11b^2$
c. $-4a^2 - 16ab - 11b^2$
d. $-4a^2 - 16ab - 5b^2$
e. none of these

21. Find the product: $(y - 13)^2$ 21. ________

a. $y^2 - 26y + 169$
b. $y^2 - 13y + 169$
c. $y^2 + 169$
d. $y^2 + 26y + 169$
e. none of these

22. Find the product: $\left(t - \frac{8}{9}\right)\left(t + \frac{8}{9}\right)$ 22. ____________

a. $t^2 - \frac{16}{9}t - \frac{64}{81}$

b. $t^2 + \frac{16}{9}t - \frac{64}{81}$

c. $t^2 - \frac{16}{9}$

d. $t^2 - \frac{64}{81}$

e. none of these

23. The difference of the square of a number and eight is equal to the square of the sum of the number and four. Find the number. 23. 

a. 2

b. -3

c. -6

d. 3

e. none of these

24. Divide and simplify: $\dfrac{24.5x^4 - 10.5x^3 + 14x}{3.5x^2}$ 24. ____________

a. $8x^2 - 3x + 4$

b. $7x^2 - 3x + 4x$

c. $7x^2 - 3x + \frac{4}{x}$

d. $7x^2 - 10.5x^3 + 14x$

e. none of these

25. Divide: $\dfrac{4 - 15x + x^3}{x + 4}$ 25. ____________

a. $x^2 - 4x + 1$

b. $x^2 - 15$

c. $x^2 - 19 + \frac{80}{x + 4}$

d. $x^2 + 4x + 1$

e. none of these

Name ______________________ Chapter 3 Form E Score ______

1. Find the value of $\left(-\frac{4}{7}\right)^4$ 1. ____________

a. $\frac{256}{2401}$

b. $\frac{16}{7}$

c. $\frac{64}{343}$

d. $\frac{1024}{16807}$

e. none of these

2. Simplify: $w^6 \cdot w^2$ 2. ____________

a. $2w^{12}$

b. w^{12}

c. w^8

d. $2w^8$

e. none of these

3. Simplify: $(z^4)^6(w^5)^4$ 3. ____________

a. $z^{10}w^9$

b. $z^{24}w^{20}$

c. $z^{10}w^{20}$

d. $z^{24}w^9$

e. none of these

4. Write the expression w^{-9} without negative exponents. 4. ____________

a. $-9w$

b. $-w^9$

c. $-1/w^9$

d. $1/w^9$

e. none of these

5. Simplify and write your answer without negative exponents: $\left(\frac{4m}{n}\right)^{-3}$ 5. ____________

a. $-12m^3/n^3$

b. $-n^3/64m^3$

c. $n^3/64m^3$

d. $-\frac{64m^3}{n^3}$

e. none of these

6. Write 34.5×10^6 in standard notation. 6. ____________

a. 34,500,000
b. 0.0000345
c. 345,000
d. 3,450,000
e. none of these

7. Evaluate using scientific notation and write your answer in standard form. (83500)(0.0004) 7. ____________

a. 334
b. 3.34
c. 0.00334
d. 33.4
e. none of these

8. Multiply $-\frac{5}{8}(c^3d^4)^2$ by $(-16cd^3)^2$. 8. ____________

a. $160c^8d^{14}$
b. $-160c^{10}d^{25}$
c. $100c^8d^{14}$
d. $\frac{-5}{2048}c^4d^2$
e. none of these

9. Simplify the expression: $\frac{5}{6}(18xy^3z)(xy^5)(yz^4)$ 9. ____________

a. $15xy^{15}z^4$
b. $15x^2y^9z^5$
c. $15x^2y^{16}z^5$
d. $15x^2y^8z^5$
e. none of these

10. Simplify the expression writing your answer without negative exponents: $\frac{10m^2n^3p^2(-6)mn^2p^4}{14m^6np^8}$ 10. ____________

a. $-\frac{30n^4}{7m^3p^2}$
b. $-\frac{30n^5}{7m^3p^2}$
c. $-\frac{30n^5}{7m^3}$
d. $-\frac{30n^4}{7m^2p^2}$
e. none of these

11. Find the degree of the polynomial 11. ____________

$$-\frac{5}{8}x^7 - \frac{3x}{2} + \frac{7x^4}{9} - 1$$

a. 11
b. 4
c. 7
d. 1
e. none of these

12. Simplify the polynomial and write your answer in descending order of the exponents: 12. ____________

$$\frac{4}{9}y^3 - \frac{1}{3}y - \frac{17}{18}y^3 + \frac{8}{9}y^3 + \frac{5}{6}y$$

a. $-\frac{5}{18}y^3 + \frac{1}{2}y$
b. $-\frac{1}{18}y^3 + \frac{1}{2}y$
c. $\frac{41}{18}y^3 + \frac{1}{2}y$
d. $\frac{7}{18}y^3 + \frac{4}{3}y$
e. none of these

13. Evaluate $\frac{5}{6}z^4 - \frac{1}{3}z - 2$ for $z = -2$ 13. ____________

a. $6\frac{31}{81}$
b. $10\frac{2}{3}$
c. -8
d. 12
e. none of these

14. Add the polynomials: 14. ____________

$$(t^4 - 4t + 3t^2 - 3) + (6t^2 + 5t - t^3 - 6)$$

a. $t^4 - t^3 + 9t^2 + t - 9$
b. $t^4 - t^3 + 3t^2 + t - 9$
c. $t^4 - t^3 + 9t^2 + 9t - 9$
d. $6t^6 + 3t - 9$
e. none of these

15. Subtract: 15. ____________

$$(4.1w^6 - 3.6w^3 - w - 1) - (5.6w - 8.5w^3 + w^6)$$

a. $3.1w^6 - 12.1w^3 - 6.6w - 1$
b. $3.1w^6 + 4.9w^3 - 6.6w - 1$
c. $3.1w^6 + 5.1w^3 - 6.6w - 1$
d. $3.1w^6 - 12.1w^3 + 4.6w - 1$
e. none of these

16. Simplify. Write your answer in descending order of exponents.

$(-9p^5 - 4p^2) - (7p^3 - 3p^5) - (p^5 - 8p^3 + 6p^2)$

a. $-5p^5 + p^3 + 2p^2$
b. $-13p^5 - p^3 - 10p^2$
c. $-7p^5 + p^3 - 10p^2$
d. $-7p^5 - 15p^3 - 10p^2$
e. none of these

16. ____________

17. Subtract the sum of $(-z^3 - 2z + 3)$ and $(5z - 2z^3)$ from $(15z^3 - 12z - 6)$.

a. $-18z^3 + 15z + 9$
b. $12z^3 - 9z - 3$
c. $12z^2 - 15z - 9$
d. $18z^3 - 15z - 9$
e. none of these

17. ____________

18. Simplify: $13y - [18y - (7 - y)]$

a. $-4y - 7$
b. $-6y + 7$
c. $-4y + 7$
d. $-6y - 7$
e. none of these

18. ____________

19. Simplify: $(4x + 3)(7x^2 - 8x - 1)$

a. $28x^3 - 32x^2 - 24x - 3$
b. $28x^3 - 9x^2 - 28x - 3$
c. $28x^3 - 53x^2 - 28x - 3$
d. $28x^3 - 9x^2 - 20x - 3$
e. none of these

19. ____________

20. Simplify: $(7d + 5)(3d - 4) - 8(6 - d)$

a. $21d^2 + 8d - 68$
b. $21d^2 - 14d - 68$
c. $21d^2 - 21d - 68$
d. $21d^2 - 5d - 68$
e. none of these

20. ____________

21. Find the product: $(8m - p)^2$

a. $64m^2 + p^2$
b. $64m^2 - 16mp - p^2$
c. $64m^2 - 16mp + p^2$
d. $16m - 2p$
e. none of these

21. ____________

22. Find the product: $\left(\frac{2}{5} + \frac{5}{4}m\right)\left(\frac{2}{5} - \frac{5}{4}m\right)$ 22. ____________

a. $\frac{4}{25} - \frac{25}{16}m^2$

b. $\frac{4}{25} - m - \frac{25}{16}m^2$

c. $\frac{4}{25} - m + \frac{25}{16}m^2$

d. $\frac{4}{25} + \frac{25}{16}m^2$

e. none of these

23. Find two consecutive odd integers so that the difference of their squares is 168. 23. ____________

a. 39 and 41
b. 9 and 11
c. 43 and 45
d. 41 and 43
e. none of these

24. Divide and simplify: $\dfrac{48z^5 - 24z^4 - 16z^3}{8z^5}$ 24. ____________

a. $6 - \frac{3}{z} - \frac{2}{z^2}$

b. $6 - 3z - 2z^2$

c. $6 - 24z^4 - 16z^3$

d. $6 - \frac{3}{z} - \frac{8}{z^2}$

e. none of these

25. Divide: $(2y^2 + y^6 - 4y^4 - 4) \div (y^2 - 2)$ 25. ____________

a. $y^4 - 2y^2 - 2$

b. $y^4 - 2y^2 - 2 + \frac{-8}{y^2 - 2}$

c. $y^4 - 6y^2 + 14 + \frac{-32}{y^2 - 2}$

d. $y^3 - 4y^2 + 2y + 5 + \frac{y + 6}{y^2 - 2}$

e. none of these

Name ____________________ Chapter 3 Form F Score ________

1. Find the value of -2^4 1. ____________
   a. 16
   b. -8
   c. -32
   d. -16
   e. none of these
2. Simplify: $t^{12}t^3w^{17}w$ 2. ____________
   a. $t^{36}w^{17}$
   b. $t^{15}w^{18}$
   c. $t^{36}w^{18}$
   d. $t^{15}w^{17}$
   e. none of these
3. Simplify: $(-\frac{4}{5}a^3b)^3$ 3. ____________
   a. $-\frac{64}{125}a^6b^4$
   b. $-\frac{12}{5}a^9b^3$
   c. $-\frac{64}{125}a^9b$
   d. $-\frac{64}{125}a^6b^3$
   e. none of these
4. Write the expression $(2a^2b^2)^{-6}$ without negative exponents. 4. ____________
   a. $\frac{1}{64a^{12}b^{12}}$
   b. $-\frac{1}{64a^{12}b^2}$
   c. $-12a^2b^2$
   d. $\frac{1}{64a^4b^4}$
   e. none of these
5. Simplify and write your answer without negative exponents: $(m^{-4}n)^{-1}(mn^5)^{-2}$ 5. ____________
   a. m^2n^2
   b. m^2n^{10}
   c. $\frac{1}{m^2n^{11}}$
   d. $\frac{m^2}{n^{11}}$
   e. none of these

6. Write 3569210 in scientific notation. 6. ____________

   a. $3.56921 \cdot 10^7$
   b. $3.56921 \cdot 10^5$
   c. $3.56921 \cdot 10^6$
   d. $3.56921 \cdot 10^{-6}$
   e. none of these

7. Evaluate using scientific notation and write your answer in standard form. $\dfrac{(48000)(0.000006)}{(0.009)(20000)}$ 7. ____________

   a. 1600
   b. 0.0016
   c. 0.0000000016
   d. 0.016
   e. none of these

8. Divide $\frac{3}{4}r^2t$ by $\frac{1}{2}t^4$. 8. ____________

   a. $\dfrac{3r^2}{2t^3}$
   b. $\frac{3}{8}r^2t^5$
   c. $\dfrac{2t^3}{3r^2}$
   d. $\frac{3}{2}r^2t^5$
   e. none of these

9. Simplify the expression: $(-\frac{2}{3}tw)^3(-9t^4w^3)^2$ 9. ____________

   a. $-24t^9w^8$
   b. $-24t^{24}w^{18}$
   c. $36t^{11}w^9$
   d. $-24t^{11}w^9$
   e. none of these

10. Simplify the expression writing your answer without negative exponents: $\dfrac{2.43(x^4y^3z)^6}{9(x^3y)^3(y^3z^4)}$ 10. ____________

   a. $0.27x^{15}y^3z^2$
   b. $0.27x^{15}y^2z^2$
   c. $0.27x^4y^3z^2$
   d. $0.27x^{8/3}y^3z^{3/2}$
   e. none of these

11. Find the degree of the polynomial 11. ____________

$$3m^5 + 5m^7 - 4m^9 - 2m$$

a. 5
b. 7
c. 22
d. 9
e. none of these

12. Simplify the polynomial and write your answer in descending order of the exponents: 12. ____________

$$8(t^3 - 3t + 2) - \frac{3}{4}(12t - 8t^3)$$

a. $14t^3 - 33t + 16$
b. $16t^3 - 33t + 16$
c. $2t^3 - 33t + 16$
d. $-12t + 2$
e. none of these

13. The daily cost C (in dollars) of making x refrigerators is given by $C = 160x - 3x^2 + \frac{1}{4}x^3 + 400$ 13. ____________

Find the cost if 6 refrigerators are made in a single day.

a. \$1090
b. \$1039.38
c. \$1306
d. \$1316
e. none of these

14. Add the polynomials: 14. ____________

$$(15 - 8z^3 + 7z + z^4) + (11z - 6z^3 - 9z^4 - 1)$$

a. $-10z^4 - 14z^3 + 18z + 14$
b. $-8z^4 - 2z^3 + 18z + 14$
c. $-8z^4 - 14z^3 + 18z + 14$
d. $10z^4 - 14z^3 + 4z + 14$
e. none of these

15. Subtract: 15. ____________

$$\left(\frac{1}{3}x^5 - \frac{7}{9}x^3 + \frac{2}{3}\right) - \left(\frac{4}{9}x^4 - \frac{2}{3}x^3 - \frac{5}{9}\right)$$

a. $\frac{1}{3}x^5 - \frac{4}{9}x^4 - \frac{1}{9}x^3 + \frac{11}{9}$

b. $\frac{1}{3}x^5 - \frac{4}{9}x^4 - \frac{13}{9}x^3 + \frac{1}{9}$

c. $\frac{1}{3}x^5 - \frac{4}{9}x^4 - \frac{1}{9}x^3 + \frac{1}{9}$

d. $\frac{1}{3}x^5 - \frac{4}{9}x^4 - \frac{13}{9}x^3 + \frac{11}{9}$

e. none of these

16. Simplify. Write your answer in descending order of exponents. 16. ____________

$$14b^4 - 2b^3 - [8b^3 - (4b^3 - 3b^4)]$$

a. $11b^4 - 14b^3$
b. $11b^4 - 6b^3$
c. $17b^4 - 6b^3$
d. $17b^4 - 14b^3$
e. none of these

17. Subtract the sum of $(23x^2 - 12xy - 11y^2)$ and $(21y^2 + 3xy - 15x^2)$. 17. ____________

a. $43x^2 - 9xy - 26y^2$
b. $8x^2 - 15xy + 10y^2$
c. $12x^2 - 9xy + 10y^2$
d. $8x^2 - 9xy - 10y^2$
e. none of these

18. Simplify: $-17w - \{11w - [15 - (4 - 8w)]\}$ 18. ____________

a. $-36w - 19$
b. $-14w + 11$
c. $-20w + 11$
d. $-20w - 11$
e. none of these

19. Simplify: $(x + 7)(x^2 + 6x + 2)$ 19. ____________

a. $x^3 + 6x + 14$
b. $x^3 + x^2 + 40x + 14$
c. $x^3 + 13x^2 + 15x + 14$
d. $x^3 + 13x^2 + 44x + 14$
e. none of these

20. Simplify: $(5x + 3)(2x - 4) - (7x - 1)(x + 6)$ 20. ____________

a. $3x^2 + 27x - 18$
b. $3x^2 - 55x - 6$
c. $3x^2 - 6$
d. $3x^2 + 27x - 6$
e. none of these

21. Find the product: $\left(\frac{5}{6}u^2 + \frac{1}{6}t^2\right)^2$ 21. ____________

a. $\frac{25}{36}u^4 + \frac{1}{36}t^4$
b. $\frac{25}{36}u^4 + \frac{5}{36}u^2t^2 + \frac{1}{36}t^4$
c. $\frac{5}{3}u^4 + \frac{5}{18}u^2t^2 + \frac{1}{3}t^4$
d. $\frac{25}{36}u^4 + \frac{5}{18}u^2t^2 + \frac{1}{36}t^4$
e. none of these

22. Find the product: $(s^4 + 3t)(s^4 - 3t)$ 22. ________

a. $s^8 + 6ts^4 - 9t^2$
b. $s^8 - 9t^2$
c. $s^8 - 6ts^4 - 9t^2$
d. $s^{16} - 9t^2$
e. none of these

23. The square of the difference of four times a number and five is equal to sixteen times the sum of the square of the number and five. 23. ________

a. $-\frac{11}{8}$
b. $\frac{1}{2}$
c. $-\frac{21}{8}$
d. $-\frac{13}{8}$
e. none of these

24. Divide and simplify: $\dfrac{102t^{12} - 51t^8 - 17t^4}{17t^4}$ 24. ________

a. $6t^3 - 3t^2 - 1$
b. $6t^8 - 3t^4 - 1$
c. $6t^8 - 3t^2 - 1$
d. $6t^3 - 3t^4 - 1$
e. none of these

25. Divide: $\dfrac{3z^4 - 15z^3 + z^2 - 7z + 10}{z - 5}$ 25. ________

a. $3z^3 + z - 12 + \dfrac{-50}{z-5}$
b. $3z^3 - 15z^2 + z - 9$
c. $3z^3 + z - 2$
d. $3z^3 + z - 7 + \dfrac{-20}{z-5}$
e. none of these

CHAPTER # 3 TEST KEYS

Form A		Form B	
1.	4096	1.	$\frac{125}{729}$
2.	1	2.	y^{13}
3.	x^{21}	3.	$x^{12}y^{21}$
4.	$\frac{1}{8}$	4.	$\frac{1}{y^{12}}$
5.	$\frac{4}{m^3}$	5.	$\frac{z^4}{81y^4}$
6.	0.0008	6.	$2{,}350$
7.	32000	7.	1.104
8.	$\frac{5}{6}m^4n^6$	8.	$-12w^8y^9$
9.	$-6a^4b^3c^6$	9.	$14m^6n^4p^8$
10.	$\frac{-2y^2}{7x^4}$	10	$\frac{-8y^2w}{x^3}$
11.	5	11.	4
12.	$-8y^4 + 9y^3 + 6$	12.	$2w^2 - \frac{6}{5}w$
13.	-33	13.	$-11\frac{3}{4}$
14.	$13x^4 - 9x^2 - x + 6$	14.	$m^5 - m^4 - 4m^3 + m - 5$
15.	$x^4 + 9x^2 - 5x + 12$	15.	$-2.7d^5 + 4.5d^3 - 4d + 7$
16.	$13z^2 - 9z - 14$	16.	$5y^4 - 9y^3 + 9y^2$
17.	$9x^2 + 11x - 2$	17.	$3x^4 + 12x^2 + x - 9$
18.	$-5x^2 + 10$	18.	$17x - 3$
19.	$5x^3 - 33x^2 - 27x + 27$	19.	$12x^3 - 14x^2 - 15x - 3$
20.	$-9x^2 + 2xy - 10y^2$	20.	$12m^2 - 34m + 16$
21.	$x^2 - 24x + 144$	21.	$49w^2 - 14wt + t^2$
22.	$a^2 - \frac{49}{64}$	22.	$\frac{9}{49} - \frac{1}{9}k^2$
23.	-2	23.	29 and 31
24.	$3m^3 - 2m + \frac{5}{m}$	24.	$5 - \frac{4}{y^2} + \frac{2}{y^3}$
25.	$y^2 - 3y + 1$	25.	$y^4 - 6y^2 + 21 + \frac{-54}{y^2 + 3}$

CHAPTER # 3 TEST KEYS

Form C

1. -81
2. $a^{17}b^{15}$
3. $-\frac{27}{125}m^3t^6$
4. $\frac{1}{(3p^2t)^4}$
5. $\frac{a^5}{b^5}$
6. 4.83×10^{-3}
7. 0.0325
8. $\frac{y^5}{4x^2}$
9. $\frac{4}{9}m^{12}n^{14}$
10. $0.3m^2h^7$
11. 7
12. $14d^4 - 16d^2 + 4d$
13. $1616
14. $8w^4 + 6w^3 - w^2 - 9w + 15$
15. $\frac{3}{4}t^4 - \frac{5}{6}t^3 + \frac{1}{3}t + \frac{3}{4}$
16. $15x^3 - 17x^2$
17. $-8x^2 - 8xy + 7y^2$
18. -4
19. $x^3 + 11x^2 + 25x + 8$
20. $12y - 13$
21. $x^4 + 18x^2y^2 + 81y^4$
22. $p^6 - q^2$
23. $-\frac{8}{3}$
24. $4b^6 - 2b^3 - 1$
25. $2x^3 - 4x^2 + 1$

Form D

1. c) 64
2. a) 1
3. d) m^{22}
4. b) $\frac{1}{6}$
5. a) $\frac{3}{4}x^4$
6. b) 0.006
7. e) None of these
8. d) $\frac{1}{2}p^4q^6$
9. c) $12x^4y^6z^4$
10. c) $-\frac{3m}{7n^4}$
11. b) 7
12. d) $-7z^4 + 2z^2 + 23$
13. e) None of these
14. b) $y^5 + 4y^3 - 4$
15. c) $-10y^3 + 2y^2 + y - 3$
16. a) $12m^2 + 10m - 11$
17. c) $18t^2 - 2t - 7$
18. e) None of these
19. a) $8x^3 - 21x^2 - 46x + 35$
20. d) $-4a^2 - 16ab - 5b^2$
21. a) $y^2 - 26y + 169$
22. d) $t^2 - \frac{64}{81}$
23. b) -3
24. c) $7x^2 - 3x + \frac{4}{x}$
25. a) $x^2 - 4x + 1$

CHAPTER # 3 TEST KEYS

Form E

1. a) $\frac{256}{2401}$
2. c) w^8
3. b) $z^{24}w^{20}$
4. d) $\frac{1}{w^9}$
5. c) $n^3/64m^3$
6. a) 34,500,000
7. d) 33.4
8. e) none of these
9. b) $15x^2y^9z^5$
10. a) $-30n^4/7m^3p^2$
11. c) 7
12. e) none of these
13. d) 12
14. a) $t^4 - t^3 + 9t^2 + t - 9$
15. b) $3.1w^6 + 4.9w^3 - 6.6w - 1$
16. c) $-7p^5 + p^3 - 10p^2$
17. d) $18z^3 - 15z - 9$
18. b) $-6y + 7$
19. b) $28x^3 - 9x^2 - 28x - 3$
20. e) none of these
21. c) $64m^2 - 16mp + p^2$
22. a) $\frac{4}{25} - \frac{25}{16}m^2$
23. d) 41 and 43
24. a) $6 - \frac{3}{z} - \frac{2}{z^2}$
25. b) $y^4 - 2y^2 - 2 + \frac{-8}{y^2 - 2}$

Form F

1. d) -16
2. b) $t^{15}w^{18}$
3. e) none of these
4. a) $\frac{1}{64a^{12}b^{12}}$
5. d) m^2/n^{11}
6. c) $3.56921 \cdot 10^6$
7. b) 0.0016
8. a) $3r^2/2t^3$
9. d) $-24t^{11}w^9$
10. e) none of these
11. d) 9
12. a) $14t^3 - 33t + 16$
13. c) $1306
14. c) $-8z^4 - 14z^3 + 18z + 14$
15. a) $\frac{1}{3}x^5 - \frac{4}{9}x^4 - \frac{1}{9}x^3 + \frac{11}{9}$
16. b) $11b^4 - 6b^3$
17. e) none of these
18. c) $-20w + 11$
19. d) $x^3 + 13x^2 + 44x + 14$
20. b) $3x^2 - 55x - 6$
21. d) $\frac{25}{36}u^4 + \frac{5}{18}u^2t^2 + \frac{1}{36}t^4$
22. b) $s^8 - 9t^2$
23. a) $-\frac{11}{8}$
24. b) $6t^8 - 3t^4 - 1$
25. c) $3z^3 + z - 2$

Name ______________________ Chapter 4 Form A Score ______

1. Determine if 51 is composite or prime 1. ____________

2. Factor 144 into primes. 2. ____________

3. Find the missing factor: $27x^{12} = 3x^3 (?)$ 3. ____________

4. Factor out the greatest common factor: 4. ____________

$24y^6 - 6y^4 + 15y^3$

5. Factor completely: $x^2 + 2x - 35$ 5. ____________

6. Factor completely: $m^4 - 3m^3 - 10m^2$ 6. ____________

7. Factor completely: $a^2 + ab - 6b^2$ 7. ____________

8. Factor completely: $2x^2 -13x + 20$ 8. ____________

9. Factor completely: $6n^2 - 11mn - 10m^2$ 9. ____________

10. Factor completely: $24x^5 - 32x^4 + 10x^3$ 10. ____________

11. Factor completely: $x^2 - 9y^2$ 11. ____________

12. Factor completely: $4x^2 - 12x + 9$ 12. ____________

13. Factor completely: $27y^3 + 64$ 13. ____________

14. Factor completely: $z^5 - 8z^2$ 14. ____________

15 Factor completely: $6n - mn + 3m - 18$ 15. ____________

16. Factor completely: $x^2y^2 - 9y^2 - x^2 + 9$ 16. ____________

17. Factor completely: $9x^6 + 36x^4$ 17. ____________

18. Factor completely: $45x^5y^2 - 60x^4y^2 + 15x^3y^2$ 18. ____________

19. Solve the equation. $5t(t - 8)(2t + 5) = 0$ 19. ____________

20. Solve the equation. $15x^2 - 7x - 2 = 0$ 20. ____________

21. Solve the equation. $9t^3 - 36t = 0$ 21. ____________

22. Solve the equation. $6w(2w - 3) = 4(2w - 3)$ 22. ____________

23. One number is 8 more than 3 times another number. If their product is 3, find the two numbers. 23. ____________

24. The width of a rectangle is 2 inches more than $\frac{2}{3}$ of its length. If the area is 432 square inches, find the length and width. 24. ____________

25. The shorter leg of a right triangle is 2 feet less than the longer leg. The hypotenuse is 2 feet more than the longer leg. Find the length of the hypotenuse. 25. ____________

Name ______________________ Chapter 4 Form B Score ______

1. Determine if 57 is composite or prime 1. __________

2. Factor 240 into primes. 2. __________

3. Find the missing factor: $28x^{10} = 4x^2\ (\ ?\ )$ 3. __________

4. Factor out the greatest common factor: 4. __________
$30w^6 - 15w^4 - 20w^2$

5. Factor completely: $x^2 + 4x - 32$ 5. __________

6. Factor completely: $y^4 - 2y^3 - 8y^2$ 6. __________

7. Factor completely: $a^2 + ab - 12b^2$ 7. __________

8. Factor completely: $3x^2 - 19x + 20$ 8. __________

9. Factor completely: $8n^2 - 14mn - 15m^2$ 9. __________

10. Factor completely: $16x^6 - 44x^5 + 10x^4$ 10. ____________

11. Factor completely: $a^2 - 16b^2$ 11. ____________

12. Factor completely: $9y^2 - 12y + 4$ 12. ____________

13. Factor completely: $8x^3 + 27$ 13. ____________

14. Factor completely: $x^7 - 64x^4$ 14. ____________

15 Factor completely: $5y - xy + 4x - 20$ 15. ____________

16. Factor completely: $a^2b^2 - 16b^2 - a^2 + 16$ 16. ____________

17. Factor completely: $8y^4 + 128y^2$ 17. ____________

18. Factor completely: $48x^4y^3 - 108x^3y^3 + 24x^2y^3$ 18. ____________

19. Solve the equation. $4t(t - 6)(3t + 4) = 0$ 19. ____________

20. Solve the equation. $10x^2 - x - 3 = 0$ 20. ____________

21. Solve the equation. $7t^3 - 63t = 0$ 21. ____________

22. Solve the equation. $3w(5w - 2) = 7(5w - 2)$ 22. ____________

23. One number is 4 more than 4 times another number. If their product is 3, find the two numbers. 23. ____________

24. The width of a rectangle is 3 cm. less than $\frac{4}{5}$ of its length. If the area is 135 square cm., find the length and width. 24. ____________

25. The shorter leg of a right triangle is 3 inches less than the longer leg. The hypotenuse is 3 inches more than the longer leg. Find the length of the hypotenuse. 25. ____________

Name ____________________ Chapter 4 Form C Score ______

1. Determine if 59 is composite or prime 1. ____________

2. Factor 168 into primes. 2. ____________

3. Find the missing factor: $24y^8 = 6y^2 (?)$ 3. ____________

4. Factor out the greatest common factor: 4. ____________
$28y^{12} - 8y^6 + 16y^3$

5. Factor completely: $x^2 + 3x - 28$ 5. ____________

6. Factor completely: $w^4 - 5w^3 - 14w^2$ 6. ____________

7. Factor completely: $a^2 + ab - 20b^2$ 7. ____________

8. Factor completely: $3x^2 - 17x + 20$ 8. ____________

9. Factor completely: $6n^2 - 5mn - 6m^2$ 9. ____________

10. Factor completely: $30x^5 - 26x^4 + 4x^3$ 10. __________

11. Factor completely: $t^2 - 49w^2$ 11. __________

12. Factor completely: $9a^2 - 24a + 16$ 12. __________

13. Factor completely: $64w^3 + 125$ 13. __________

14. Factor completely: $y^6 - 27y^3$ 14. __________

15 Factor completely: $7n - mn + 3m - 21$ 15. __________

16. Factor completely: $m^2n^2 - 25m^2 - n^2 + 25$ 16. __________

17. Factor completely: $4z^8 + 100z^6$ 17. __________

18. Factor completely: $45x^4y^3 - 54x^3y^3 + 9x^2y^3$ 18. __________

19. Solve the equation. $6t(t - 7)(5t + 2) = 0$ 19. ____________

20. Solve the equation. $15x^2 - 7x - 4 = 0$ 20. ____________

21. Solve the equation. $6t^3 - 96t = 0$ 21. ____________

22. Solve the equation. $4w(6w - 5) = 6(6w - 5)$ 22. ____________

23. One number is 5 more than 12 times another number. If their product is 2, find the two numbers. 23. ____________

24. The width of a rectangle is 3 inches less than $\frac{3}{8}$ of its length. If the area is 144 square inches, find the length and width. 24. ____________

25. The shorter leg of a right triangle is 5 cm. less than the longer leg. The hypotenuse is 5 cm. more than the longer leg. Find the length of the hypotenuse. 25. ____________

Name ______________________ Chapter 4 Form D Score ______

1. Of the numbers 51, 61, 71, 81, and 91, which numbers are composite? 1. ____________
   a. 51, 81, and 91
   b. 61 and 71
   c. 51 and 81
   d. 81 and 91
   e. none of these

2. Factor 112 into primes 2. ____________
   a. $2 \cdot 3 \cdot 17$
   b. $4^2 \cdot 7$
   c. $2^3 \cdot 7$
   d. $2^4 \cdot 7$
   e. none of these

3. Find the missing factor: $56x^9 = 4x^3(\underline{\ ?\ })$ 3. ____________
   a. $16x^3$
   b. $14x^6$
   c. $14x^3$
   d. $16x^6$
   e. none of these

4. Factor out the greatest common factor: 4. ____________
   $$28y^{12} - 12y^6 + 24y^4$$
   a. $4y^4(7y^3 - 3y^2 + 6y)$
   b. $4y^4(7y^3 - 3y^2 + 6)$
   c. $4y^4(7y^8 - 3y^2 + 6)$
   d. $4y^4(7y^8 - 3y^2 + 6y)$
   e. none of these

5. Factor completely: $x^2 + 3x - 28$ 5. ____________
   a. $(x + 7)(x + 4)$
   b. $(x + 7)(x - 4)$
   c. $(x - 7)(x + 4)$
   d. $(x - 7)(x - 4)$
   e. none of these

6. Factor completely: $m^4 - 3m^3 - 18m^2$ 6. ____________
   a. $m^2(m + 3)(m - 6)$
   b. $(m^2 - 6m)(m^2 + 3m)$
   c. $(m^2 + 6m)(m^2 - 3m)$
   d. $m^2(m - 3)(m + 6)$
   e. none of these

7. Factor completely: $a^2 - 8ab + 12b^2$ 7. ____________

a. $(a - 3b)(a - 4b)$
b. $(a + 2b)(a + 6b)$
c. $(a - 2b)(a - 6b)$
d. $(a - 6b)(a + 2b)$
e. none of these

8. Factor completely: $2x^2 - 19x + 24$ 8. ____________

a. $(2x + 3)(x - 8)$
b. $(2x - 8)(x - 3)$
c. $(2x - 3)(x + 8)$
d. $(2x - 3)(x - 8)$
e. none of these

9. Factor completely: $6n^2 - 23mn + 20m^2$ 9. ____________

a. $(3n - 4m)(2n - 5m)$
b. $(6n - 5m)(n - 4m)$
c. $(6n - 10m)(n - 2m)$
d. $(3n - 5m)(2n - 4m)$
e. none of these

10. Factor completely: $24x^5 - 30x^4 + 9x^3$ 10. ____________

a. $3x^3(4x + 1)(2x - 3)$
b. $3x^3(4x + 1)(2x + 3)$
c. $3x^3(4x - 1)(2x - 3)$
d. $3x^3(4x - 1)(2x - 3)$
e. none of these

11. Factor completely: $x^2 - 81y^2$ 11. ____________

a. $(x - 9y)(x - 9y)$
b. $(x + 9y)(x + 3y)(x - 3y)$
c. $(x - 9y)(x + 9y)$
d. $(x + 9y)(x - 3y)(x - 3y)$
e. none of these

12. Factor completely: $4x^2 - 20x + 25$ 12. ____________

a. $(2x + 5)(2x + 5)$
b. $(4x - 5)(x - 5)$
c. $(2x - 5)(2x - 5)$
d. $(4x - 5)(4x - 5)$
e. none of these

13. Factor completely: $8a^3 + 125$ 13. ____________

a. $(2a + 5)(4a^2 - 10a + 25)$

b. $(2a + 5)^3$

c. $(2a + 5)(4a^2 + 10a + 25)$

d. $(2a + 5)(4a^2 - 5a + 25)$

e. none of these

14. Factor completely: $x^6 - 125x^3$ 14. ____________

a. $(x^2 - 5x)(x^4 + 5x^3 + 25x^2)$

b. $x^3(x - 5)(x^2 + 5x + 25)$

c. $(x^2 - 5x)^3$

d. $x^3(x - 5)(x^2 + 5x + 25)$

e. none of these

15. Factor completely: $7x - xy + 4y - 28$ 15. ____________

a. $(x + 4)(7 - y)(y - 7)$

b. $(x - 4)(y - 7)$

c. $(x + 4)(7 - y)$

d. $(x - 4)(7 - y)$

e. none of these

16. Factor completely: $x^2y^2 - 36x^2 - y^2 + 36$ 16. ____________

a. $(x + 1)(x - 1)(y + 6)(y - 6)(y^2 + 36)$

b. $(x - 1)(x - 1)(y - 6)(y + 6)$

c. $(x + 1)(x - 1)(y + 6)(y + 6)$

d. $(x + 1)(x - 1)(y^2 + 36)$

e. none of these

17. Factor completely: $-8x^4 - 72x^2$ 17. ____________

a. $-8x^2(x + 3)(x - 3)$

b. $-8x^2(x^2 + 9)$

c. $-8x^2(x - 3)(x - 3)$

d. $-8x^2(x + 3)(x + 3)$

e. none of these

18. Factor completely: $16x^6y^2 - 40x^5y^2 + 24x^4y^2$ 18. ____________

a. $4x^4y^2(2x - 3)(2x - 2)$

b. $8x^4y^2(2x^2 - 5x + 3)$

c. $8x^4y^2(2x - 1)(x - 3)$

d. $8x^4y^2(x - 1)(2x - 3)$

e. none of these

19. Solve the equation: $3t(t - 9)(3t + 4) = 0$ 19. ____________

a. $t = 0, t = -9, \text{ or } t = \frac{4}{3}$

b. $t = 3, t = 9, \text{ or } t = -\frac{4}{3}$

c. $t = 0, t = 9, \text{ or } t = -\frac{4}{3}$

d. $t = 0, t = 9, \text{ or } t = -\frac{3}{4}$

e. none of these

20. Solve the equation: $20x^2 - 7x - 3 = 0$ 20. ____________

a. $x = -\frac{1}{4} \text{ or } x = -\frac{3}{5}$

b. $x = \frac{1}{4} \text{ or } x = -\frac{3}{5}$

c. $x = \frac{1}{4} \text{ or } x = \frac{3}{5}$

d. $x = -4 \text{ or } x = \frac{5}{3}$

e. none of these

21. Solve the equation: $8t^3 - 200t = 0$ 21. ____________

a. $t = 0 \text{ or } t = 5$

b. $t = 8, t = 5, \text{ or } t = -5$

c. $t = 8 \text{ or } t = 5$

d. $t = 0, t = 5, \text{ or } t = -5$

e. none of these

22. Solve the equation: $5x(4x - 2) = 6(4x - 2)$ 22. ____________

a. $x = \frac{6}{5}$

b. $x = \frac{6}{5} \text{ or } x = \frac{1}{2}$

c. $x = 0 \text{ or } x = \frac{6}{5}$

d. $x = \frac{5}{6} \text{ or } x = 2$

e none of these

23. One number is 10 more than twice another number. If their product is -8, find the two numbers.

23. ____________

a. $\frac{1}{4}$ and $\frac{21}{2}$ or -1 and 8

b. -4 and 2 or -1 and 8

c. 4 and 18 or 1 and 12

d. -4 and -1

e. none of these

24. The length of a rectangle is 9 cm. more than $\frac{4}{5}$ its width. If the area is 170 square cm., find the length of the rectangle.

24. ____________

a. 17 cm.

b. 10 cm.

c. 26 cm.

d. 21.25 cm.

e. none of these

25. The longer leg of a right triangle is 4 feet more than the shorter leg. The hypotenuse is 4 feet less than twice the shorter leg. Find the length of the hypotenuse.

25. ____________

a. 12 feet

b. 4 feet

c. 16 feet

d. 20 feet

e. none of these

Name ______________________ Chapter 4 Form E Score ______

1. Of the numbers 53, 63, 73, 83, and 93, which numbers are composite? 1. ____________
   a. 53, 63, and 93
   b. 63 and 83
   c. only 63
   d. 63, 83, and 93
   e. none of these

2. Factor 216 into primes 2. ____________
   a. $2^4 \cdot 3^3$
   b. $2^4 \cdot 11$
   c. $2^3 \cdot 3^3$
   d. $3 \cdot 73$
   e. none of these

3. Find the missing factor: $42x^{15} = 3x^3(\underline{\ ?\ })$ 3. ____________
   a. $14x^{12}$
   b. $14x^5$
   c. $18x^{12}$
   d. $18x^5$
   e. none of these

4. Factor out the greatest common factor: 4. ____________

$$20y^{10} - 12y^6 - 4y^2$$

   a. $4y^2(5y^5 - 3y^3 - 1)$
   b. $4y^2(5y^8 - 3y^4)$
   c. $4y^2(5y^5 - 3y^3)$
   d. $4y^2(5y^8 - 3y^4 - 1)$
   e. none of these

5. Factor completely: $x^2 + 6x - 27$ 5. ____________
   a. $(x - 9)(x + 3)$
   b. $(x - 9)(x - 3)$
   c. $(x + 9)(x - 3)$
   d. $(x + 9)(x + 3)$
   e. none of these

6. Factor completely: $m^4 - 2m^3 - 24m^2$ 6. ____________
   a. $m^2(m - 4)(m + 6)$
   b. $(m^2 + 4m)(m^2 - 6m)$
   c. $(m^2 - 4m)(m^2 + 6m)$
   d. $m^2(m + 4)(m - 6)$
   e. none of these

7. Factor completely: $a^2 - 10ab + 24b^2$

7. ____________

a. $(a - 4b)(a - 6b)$
b. $(a - 8b)(a - 2b)$
c. $(a - 12b)(a + 2b)$
d. $(a + 4b)(a + 6b)$
e. none of these

8. Factor completely: $3x^2 - 17x - 10$

8. ____________

a. $(3x - 2)(x + 5)$
b. $(3x - 2)(x - 5)$
c. $(3x + 2)(x - 5)$
d. $(3x - 5)(x + 2)$
e. none of these

9. Factor completely: $6n^2 - 25mn + 24m^2$

9. ____________

a. $(3n - 3m)(2n - 8m)$
b. $(3n - 8m)(2n - 3m)$
c. $(6n - 12m)(n - 2m)$
d. $(6n - 8m)(n - 3m)$
e. none of these

10. Factor completely: $24x^4 - 40x^3 + 6x^2$

10. ____________

a. $2x^2(6x - 3)(2x - 1)$
b. $2x^2(4x - 1)(3x - 3)$
c. $2x^2(4x - 3)(3x - 1)$
d. $2x^2(6x - 1)(2x - 3)$
e. none of these

11. Factor completely: $m^2 - 36n^2$

11. ____________

a. $(m - 6n)(m - 6n)$
b. $(m - 6n)(m + 6n)$
c. $(m - 9n)(m - 4n)$
d. $(m - 9n)(m + 4n)$
e. none of these

12. Factor completely: $9m^2 - 24m + 16$

12. ____________

a. $(9m - 16)(m - 1)$
b. $(3m - 4)(3m - 4)$
c. $(3m + 4)(3m + 4)$
d. $(9m - 8)(m - 2)$
e. none of these

13. Factor completely: $27x^3 + 125$ 13. ____________

a. $(3x + 5)^3$
b. $(3x + 5)(9x^2 + 15x + 25)$
c. $(3x + 5)(9x^2 + 5x + 25)$
d. $(3x + 5)(9x^2 + 25)$
e. none of these

14. Factor completely: $w^8 - 216w^5$ 14. ____________

a. $w^5(w - 6)(w^2 + 36)$
b. $w^5(w - 6)^3$
c. $w^5(w - 6)(w^2 + 6w + 36)$
d. $w^5(w - 6)(w^2 - 6w + 36)$
e. none of these

15. Factor completely: $8n - nm + 5m - 40$ 15. ____________

a. $(n + 5)(8 - m)$
b. $(n - 5)(8 - m)$
c. $(n - 5) (m - 8)$
d. $(n + 5)(8 - m) (m - 8)$
e. none of these

16. Factor completely: $w^2z^2 - 4z^2 - 25w^2 + 100$ 16. ____________

a. $(w + 2)(w - 2)(z + 5)(z - 5)$
b. $(z^2 - 25)(w^2 - 4)$
c. $(z - 5)^2(w - 2)^2$
d. $(z + 5)(z - 5)(w + 2)(w - 2)(w^2 + 4)$
e. none of these

17. Factor completely: $-4m^5 - 16m^3$ 17. ____________

a. $-4m^3(m + 2)(m - 2)$
b. $-4m^3(m - 2)(m - 2)$
c. $-4m^3(m^2 + 4)$
d. $-4m^3(m + 2)(m + 2)$
e. none of these

18. Factor completely: $32x^3y^3 - 48x^2y^3 + 16xy^3$ 18. ____________

a. $16xy^3(2x - 1)(x - 1)$
b. $16xy^3(2x^2 - 3x + 1)$
c. $8xy^3(2x - 2)(2x - 1)$
d. $16xy^3(2x + 1)(x + 1)$
e. none of these

19. Solve the equation: $7t(t - 2)(5t + 3) = 0$ 19. ____________

a. $t = 7, t = 2, \text{ or } t = -\frac{3}{5}$

b. $t = 0, t = 2, \text{ or } t = -\frac{3}{5}$

c. $t = 0, t = -2, \text{ or } t = \frac{3}{5}$

d. $t = 0, t = 2, \text{ or } t = -\frac{5}{3}$

e. none of these

20. Solve the equation: $12x^2 - 11x - 15 = 0$ 20. ____________

a. $x = -\frac{5}{3}$ or $x = \frac{3}{4}$

b. $x = \frac{3}{5}$ or $x = -\frac{4}{3}$

c. $x = \frac{5}{3}$ or $x = \frac{3}{4}$

d. $x = \frac{5}{3}$ or $x = -\frac{3}{4}$

e. none of these

21. Solve the equation: $4t^3 - 4t = 0$ 21. ____________

a. $t = 1$

b. $t = 0$ or $t = 1$

c. $t = 1$ or $t = -1$

d. $t = 4$ or $t = 1$

e. none of these

22. Solve the equation: $2x(7 - 3x) = 12(7 - 3x)$ 22. ____________

a. $x = \frac{7}{3}$ or $x = 6$

b. $x = 6$

c. $x = \frac{3}{7}$ or $x = 6$

d. $x = -\frac{7}{3}$ or $x = -6$

e none of these

23. One number is 3 less than 4 times another number. If their product is 10, find the two numbers. 23. ____________

a. $\frac{5}{2}$ and 7 or -1 and -7

b. $\frac{5}{4}$ and 2 or 2 and 5

c. 2 and 5

d. $-\frac{5}{4}$ and -8 or 2 and 5

e. none of these

24. The length of a rectangle is 5 inches more than $\frac{2}{3}$ of its width. If the area is 99 square inches, find the length of the rectangle. 24. ____________

a. 16.5 inches

b. 9 inches

c. 11 inches

d. 16 inches

e. none of these

25. The longer leg of a right triangle is 7 cm. more than the shorter leg. The hypotenuse is 1 cm. more than twice the shorter leg. Find the length of the hypotenuse. 25. ____________

a. 7 cm.

b. 15 cm.

c. 17 cm.

d. 8 cm.

e. none of these

Name ______________________ Chapter 4 Form F Score ______

1. Of the numbers 57, 67, 77, 87, and 97, which numbers are composite? 1. ____________
   a. 57, 67, and 77
   b. 57, 77 and 97
   c. 57, 77, and 87
   d. 77 and 87
   e. none of these

2. Factor 162 into primes 2. ____________
   a. $2 \cdot 3^4$
   b. $2 \cdot 9^2$
   c. 3^5
   d. $2 \cdot 3^3$
   e. none of these

3. Find the missing factor: $68x^8 = 4x^2(\underline{\ ?\ })$ 3. ____________
   a. $17x^4$
   b. $12x^6$
   c. $12x^4$
   d. $17x^6$
   e. none of these

4. Factor out the greatest common factor: 4. ____________
   $18y^{12} - 9y^6 - 3y^3$
   a. $3y^3(6y^4 - 3y^2 - 1)$
   b. $3y^3(6y^9 - 3y^3 - 1)$
   c. $3y^3(6y^4 - 3y^2)$
   d. $3y^3(6y^9 - 3y^3)$
   e. none of these

5. Factor completely: $x^2 + 4x - 32$ 5. ____________
   a. $(x + 8)(x - 4)$
   b. $(x - 8)(x + 4)$
   c. $(x + 8)(x + 4)$
   d. $(x - 8)(x - 4)$
   e. none of these

6. Factor completely: $m^4 - 7m^3 - 18m^2$ 6. ____________
   a. $(m^2 - 9m)(m^2 + 2m)$
   b. $m^2(m + 9)(m - 2)$
   c. $m^2(m - 9)(m + 2)$
   d. $(m^2 + 9m)(m^2 - 2m)$
   e. none of these

7. Factor completely: $a^2 - 11ab + 28b^2$ 7. ____________

a. $(a - 14b)(a + 2b)$
b. $(a - 9b)(a - 2b)$
c. $(a + 7b)(a + 4b)$
d. $(a - 7b)(a - 4b)$
e. none of these

8. Factor completely: $3x^2 - 5x - 12$ 8. ____________

a. $(3x - 4)(x + 3)$
b. $(3x + 4)(x + 3)$
c. $(3x + 4)(x - 3)$
d. $(3x - 4)(x - 3)$
e. none of these

9. Factor completely: $6n^2 - 7mn + 20m^2$ 9. ____________

a. $(3n - 5m)(2n - 4m)$
b. $(3n - 4m)(2n + 5m)$
c. $(3n + 4m)(2n - 5m)$
d. $(3n - 4m)(2n - 5m)$
e. none of these

10. Factor completely: $24x^4 - 57x^3 + 18x^2$ 10. ____________

a. $3x^2(8x - 2)(x - 3)$
b. $3x^2(8x - 3)(x - 2)$
c. $3x^2(4x - 6)(2x - 1)$
d. $3x^2(4x - 1)(2x - 6)$
e. none of these

11. Factor completely: $a^2 - 64b^2$ 11. ____________

a. $(a - 8b)(a - 8b)$
b. $(a + 16b)(a - 4b)$
c. $(a - 4b)^2$
d. $(a + 8b)(a - 8b)$
e. none of these

12. Factor completely: $16y^2 - 72y + 81$ 12. ____________

a. $(4y - 9)(4y - 9)$
b. $(8y - 27)(2y - 2)$
c. $(8y - 9)(2y - 9)$
d. $(16y - 27)(y - 3)$
e. none of these

13. Factor completely: $y^3 + 125$ 13. ____________

a. $(y + 5)^3$
b. $(y + 5)(y^2 - 5y + 25)$
c. $(y + 5)(y^2 + 25)$
d. $(y + 5)(y^2 + 5y + 25)$
e. none of these

14. Factor completely: $w^9 - 27w^6$ 14. ____________

a. $w^6(w - 3)^3$
b. $w^6(w - 3)(w^2 - 3w + 9)$
c. $w^6(w - 3)(w^2 + 9)$
d. $(w^3 - 3w^2)(w^6 + 3w^5 + 9w^4)$
e. none of these

15. Factor completely: $6a - ab + 3b - 18$ 15. ____________

a. $(6 - b)(a - 3)$
b. $(a + 3)(6 - b)(b - 6)$
c. $(a + 3)(6 - b)$
d. $(a - 3)(b - 6)$
e. none of these

16. Factor completely: $a^2b^2 - 49b^2 - a^2 + 49$ 16. ____________

a. $(b + 1)(b - 1)(a - 7)(a + 7)(a^2 + 49)$
b. $(a - 7)^2(b - 1)^2$
c. $(a - 7)(a + 7)(b - 1)(b + 1)$
d. $(b + 1)(b - 1)(a^2 + 49)$
e. none of these

17. Factor completely: $-6z^6 - 216z^4$ 17. ____________

a. $-6z^4(z + 6)(z + 6)$
b. $-6z^4(z + 6)(z - 6)$
c. $-6z^4(z - 6)(z - 6)$
d. $-6z^4(z^2 + 36)$
e. none of these

18. Factor completely: $20x^6y^3 - 50x^5y^3 + 30x^4y^3$ 18. ____________

a. $10x^4y^3(x - 1)(2x + 3)$
b. $10x^4y^3(x - 3)(2x + 1)$
c. $10x^4y^3(x + 1)(2x - 3)$
d. $10x^4y^3(x + 3)(2x - 1)$
e. none of these

19. Solve the equation: $8t(t - 6)(7t + 4) = 0$ 19. ____________

a. $t = 8, t = 6, \text{ or } t = -\frac{4}{7}$

b. $t = 0, t = -6, \text{ or } t = \frac{4}{7}$

c. $t = 0, t = 6, \text{ or } t = -\frac{7}{4}$

d. $t = 0, t = 6, \text{ or } t = -\frac{4}{7}$

e. none of these

20. Solve the equation: $8x^2 + 2x - 15 = 0$ 20. ____________

a. $x = \frac{5}{4}$ or $x = \frac{3}{2}$

b. $x = \frac{4}{5}$ or $x = -\frac{2}{3}$

c. $x = \frac{5}{4}$ or $x = -\frac{3}{2}$

d. $x = -\frac{5}{4}$ or $x = \frac{3}{2}$

e. none of these

21. Solve the equation: $5t^3 - 180t = 0$ 21. ____________

a. $t = 0$ or $t = 6$

b. $t = 0, t = 6,$ or $t = -6$

c. $t = 5$ or $t = 6$

d. $t = 5, t = 6,$ or $t = -6$

e. none of these

22. Solve the equation: $8x(5 - 2x) = 16(5 - 2x)$ 22. ____________

a. $x = \frac{2}{5}$ or $x = 2$

b. $x = -\frac{5}{2}$ or $x = -2$

c. $x = \frac{5}{2}$ or $x = 2$

d. $x = 2$

e none of these

23. One number is 5 less than 6 times another number. If their product is 11, find the two numbers. 23. ________

a. $\frac{11}{6}$ and 6 or -1 and -11

b. $-\frac{11}{6}$ and -6 or 1 and 11

c. -1 and -11

d. $-\frac{11}{6}$ and -6 or -1 and -11

e. none of these

24. The length of a rectangle is 4 feet more than $\frac{3}{4}$ of its width. If the area is 156 square feet, find the length of the rectangle. 24. ________

a. 14 ft.

b. 20 ft.

c. $17\frac{1}{3}$ ft.

d. 12 ft.

e. none of these

25. The longer leg of a right triangle is 6 inches more than the shorter leg. The hypotenuse is 6 inches less than twice the shorter leg. Find the length of the hypotenuse. 25. ________

a. 18 inches

b. 30 inches

c. 24 inches

d. 36 inches

e. none of these

CHAPTER #4 TEST KEYS

Form A

1. composite
2. $2^4 \cdot 3^2$
3. $9x^9$
4. $3y^3(8y^3 - 2y + 5)$
5. $(x + 7)(x - 5)$
6. $m^2(m - 5)(m + 2)$
7. $(a + 3b)(a - 2b)$
8. $(2x - 5)(x - 4)$
9. $(3n + 2m)(2n - 5m)$
10. $2x^3(2x - 1)(6x - 5)$
11. $(x + 3y)(x - 3y)$
12. $(2x - 3)^2$
13. $(3y + 4)(9y^2 - 12y + 16)$
14. $z^2(z - 2)(z^2 + 2z + 4)$
15. $(n - 3)(6 - m)$
16. $(y + 1)(y - 1)(x + 3)(x - 3)$
17. $9x^4(x^2 + 4)$
18. $15x^3y^2(3x - 1)(x - 1)$
19. $t = 0$, $t = 8$, or $t = -\frac{5}{2}$
20. $x = -\frac{1}{5}$ or $x = \frac{2}{3}$
21. $t = 0$, $t = 2$, or $t = -2$
22. $w = \frac{2}{3}$ or $w = \frac{3}{2}$
23. $\frac{1}{3}$ and 9 or -3 and -1
24. 24 inches by 18 inches
25. 10 feet

Form B

1. composite
2. $2^4 \cdot 3 \cdot 5$
3. $7x^8$
4. $5w^2(6w^4 - 3w^2 - 4)$
5. $(x + 8)(x - 4)$
6. $y^2(y - 4)(y + 2)$
7. $(a + 4b)(a - 3b)$
8. $(3x - 4)(x - 5)$
9. $(2n - 5m)(4n + 3m)$
10. $2x^4(2x - 5)(4x - 1)$
11. $(a - 4b)(a + 4b)$
12. $(3y - 2)^2$
13. $(2x + 3)(4x^2 - 6x + 9)$
14. $x^4(x - 4)(x^2 + 4x + 16)$
15. $(y - 4)(5 - x)$
16. $(b + 1)(b - 1)(a + 4)(a - 4)$
17. $8y^2(y^2 + 16)$
18. $12x^2y^3(4x - 1)(x - 2)$
19. $t = 0$, $t = 6$, or $t = -\frac{4}{3}$
20. $x = \frac{3}{5}$ or $x = -\frac{1}{2}$
21. $t = 0$, $t = 3$, or $t = -3$
22. $w = \frac{2}{5}$ or $w = \frac{7}{3}$
23. $-\frac{3}{2}$ and -2 or $\frac{1}{2}$ and 6
24. 15 cm. by 9 cm.
25. 15 inches

Chapter #4 Test Keys

Form C

1. Prime
2. $2^3 \cdot 3 \cdot 7$
3. $4y^6$
4. $4y^3(7y^9 - 2y^3 + 4)$
5. $(x + 7)(x - 4)$
6. $w^2(w - 7)(w + 2)$
7. $(a + 5b)(a - 4b)$
8. $(3x - 5)(x - 4)$
9. $(3n + 2m)(2n - 3m)$
10. $2x^3(5x - 1)(3x - 2)$
11. $(t + 7w)(t - 7w)$
12. $(3a - 4)^2$
13. $(4w + 5)(16w^2 - 20w + 25)$
14. $y^3(y - 3)(y^2 + 3y + 9)$
15. $(n - 3)(7 - m)$
16. $(m + 1)(m - 1)(n + 5)(n - 5)$
17. $4z^6(z^2 + 25)$
18. $9x^2y^3(5x - 1)(x - 1)$
19. $t = 0, t = 7, \text{or } t = -\frac{2}{5}$
20. $x = \frac{4}{5}$ or $x = -\frac{1}{3}$
21. $t = 0, t = 4, \text{or } t = -4$
22. $w = \frac{5}{6}$ or $w = \frac{3}{2}$
23. -3 and $-\frac{2}{3}$ or $\frac{1}{4}$ and 8
24. 24 inches by 6 inches
25. 25 cm.

Form D

1. a 51, 81, and 91
2. d $2^4 \cdot 7$
3. b $14x^6$
4. c $4y^4(7y^8 - 3y^2 + 6)$
5. b $(x + 7)(x - 4)$
6. a $m^2(m + 3)(m - 6)$
7. c $(a - 2b)(a - 6b)$
8. d $(2x - 3)(x - 8)$
9. a $(3n - 4m)(2n - 5m)$
10. e none of these
11. c $(x - 9y)(x + 9y)$
12. c $(2x - 5)(2x - 5)$
13. a $(2a + 5)(4a^2 - 10a + 25)$
14. b $x^3(x - 5)(x^2 + 5x + 25)$
15. d $(x - 4)(7 - y)$
16. e none of these
17. b $-8x^2(x^2 + 9)$
18. d $8x^4y^2(x - 1)(2x - 3)$
19. c $t = 0, t = 9, \text{or } t = -\frac{4}{3}$
20. e none of these
21. d $t = 0, t = 5, \text{or } t = -5$
22. b $x = \frac{6}{5}$ or $x = \frac{1}{2}$
23. b -4 and 2 or -1 and 8
24. a 17 cm.
25. d 20 feet

Chapter #4 Test Keys

Form E

1. b 63 and 93
2. c $2^3 \cdot 3^3$
3. a $14x^{12}$
4. d $4y^2(5y^8 - 3y^4 - 1)$
5. c $(x + 9)(x - 3)$
6. d $m^2(m + 4)(m - 6)$
7. a $(a - 4b)(a - 6b)$
8. e none of these
9. b $(3n - 8m)(2n - 3m)$
10. d $2x^2(6x - 1)(2x - 3)$
11. b $(m - 6n)(m + 6n)$
12. b $(3m - 4)(3m - 4)$
13. e none of these
14. c $w^5(w - 6)(w^2 + 6w + 36)$
15. b $(n - 5)(8 - m)$
16. a $(w + 2)(w - 2)(z + 5)(z - 5)$
17. c $-4m^3(m^2 + 4)$
18. a $16xy^3(2x - 1)(x - 1)$
19. b $t = 0$, $t = 2$, or $t = -\frac{3}{5}$
20. d $x = \frac{5}{3}$ or $x = -\frac{3}{4}$
21. e none of these
22. a $x = \frac{7}{3}$ or $x = 6$
23. d $-\frac{5}{4}$ and -8 or 2 and 5
24. c 11 inches
25. c 17 cm.

Form F

1. c 57, 77, and 87
2. a $2 \cdot 3^4$
3. d $17x^6$
4. b $3y^3(6y^9 - 3y^3 - 1)$
5. a $(x + 8)(x - 4)$
6. c $m^2(m - 9)(m + 2)$
7. d $(a - 7b)(a - 4b)$
8. c $(3x + 4)(x - 3)$
9. e none of these
10. b $3x^2(8x - 3)(x - 2)$
11. d $(a + 8b)(a - 8b)$
12. a $(4y - 9)(4y - 9)$
13. b $(y + 5)(y^2 - 5y + 25)$
14. e none of these
15. a $(6 - b)(a - 3)$
16. c $(a - 7)(a + 7)(b - 1)(b + 1)$
17. d $-6z^4(z^2 + 36)$
18. b $10x^4y^3(x - 3)(2x + 1)$
19. d $t = 0$, $t = 6$, or $t = -\frac{4}{7}$
20. c $x = \frac{5}{4}$ or $x = -\frac{3}{2}$
21. b $t = 0$, $t = 6$, or $t = -6$
22. c $x = \frac{5}{2}$ or $x = 2$
23. a $\frac{11}{6}$ and 6 or -1 and -11
24. e none of these
25. b 30 inches

Name ______________________ Chapter 5 Form A Score ________

1. Determine any values of the variable in which the rational expression $\frac{6}{4x - 2}$ is undefined.

1. ______________

2. Write the rational expression in lowest terms:

$$\frac{8y - 24}{16y - 48}$$

2. ______________

3. Write the rational expression in lowest terms:

$$\frac{ab + yb - az - yz}{ab + 2yb - az - 2yz}$$

3. ______________

4. Multiply and write the answer in lowest terms:

$$\frac{2d^2 + 5d - 12}{2d + 1} \cdot \frac{2d^2 + 3d + 1}{d^2 + 5d + 4}$$

4. ______________

5. Divide and write the answer in lowest terms:

$$\frac{3x - 4}{6x - 12} \div \frac{4 - 3x}{2x - 4}$$

5. ______________

6. Find the least common denominator for

$$\frac{t + 3}{6 - t} \text{ and } \frac{t + 1}{t^2 - 36}$$

6. ______________

7. Find the missing numerator:

$$\frac{9w}{6(5w - 4} = \frac{}{42(4 - 5w)}$$

7. ____________

8. Add and write the answer in lowest terms:

$$\frac{4x}{(2x + 1)(x - 3)} + \frac{2}{(2x + 1)(x - 3)}$$

8. ____________

9. Subtract and write the answer in lowest terms:

$$\frac{5t}{(t - 1)(t - 3)} - \frac{15}{(t - 3)(t - 1)}$$

9. ____________

10. Add and subtract and write the answer in lowest terms: $\frac{9}{5z^2} + \frac{4}{3z} - \frac{6}{z^3}$

10. ____________

11. Simplify: $$\frac{-\frac{18}{x^4}}{\frac{63}{x^{12}}}$$

11. ____________

12. Simplify: $$\frac{\frac{4}{x} - \frac{2}{x^2}}{8 - \frac{3}{x}}$$

12. ____________

13. Solve the equation: $6x - \frac{3x}{2} = -\frac{9}{15}$ 13. ____________

14. Solve the equation: $\frac{6}{x+1} - \frac{3}{x} = \frac{9}{x^2 + x}$ 14. ____________

15. One number is three times another number. The sum of their reciprocals is 12. Find the two numbers. 15. ____________

16. Solve $\frac{y - 3xw}{y^3} = 1$ for w 16. ____________

17. Solve the proportion: $\frac{2y + 2}{y^2 + 3} = \frac{1}{y}$ 17. ____________

18. On a map, 3 inches represents 20 miles. How many miles does 10 inches represent? 18. ____________

19. Find the lengths of the missing sides in the similar triangles $\triangle ABC$ and $\triangle DEF$. 19. ____________

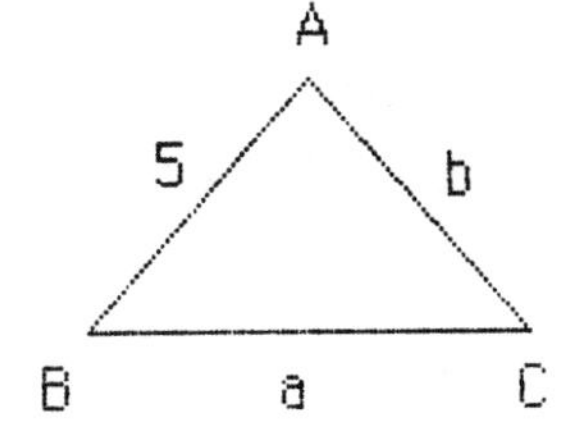

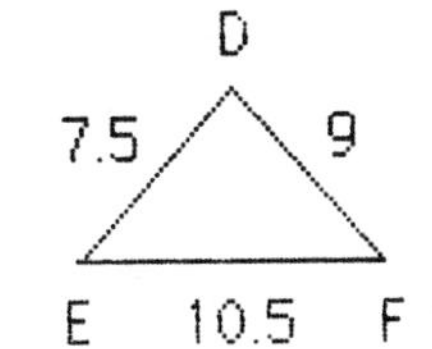

20. Find two numbers whose sum is 9 and the sum of their reciprocals is $\frac{1}{2}$.

20. ____________

21. Bob can paint a room in 6 hours and Ed can paint it in 8 hours. How long does it take them to paint the room together?

21. ____________

22. Josey took the same time to drive 84 miles as it took Carl to drive 48 miles. Josey's speed was 15 miles per hour faster than Carl's speed. How fast did Josey drive?

22. ____________

23. Suppose y varies directly as x and $y = 12$ when $x = 8$. Find y when $x = 15$.

23. ____________

24. If y varies inversely as x and y is 12 when x is 4, find y when $x = -2$.

24. ____________

25. The estimated cost of building a house at a certain time and place varies directly as the number of square feet of floor space. If it cost $50,000 for 1250 square feet, how much floor space could you expect for $72,000?

25. ____________

Name ____________________ Chapter 5 Form B  Score ______

1. Determine any values of the variable for which the rational expression $\frac{6 - 5m}{9 + n^2}$ is undefined. 1. ____________

2. Write the rational expression in lowest terms: 2. ____________

$$\frac{56\,a^{15}b^{9}}{63\,a^{18}b^{3}}$$

3. Write the rational expression in lowest terms: 3. ____________

$$\frac{m - 8}{8 - m}$$

4. Multiply and write the answer in lowest terms: 4. ____________

$$\frac{3t + 15}{8t} \cdot \frac{28}{t + 5}$$

5. Divide and write the answer in lowest terms: 5. ____________

$$\frac{b^2 - 25}{b - 3} \div \frac{b + 5}{b^2 - 9}$$

6. Find the least common denominator for 6. ____________

$$\frac{6z}{z^2 + 4z} \text{ and } \frac{2z - 3}{4z^2 + 16z}$$

7. Find the missing numerators:

$$\frac{5 - 3t}{4t - 28} = \frac{\quad}{140 - 20t}$$

7. ____________

8. Add and write the answer in lowest terms:

$$\frac{3y}{y + 3} + \frac{y - 3}{y^2 - 9}$$

8. ____________

9. Subtract and write the answer in lowest terms:

$$\frac{2x + 1}{x + 4} - \frac{3x - 12}{x^2 - 16}$$

9. ____________

10. Add and subtract and write the answer in lowest terms: $\frac{u}{x^2 - u^2} + \frac{1}{x - u} - \frac{1}{x + u}$

10. ____________

11. Simplify:

$$\frac{\frac{1}{16} + \frac{3}{4}}{2 + \frac{1}{8}}$$

11. ____________

12. Simplify:

$$\frac{\frac{9}{w^4} - \frac{4}{w^2}}{\frac{3}{w} + \frac{2}{w^2}}$$

12. ____________

13. Solve the equation: $\frac{4x - 3}{4} - \frac{6x}{8} = 3$

13. ____________

14. Solve the equation: $\frac{x}{x + 1} = \frac{2z + 6}{x + 3}$

14. ____________

15. One number is three less than another number. The larger number divided by the smaller number is two. Find the two numbers.

15. ____________

16. Solve $y = \frac{1}{3 - x}$ for x

16. ____________

17. Solve the proportion: $\frac{3x}{x - 4} = \frac{x + 4}{2}$

17. ____________

18. A piece of rope 27 feet long is to be cut into two pieces whose lengths have the ratio 2 to 7. Find the length of each piece.

18. ____________

19. Find the lengths of the missing sides in the similar triangles $\triangle ABC$ and $\triangle DEF$. 19. ____________

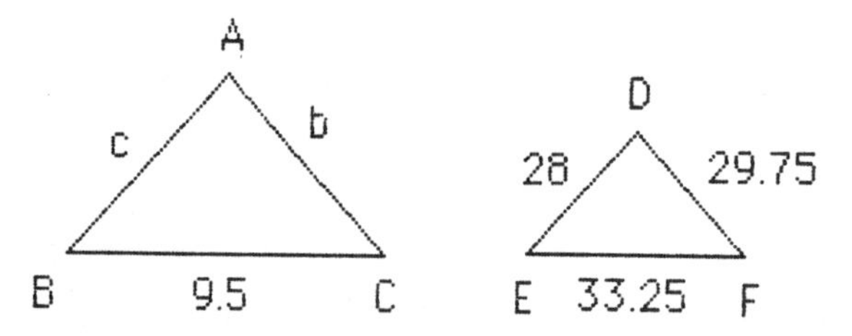

20. What number must be added to the numerator and denominator of $\frac{1}{3}$ to make a fraction equivalent to $\frac{3}{4}$? 20. ____________

21. A gardener can mow a lawn in 9 hours. When his assistant aids him, it takes the two together only 6 hours. How long does it take the assistant alone to mow the lawn? 21. ____________

22. Jonathan bicycled 11 miles in the same time it took Randy to walk 3 miles. Jonathan's rate was 2 miles per hour faster than Randy's. How fast does Jonathan ride? 22. ____________

23. Suppose y varies directly as the square of w, If $y = 27$ when $w = -3$, find y when $w = 5$. 23. ____________

24. Given that N varies inversely as m and that $N = 3$ when $m = \frac{2}{5}$, find N when $m = 10$.

24. ____________

25. The height of a cylinder of constant volume varies inversely as the square of the radius of the base. The height of a cylinder is 8 inches and the radius of the base is $\frac{3}{4}$ inch. Find the height of a cylinder with the same volume that has a base radius of 4 inches.

25. ____________

Name ____________________ Chapter 5 Form C Score

1. Determine any values of the variable for which the rational expression $\dfrac{k+1}{2k^2+3k+1}$ is undefined. 1. ______

2. Write the rational expression in lowest terms: 2. ______
$$\frac{x^2+x-12}{x^2-2x-24}$$

3. Write the rational expression in lowest terms: 3. ______
$$\frac{-3m^2+5m+2}{6m^2-m-1}$$

4. Multiply and write the answer in lowest terms: 4. ______
$$\frac{x^2+4x}{3x+12} \cdot \frac{2x^2-3x}{10x-15}$$

5. Divide and write the answer in lowest terms: 5. ______
$$\frac{4-x^2}{5x^4+10x^3} \div \frac{x^2-4x+4}{15x^5}$$

6. Find the least common denominator for 6. ______
$$\frac{x}{x^2-2x-3} \text{ and } \frac{18}{x^2-4x+3}$$

7. Find the missing numerators:

$$\frac{5x + 1}{x^2 + 9x + 14} = \frac{\quad}{3x(x + 7)(x + 2)}$$

7. ________

8. Add and write the answer in lowest terms:

$$(w + 4) + \frac{5}{w + 1}$$

8. ________

9. Subtract and write the answer in lowest terms:

$$\frac{x^2 + 5}{4x^2 + 5x + 1} - \frac{x + 3}{4x + 1}$$

9. ________

10. Add and subtract and write the answer in lowest terms: $\frac{2}{a^3} + \frac{1}{a^2 - 9a} - \frac{1}{9a^2 - a^3}$

10. ________

11. Simplify: $\dfrac{d^8}{-\dfrac{15}{d^2}}$

11. ________

12. Simplify: $\dfrac{\dfrac{1}{a+1} - \dfrac{1}{a-1}}{\dfrac{1}{a^2-1}}$

12. ____________

13. Solve the equation: $\dfrac{t+2}{4} - \dfrac{3t-6}{8} = 2t$

13. ____________

14. Solve the equation: $\dfrac{1}{x^2-1} + \dfrac{1}{x-1} = \dfrac{4}{x+1}$

14. ____________

15. A number is equal to negative four divided by the sum of the number and four. Find the number.

15. ____________

16. Solve $A = p\left(\dfrac{1}{a} - \dfrac{1}{b}\right)$ for b

16. ____________

17. Solve the proportion: $\dfrac{3a+1}{a+1} = \dfrac{1+a}{a}$

17. ____________

18. Two brothers are to split an inheritance of $27000 with a ratio of 3 to 5. How much will each brother receive ?

18. 

19. Find the lengths of the missing sides in the similar triangles $\triangle ABC$ and $\triangle DEF$.

19. 

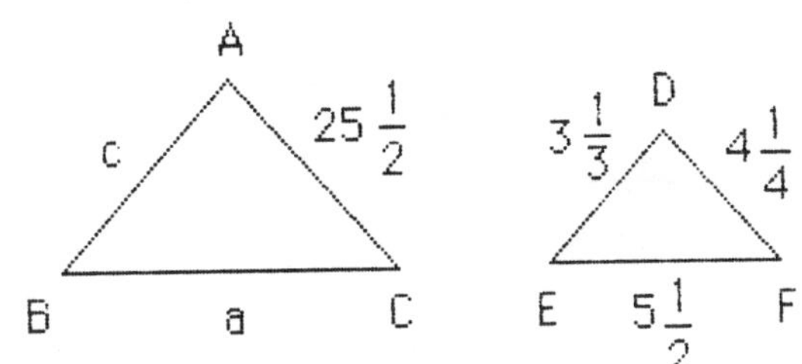

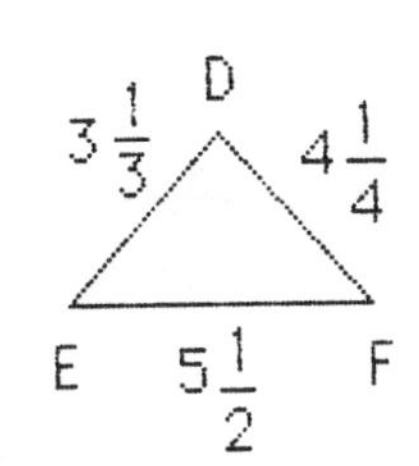

20. One number is 10 smaller than another number. The quotient of the larger number divided by the smaller number is $-2\frac{1}{3}$. Find the two numbers.

20. ______________

21. One pipe can fill a tank in 15 minutes. A second pipe can empty a full tank in 18 minutes. If both pipes are open, how long does it take to fill the tank, when empty?

21. ______________

22. A river has a current of 4 miles per hour. A ship went 48 miles downriver in the same amount of time it took to go 36 miles upriver. What is the rate of the ship in still water?

22. ______________

23. Suppose N varies directly as the square of p. If $N = 48$ when $p = 8$, find N when $p = 3$.

24. If w varies inversely as the square of x and $w = 256$ when $x = \frac{3}{16}$, find w when $x = \frac{1}{2}$.

24. ____________

25. On a roadmap, $1\frac{3}{4}$ inches represents 225 miles.

If two cities are $2\frac{3}{8}$ inches apart, what is the actual distance between the two cities? Round answer to the nearest mile.

25. ____________

Name ______________________ Chapter 5 Form D Score ________

1. Determine any values of the variable for which the rational expression $\frac{5}{3x-6}$ is undefined. 1. ____________

a. -2
b. 2
c. 0
d. 3
e. none of these

2. Write the rational expression in lowest terms: 2. ____________

$$\frac{6y-30}{12y-60}$$

a. $\frac{1}{6}$
b. $\frac{1}{4}$
c. 0
d. $\frac{1}{2}$
e. none of these

3. Write the rational expression in lowest terms: 3. ____________

$$\frac{mt-nt+2m-2n}{2mt-2nt+2mz-2nz}$$

a. $\frac{t+2}{2(t+z)}$
b. $\frac{t}{2t+z}$
c. $\frac{1}{2}$
d. 0
e. none of these

4. Multiply and write the answer in lowest terms: 4. ____________

$$\frac{3m^2+m-2}{2m-1} \cdot \frac{2m^2+7m-4}{m^2+5m+4}$$

a. $\frac{(3m-2)(m-4)}{m+4}$
b. $-\frac{27m^2}{5}$
c. $\frac{(3m-2)(2m+1)}{2m-1}$
d. $\frac{(3m+1)(m-2)}{m+1}$
e. none of these

5. Divide and write the answer in lowest terms:

$$\frac{5x - 6}{3x - 12} \div \frac{6 - 5x}{9x - 36}$$

5. ____________

a. -3
b. $\frac{3(5x - 6)}{6 - 5x}$
c. -1
d. 3
e. none of these

6. Find the least common denominator for

$$\frac{d + 7}{9 - d} \text{ and } \frac{d + 2}{d^2 - 81}$$

6. ____________

a. $(9 - d)(d - 9)(d + 9)$
b. $d - 9$
c. $(d - 9)(d + 9)$
d. $(d + 7)(d + 2)$
e. none of these

7. Find the missing numerators:

$$\frac{10z}{5(9z - 2)} = \frac{}{45(2 - 9z)}$$

7. ____________

a. $2z$
b. $-90z$
c. -9
d. $90z$
e. none of these

8. Add and write the answer in lowest terms:

$$\frac{5w}{(w + 3)(w + 5)} + \frac{15}{(w + 5)(w + 3)}$$

8. ____________

a. $\frac{5}{w + 5}$
b. $\frac{1}{w}$
c. $\frac{5}{w}$
d. $\frac{20w}{(w + 3)(w + 5)}$
e. none of these

9. Subtract and write the answer in lowest terms: 9. ____________

$$\frac{9x^2}{(4x-1)(x-1)} - \frac{9x}{(4x-1)(x-1)}$$

a. $-3x + 3$

b. 3

c. $\frac{x}{(4x-1)(x-1)}$

d. $\frac{9x}{4x-1}$

e. none of these

10. Add and subtract and write the answer in lowest terms: $\frac{12}{6x^2} + \frac{8}{x^3} - \frac{3}{4x}$ 10. ____________

a. $\frac{8x^3 + 32x^2 - 3x^5}{4x^6}$

b. $\frac{98 - 9x^2}{x^2}$

c. $\frac{-3x^2 + 8x + 32}{4x^3}$

d. $\frac{17}{2x^4}$

e. none of these

11. Simplify: $\frac{-\frac{32}{y^6}}{\frac{56}{y^{12}}}$ 11. 

a. $\frac{-4y^{12}}{7y^6}$

b. $\frac{-4y^2}{7}$

c. $\frac{-1792}{y^{18}}$

d. $\frac{-4y^6}{7}$

e. none of these

12. Simplify: $\dfrac{\dfrac{1}{a^2} + \dfrac{1}{a}}{a - \dfrac{1}{a}}$ 12. ____________

a. $\dfrac{1}{a^2 - 1}$

b. $\dfrac{2}{(a + 1)(a - 1)}$

c. $\dfrac{1 + a}{a(a - 1)}$

d. $\dfrac{1 + a}{a(a^2 - 1)}$

e. none of these

13. Solve the equation: $8y - \dfrac{5y}{4} = -\dfrac{9}{2}$ 13. ____________

a. $y = 9$

b. $y = -\dfrac{2}{3}$

c. $y = -6$

d. $y = -\dfrac{3}{2}$

e. none of these

14. Solve the equation: $\dfrac{9}{y + 3} - \dfrac{6}{y} = \dfrac{12}{y^2 + 3y}$ 14. ____________

a. $y = 3$

b. $y = 2$

c. $y = 10$

d. $y = -2$

e. none of these

15. One number is twice another number. The sum of their reciprocals is 15. Find the two numbers. 15. ____________

a. $\dfrac{1}{10}$ and $\dfrac{1}{5}$

b. $\dfrac{1}{9}$ and $\dfrac{1}{6}$

c. 10 and 5

d. 9 and 6

e. none of these

16. Solve $\dfrac{2a - 5bc}{a^3} = 1$ for b.

16. ____________

a. $b = \dfrac{a^3 - 2a}{5c}$

b. $b = \dfrac{2a - a^3}{5c}$

c. $b = 2a - a^3 - 5c$

d. $b = a^3 - 2a + 5c$

e. none of these

17. Solve the preportion: $\dfrac{3y + 2}{y^2 + 4} = \dfrac{1}{y}$

17. ____________

a. $y = 2$

b. $y = 1$ or $y = -1$

c. $y = 1$

d. $y = 1$ or $y = -2$

e. none of these

18. On a map 5 inches represents 16 miles. How many miles does 18 inches represent?

18. ____________

a. 48.2 miles

b. 56.25 miles

c. 57.6 miles

d. $5\frac{5}{8}$ miles

e. none of these

19. Find the lengths of the missing sides in the similar triangles $\triangle ABC$ and $\triangle DEF$.

19. ____________

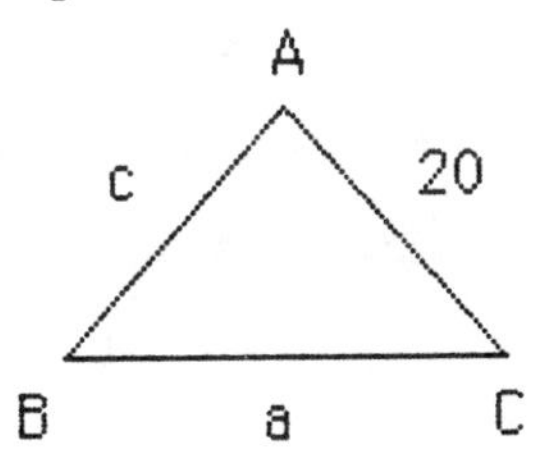

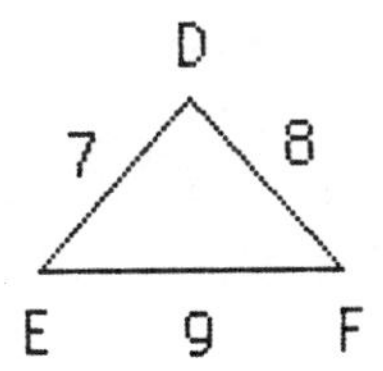

a. a = 3.6 and c = 2.8

b. a = 21 and c = 19

c. a = 18.5 and c = 14.5

d. a = 22.5 and c = 17.5

e. none of these

20. Find two numbers whose sum is 18 and the sum of their reciprocals is $\frac{1}{4}$.

20. ____________

a. 7 and 11
b. 6 and 12
c. 14 amd 4
d. 5 and 13
e. none of these

21. Bob can paint a barn in 10 hours. Joe can paint it in 12 hours. How long does it take them together to paint the barn?

21. ____________

a. $5\frac{1}{12}$ hours
b. 6 hours
c. 11 hours
d. $5\frac{1}{6}$ hours
e. none of these

22. Jeanette took the same time to drive 30 miles as it took Larry to drive 25 miles. Jeanette's speed was 10 miles per hour faster than Larry's speed. How fast did Jeanette drive?

22. ____________

a. 50 m.p.h.
b. 12 m.p.h.
c. 60 m.p.h.
d. 55 m.p.h.
e. none of these

23. Suppose y varies directly as x and $y = 14$ when $x = 9$. Find y when $x = 12$.

23. ____________

a. $y = 7\frac{5}{7}$
b. $y = 18\frac{2}{3}$
c. $y = 60$
d. $y = 52$
e. none of these

24. If w varies inversely as t and $w = \frac{1}{2}$ when $t = 4$, find w when $t = 8$.

24. ____________

a. $w = 1$
b. $w = 4$
c. $w = \frac{1}{4}$
d. $w = \frac{1}{6}$
e. none of these

25. Property tax is directly proportional to the assessed value of the property. A vacant lot is assessed at $5000, and the tax on it is $425. What should be the tax on a house and lot assessed at $32,500?

25. ____________

a. $2762.50
b. $3823.53
c. $2730.50
d. $2740.50
e. none of these

Name ______________________ Chapter 5 Form E Score ________

1. Determine any values of the variable for which the rational expression $\frac{8 - 2n}{16 - n^2}$

1. ____________

a. $n = 4$ and $n = -4$
b. $n = 6$
c. $n = 8$ and $n = -8$
d. $n = 4$
e. none of these

2. Write the rational expression in lowest terms: $\frac{84x^{12} y^{14}}{56x^{16} y^2}$

2. ____________

a. $\frac{3y^7}{2x}$
b. $\frac{3y^7}{2x^4}$
c. $\frac{3y^{12}}{2x^4}$
d. $\frac{3y^{12}}{2x}$
e. none of these

3. Write the rational expression in lowest terms: $\frac{-2y + 3}{-6 + 4y}$

3. ____________

a. $\frac{1}{4}$
b. $-\frac{1}{2}$
c. $-\frac{1}{4}$
d. $\frac{1}{2}$
e. none of these

4. Multiply and write the answer in lowest terms: 4. ____________

$$\frac{6m + 30}{15m} \cdot \frac{40}{2m + 10}$$

a. $\frac{6m + 2}{m}$

b. $\frac{16}{m}$

c. $\frac{12}{m}$

d. $\frac{8}{m}$

e. none of these

5. Divide and write the answer in lowest terms: 5. ____________

$$\frac{m^2 - 16}{m - 6} \div \frac{m + 4}{m^2 - 36}$$

a. $-24m^2$

b. $\frac{8}{27}$

c. $(m - 4)(m + 6)$

d. $m^2 - 24$

e. none of these

6. Find the least common denominator for 6. ____________

$$\frac{8y^2}{3y + 12y^2} \text{ and } \frac{7 + y}{8y^2 + 32y^3}$$

a. $8y^3(1 + 4y)$

b. $24y^3(1 + 4y)^2$

c. $(3y + 12y^2)(8y^2 + 32y^3)$

d. $8y^2(7 + y)$

e. none of these

7. Find the missing numerators: 7. ____________

$$\frac{4 - 6w}{12w - 8} = \frac{\quad}{56 - 84w}$$

a. $7(4 - 6w)$

b. $4 - 6w$

c. $-7(4 - 6w)$

d. $8(4 - 6w)$

e. none of these

8. Add and write the answer in lowest terms: 8. ____________

$$\frac{4x}{x+5} + \frac{x-5}{x^2-25}$$

a. $\frac{5x-5}{(x+5)(x-5)}$

b. $\frac{4x+1}{x+5}$

c. $\frac{5x-5}{x^2+x-20}$

d. $\frac{4x^2+x-10}{(x+5)(x-5)}$

e. none of these

9. Subtract and write the answer in lowest terms: 9. ____________

$$\frac{3m-1}{m-5} - \frac{m+5}{m^2-25}$$

a. $\frac{3m-2}{m-5}$

b. $\frac{2m-6}{m-5}$

c. $\frac{3m}{m-5}$

d. $\frac{3m^2-m-10}{(m+5)(m-5)}$

e. none of these

10. Add and subtract and write the answer in lowest terms: $\frac{w}{y^2-w^2} - \frac{1}{y+w} + \frac{1}{y-w}$ 10. ____________

a. $\frac{-w}{(y+w)(y-w)}$

b. $\frac{-3w}{(y+w)(y-w)}$

c. $\frac{w}{(y+w)(y-w)}$

d. $\frac{3w}{(y+w)(y-w)}$

e. none of these

11\. Simplify: $\dfrac{\dfrac{3}{16} + \dfrac{3}{4}}{3 + \dfrac{1}{8}}$ 11. ____________

a. $\dfrac{3}{5}$

b. $\dfrac{3}{10}$

c. $\dfrac{15}{8}$

d. $\dfrac{3}{40}$

e. none of these

12\. Simplify: $\dfrac{\dfrac{16}{z^3} - \dfrac{9}{z}}{\dfrac{4z}{z^4} - \dfrac{3}{z^2}}$ 12. ____________

a. $\dfrac{4 + 3z}{z}$

b. $4 + 3z$

c. $\dfrac{7}{4z - 3}$

d. 1

e. none of these

13\. Solve the equation: $\dfrac{7x - 1}{8} - \dfrac{2x}{12} = 1$ 13. ____________

a. $x = \dfrac{25}{17}$

b. $x = \dfrac{2}{5}$

c. $x = \dfrac{13}{68}$

d. $x = \dfrac{27}{17}$

e. none of these

14. Solve the equation: $\dfrac{3m - 5}{m + 1} = \dfrac{3m + 1}{m - 2}$ 14. ___________

a. $m = \dfrac{9}{4}$

b. $m = \dfrac{5}{3}$

c. $m = 1$ or $m = \dfrac{3}{8}$

d. $m = -6$

e. none of these

15. One number is six less than another number. The larger number divided by the smaller number is two. Find the smaller number. 15. ___________

a. 12
b. 0
c. -12
d. 6
e. none of these

16. Solve $m = \dfrac{2}{5 - p}$ for p. 16. ___________

a. $p = \dfrac{5m - 2}{m}$

b. $p = \dfrac{2 - 5m}{m}$

c. $p = 5m - 2$

d. $p = 2 - 4m$

e. none of these

17. Solve the preportion: $\dfrac{-2x}{x - 4} = \dfrac{x + 4}{3}$ 17. ___________

a. $x = -\dfrac{3}{2}$ or $x = -4$

b. $x = 2$ or $x = -8$

c. $x = \dfrac{3}{2}$ or $x = 4$

d. $x = 8$ or $x = -2$

e. none of these

18. A piece of rope 32 feet long is to be cut into pieces whose lengths have the ratio of 3 to 5. Find the length of the shorter piece.

18. ____________

a. 12 ft.
b. 20 ft.
c. $12\frac{4}{5}$ ft.
d. $19\frac{1}{5}$ ft.
e. none of these

19. Find the lengths of the missing sides in the similar triangles $\triangle ABC$ and $\triangle DEF$.

19. ____________

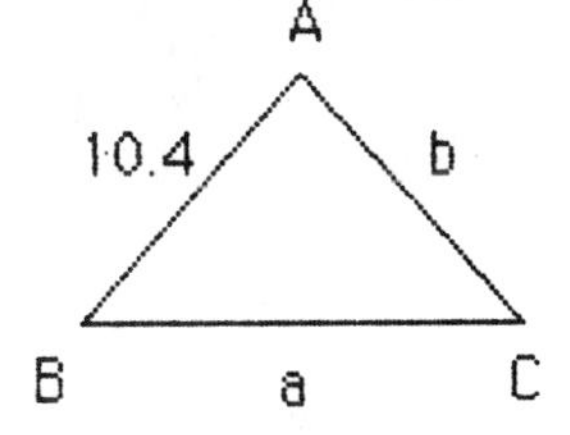

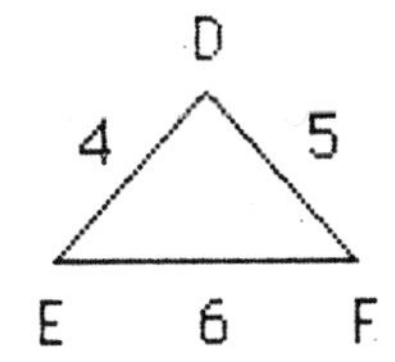

a. a = 2.3 and b = 1.9
b. $a = 6\frac{14}{15}$ and $b = 8\frac{2}{3}$
c. a = 15.6 and b = 13
d. a = 15.1 and b = 12.5
e. none of these

20. What number must be added to the numerator and denominator of $\frac{1}{8}$ to make a fraction equivalant to $\frac{2}{3}$?

20. ____________

a. 1
b. -13
c. -22
d. 13
e. none of these

21. Two privates sweep the mess hall together in 4 hours. One works twice as fast as the other. How long does it take the faster private to do the job alone?

21. ____________

a. 12 hours
b. $2\frac{2}{3}$ hours
c. 6 hours
d. $5\frac{1}{3}$ hours
e. none of these

22. Susan bicycled 8 miles in the same time it took Tamara to walk 3 miles. Susan's rate was 3 miles per hour faster than Tamara's. How fast does Susan ride?

22. ____________

a. $4\frac{4}{5}$ m.p.h.
b. $1\frac{4}{5}$ m.p.h.
c. 6 m.p.h.
d. 3 m.p.h.
e. none of these

23. Suppose A varies directly as the square of d. If $A = 6$ when $d = 3$, find A when $d = -6$.

23. ____________

a. $A = 18$
b. $A = 36$
c. $A = 54$
d. $A = 24$
e. none of these

24. Given that V varies inversely as t and that $V = 12$ when $t = \frac{1}{3}$, find V when $t = 6$.

24. ____________

a. $V = 216$
b. $V = \frac{2}{3}$
c. $V = 6$
d. $V = \frac{3}{2}$
e. none of these

25. The height of a cylinder of constant volume varies inversely as the square of the radius of the base. The height of a cylinder is 12 inches and the radius of the base is $\frac{1}{4}$ inch. Find the height of cylinder with the same volume that has a base radius of 3 inches.

25. ____________

a. $h = \frac{1}{3}$
b. $h = \frac{1}{9}$
c. $h = \frac{1}{12}$
d. $h = \frac{1}{6}$
e. none of these

Name ________________________ Chapter 5 Form F Score ________

1. Determine any values of the variable for which the rational expression $\frac{y - 2}{2y^2 - 3y - 2}$ is undefined.

1. ____________

a. $y = 2$

b. $y = -2$ and $y = \frac{1}{2}$

c. $y = -\frac{1}{2}$

d. $y = 2$ and $y = -\frac{1}{2}$

e. none of these

2. Write the rational expression in lowest terms:

$$\frac{x^2 - 3x - 10}{x^2 - x - 20}$$

2. ____________

a. $\frac{x + 2}{x + 4}$

b. $\frac{3x}{x + 2}$

c. $\frac{-3x - 10}{-x - 20}$

d. $\frac{x - 2}{x - 4}$

e. none of these

3. Write the rational expression in lowest terms:

$$\frac{-4x^2 + 11x + 3}{8x^2 - 23x - 3}$$

3. ____________

a. $\frac{4x + 1}{8x + 1}$

b. $\frac{11x}{2 - 23x}$

c. $\frac{-(x - 3)}{2x - 3}$

d. $\frac{-4x + 11}{8x - 23}$

e. none of these

4. Multiply and write the answer in lowest terms: 4. ____________

$$\frac{2y^2 - 6y}{4y + 4} \cdot \frac{y^2 + y}{6y - 18}$$

a. $\frac{y^2}{24}$

b. $\frac{y^2}{12}$

c. $\frac{3y}{10}$

d. $\frac{3(y - 3)^2}{(y + 1)^2}$

e. none of these

5. Divide and write the answer in lowest terms: 5. ____________

$$\frac{16 - x^2}{2x^3 + 8x^2} \div \frac{x^2 - 8x + 16}{6x^5}$$

a. $\frac{3x^3}{x - 4}$

b. $\frac{6x^2}{x^2 - 8x + 16}$

c. $-\frac{(x - 4)}{3x^3}$

d. $\frac{-3x^3}{x - 4}$

e. none of these

6. Find the least common denominator for 6. ____________

$$\frac{2y}{y^2 - 9y + 8} \quad \text{and} \quad \frac{12}{y^2 + 3y - 4}$$

a. $12y$

b. $(y - 8)(y - 1)(y + 4)$

c. $y - 1$

d. $(y - 8)(y + 4)(y - 1)^2$

e. none of these

7. Find the missing numerators: 7. ____________

$$\frac{2 - 11y}{y^2 + 3y - 18} = \frac{\qquad}{5y^2(3 - y)(y + 6)}$$

a. $- 5y^2(2 - 11y)$

b. $5y^2(2 - 11y)$

c. $-5y^2$

d. $5y^2(2 - 11y)(y - 3)$

e. none of these

8. Add and write the answer in lowest terms: 8. ____________

$$x + 2 + \frac{8}{x - 4}$$

a. $\frac{x^2}{x - 4}$

b. $\frac{x + 10}{x - 4}$

c. $\frac{x^2 - 2x}{x - 4}$

d. $\frac{x^2}{2}$

e. none of these

9. Subtract and write the answer in lowest terms: 9. ____________

$$\frac{x^2 + 19}{x^2 + 2x - 3} - \frac{x - 4}{x + 3}$$

a. $\frac{x^2 - x + 23}{(x + 3)(x - 1)}$

b. $\frac{5}{x - 1}$

c. $\frac{-x + 23}{2x - 3}$

d. $\frac{15}{(x + 3)(x - 1)}$

e. none of these

10. Add and subtract and write the answer in lowest terms: $\frac{2}{x^2 - 25} + \frac{1}{x + 5} - \frac{1}{x - 5}$ 10. ____________

a. $\frac{-8}{(x + 5)(x - 5)}$

b. $\frac{2}{x^2 - 15}$

c. $\frac{2}{(x + 5)(x - 5)}$

d. $\frac{12}{(x + 5)(x - 5)}$

e. none of these

11. Simplify: $\dfrac{y^{10}}{-\dfrac{12}{y^2}}$ 11. ____________

a. $-12y^8$

b. $-\dfrac{y^{20}}{12}$

c. $-\dfrac{y^{12}}{12}$

d. $\dfrac{-12}{y^{12}}$

e. none of these

12. Simplify: $\dfrac{\dfrac{1}{x+3} - \dfrac{1}{x-3}}{\dfrac{2x}{x^2-9}}$ 12. ____________

a. $\dfrac{0}{2x}$

b. $\dfrac{-12x}{(x+3)(x-3)}$

c. $\dfrac{-4}{x}$

d. $-\dfrac{3}{x}$

e. none of these

13. Solve the equation: $\dfrac{m-1}{4} - \dfrac{4m+4}{3} = m$ 13. ____________

a. $m = -\dfrac{19}{25}$

b. $m = \dfrac{3}{25}$

c. $m = -\dfrac{25}{19}$

d. $m = \dfrac{25}{3}$

e. none of these

14. Solve the equation: $\frac{5}{w} + \frac{12}{w^2 + 4w} = \frac{w + 1}{w + 4}$ 14. ________

a. $w = 8$ or $w = -4$
b. $w = -\frac{31}{4}$
c. $w = -8$ or $w = 4$
d. $w = 8$
e. none of these

15. A number is equal to a negative twenty-five divided by the difference of the number and ten. Find the number. 15. ________

a. -5
b. $-\frac{5}{2}$
c. $\frac{5}{2}$
d. $\frac{5}{13}$
e. none of these

16. Solve $D = v\left(\frac{2}{w} - \frac{1}{x}\right)$ for w. 16. ________

a. $w = \frac{2v + 2xD}{D}$
b. $w = \frac{2vx}{Dx + 1}$
c. $w = \frac{2vx}{Dx + v}$
d. $w = \frac{2vx}{Dx - v}$
e. none of these

17. Solve the proportion: $\frac{2x + 2}{x + 1} = \frac{x + 4}{x}$ 17. ________

a. $x = 4$
b. $x = 2$ or $x = -2$
c. $x = 4$ or $x = -1$
d. $x = -8$ or $x = -1$
e. none of these

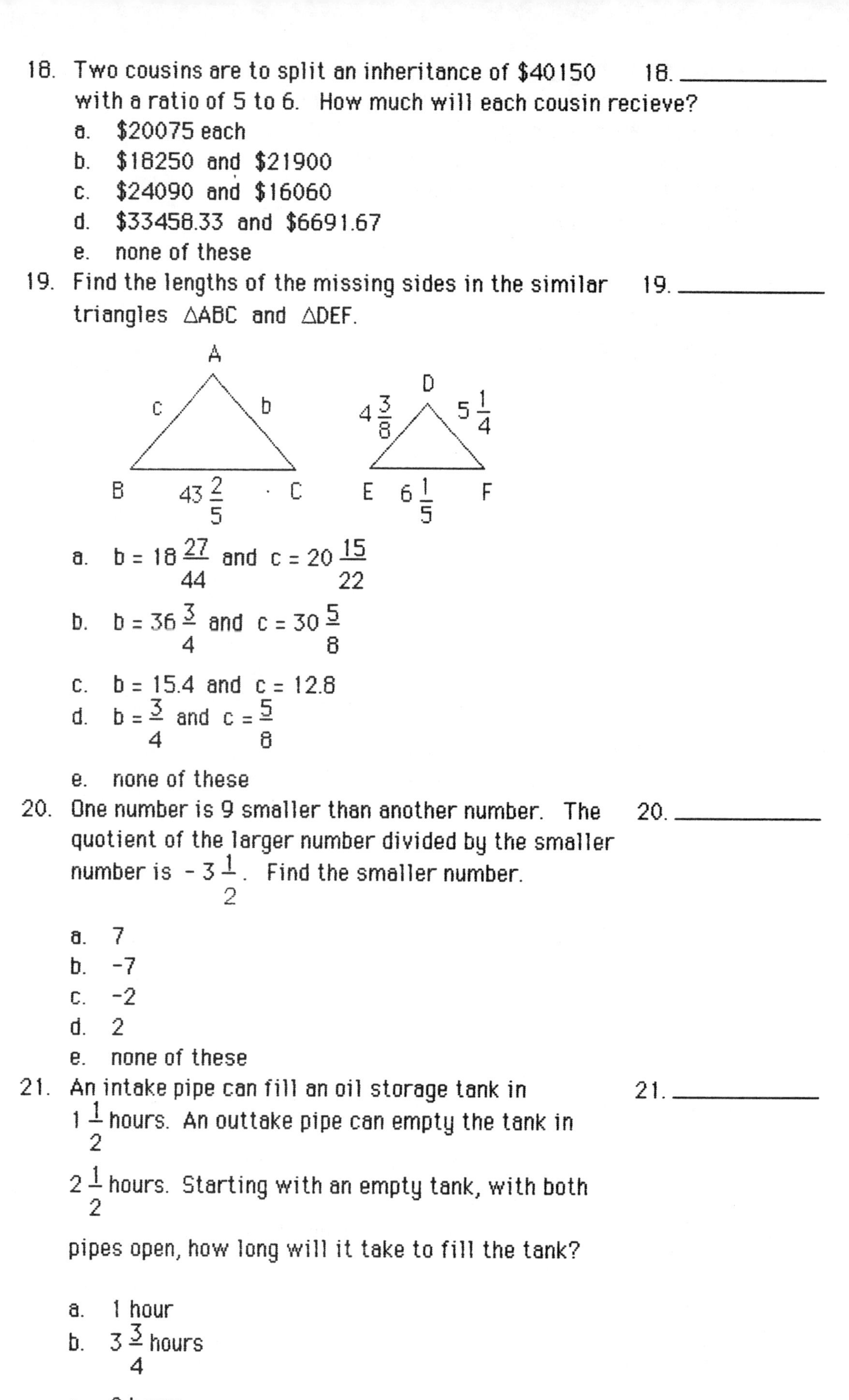

18. Two cousins are to split an inheritance of \$40150 with a ratio of 5 to 6. How much will each cousin recieve? 18. ____________
   a. \$20075 each
   b. \$18250 and \$21900
   c. \$24090 and \$16060
   d. \$33458.33 and \$6691.67
   e. none of these

19. Find the lengths of the missing sides in the similar triangles $\triangle ABC$ and $\triangle DEF$. 19. ____________

   a. $b = 18\frac{27}{44}$ and $c = 20\frac{15}{22}$
   b. $b = 36\frac{3}{4}$ and $c = 30\frac{5}{8}$
   c. $b = 15.4$ and $c = 12.8$
   d. $b = \frac{3}{4}$ and $c = \frac{5}{8}$
   e. none of these

20. One number is 9 smaller than another number. The quotient of the larger number divided by the smaller number is $-3\frac{1}{2}$. Find the smaller number. 20. ____________
   a. 7
   b. -7
   c. -2
   d. 2
   e. none of these

21. An intake pipe can fill an oil storage tank in $1\frac{1}{2}$ hours. An outtake pipe can empty the tank in $2\frac{1}{2}$ hours. Starting with an empty tank, with both pipes open, how long will it take to fill the tank? 21. ____________
   a. 1 hour
   b. $3\frac{3}{4}$ hours
   c. 2 hours
   d. 4 hours
   e. none of these

22. Irene swam 110 meters with the current in the same amount of time that it took her to swim 95 meters against the current. The current flows at 3 meters per minute. What would be her speed if she were swimming in still water?

a. $\frac{2}{5}$ meters per minute
b. 3 meters per minute
c. 45 meters per minute
d. 41 meters per minute
e. none of these

22. ____________

23. Suppose z varies directly as the square of t. If $z = 10$ when $t = -4$, find z when $t = 12$.

a. $z = 56\frac{1}{4}$
b. $z = \frac{10}{9}$
c. $z = 90$
d. $z = 180$
e. none of these

23. ____________

24. If A varies inversely as the square of w and $A = 81$ when $w = \frac{1}{3}$, find A when $w = 3$.

a. $A = \frac{1}{81}$
b. $A = 6$
c. $A = \frac{1}{6}$
d. $A = 1$
e. none of these

24. ____________

25. On a road map, $3\frac{1}{4}$ inches represents 315 miles.

If two cities are $5\frac{1}{8}$ inches apart, what is the actual distance between the two cities? Round answer off to the nearest mile.

a. 293 miles
b. 497 miles
c. 525 miles
d. 485 miles
e. none of these

25. ____________

CHAPTER # 5 TEST KEYS

Form A

1. $x = \frac{1}{2}$
2. $\frac{1}{2}$
3. $\frac{a + y}{a + 2y}$
4. $2d - 3$
5. $-\frac{1}{3}$
6. $(t - 6)(t + 6)$
7. $-63w$
8. $\frac{2}{x - 3}$
9. $\frac{5}{t - 1}$
10. $\frac{20z^2 + 27z - 90}{15z^3}$
11. $-\frac{2}{7}x^8$
12. $\frac{4x - 2}{x(8x - 3)}$
13. $x = -\frac{2}{15}$
14. $x = 4$
15. $\frac{1}{9}$ and $\frac{1}{3}$
16. $w = \frac{y^3 - y}{-3x}$
17. $y = -3$ or $y = 1$
18. $66\frac{2}{3}$ miles
19. $a = 7$ and $b = 6$
20. 6 and 3
21. $3\frac{3}{7}$ hours
22. 35 mph.
23. $y = 22\frac{1}{2}$

Form B

1. no values where undefined
2. $\frac{8b^6}{9a^3}$
3. -1
4. $\frac{21}{2t}$
5. $(b - 5)(b + 3)$
6. $4z(z + 4)$
7. $-5(5 - 3t)$
8. $\frac{3y + 1}{y + 3}$
9. $\frac{2(x - 1)}{x + 4}$
10. $\frac{3u}{x^2 - u^2}$
11. $\frac{13}{34}$
12. $\frac{3 - 2w}{w^2}$
13. $x = 15$
14. $x = -2$
15. 6 and 3
16. $x = \frac{3y - 1}{y}$
17. $x = 8$ or $x = -2$
18. 6 ft. and 21 ft.
19. $b = 8.5$ and $c = 8$
20. 5
21. 18 hours
22. $2\frac{3}{4}$ mph.
23. $y = -45$

CHAPTER # 5 TEST KEYS

Form A

24. $y = -24$

25. 1500 sq. ft.

Form B

24. $N = \frac{3}{25}$

25. $\frac{9}{32}$ inch

CHAPTER # 5 TEST KEYS

Form C

1. $k = -1$ and $k = -\frac{1}{2}$
2. $\frac{x-3}{x-6}$
3. $\frac{-(m-2)}{2m-1}$
4. $\frac{x^2}{15}$
5. $\frac{-3x^2}{x-2}$
6. $(x-3)(x+1)(x-1)$
7. $3x(5x+1)$
8. $\frac{w^2+5w+9}{w+1}$
9. $\frac{-4x+2}{(4x+1)(x+1)}$
10. $\frac{a^2+3a-18}{a^3(a-9)}$
11. $\frac{-d^{10}}{15}$
12. $-2(a+1)$
13. $t = \frac{10}{17}$
14. $x = 2$
15. $x = -2$
16. $b = \frac{aP}{p - aA}$
17. $a = 1$ or $a = -\frac{1}{2}$
18. \$10,125 and \$16,875
19. $b = 33$ and $c = 20$
20. 7 and -3
21. 90 minutes
22. 28 m.p.h.
23. $N = \frac{27}{4}$
24. $w = 36$
25. 305 miles

Form D

1. b) 2
2. d) $\frac{1}{2}$
3. a) $\frac{t+2}{2(t+z)}$
4. e) none of these
5. a) -3
6. c) $(d-9)(d+9)$
7. b) $-90z$
8. a) $\frac{5}{w+5}$
9. d) $\frac{9x}{4x-1}$
10. c) $\frac{-3x^2+8x+32}{4x^3}$
11. d) $\frac{-4y^6}{7}$
12. e) none of these
13. b) $y = -\frac{2}{3}$
14. c) $y = 10$
15. a) $\frac{1}{10}$ and $\frac{1}{5}$
16. b) $b = \frac{2a - a^3}{5c}$
17. d) $y = 1$ or $y = -2$
18. c) 57.6 miles
19. d) $a = 22.5$ and $c = 17.5$
20. b) 6 and 12
21. a) $5\frac{1}{12}$ hours
22. c) 60 m.p.h.
23. b) $y = 18\frac{2}{3}$
24. c) $w = \frac{1}{4}$
25. a) \$2762.50

CHAPTER # 5 TEST KEYS

Form E

1. a) $n = 4$ and $n = -4$
2. c) $\frac{3y^{12}}{2x^4}$
3. b) $-\frac{1}{2}$
4. d) $\frac{8}{m}$
5. c) $(m - 4)(m + 6)$
6. e) None of these
7. c) $-7(4 - 6w)$
8. b) $\frac{4x + 1}{x + 5}$
9. a) $\frac{3m - 2}{m - 5}$
10. d) $\frac{3w}{(y + w)(y - w)}$
11. b) $\frac{3}{10}$
12. b) $4 + 3z$
13. d) $x = \frac{27}{17}$
14. e) None of these
15. d) 6
16. a) $p = \frac{5m - 2}{m}$
17. b) $x = 2$ or $x = -8$
18. a) 12 ft.
19. c) $a = 15.6$ and $b = 13$
20. d) 13
21. c) 6 hours
22. a) $4\frac{4}{5}$ m.p.h.
23. d) $A = 24$
24. b) $V = \frac{2}{3}$
25. c) $h = 1/12$

Form F

1. d) $y = 2$ and $y = -\frac{1}{2}$
2. a) $\frac{x + 2}{x + 4}$
3. e) None of these
4. b) $\frac{y^2}{12}$
5. d) $\frac{-3x^3}{x - 4}$
6. b) $(y - 8)(y - 1)(y + 4)$
7. a) $-5y^2(2 - 11y)$
8. c) $\frac{x^2 - 2x}{x - 4}$
9. b) $\frac{5}{x - 1}$
10. a) $\frac{-8}{(x + 5)(x - 5)}$
11. c) $-\frac{y^{12}}{12}$
12. d) $-\frac{3}{x}$
13. a) $m = -\frac{19}{25}$
14. d) $w = 8$
15. e) None of these
16. c) $w = \frac{2vx}{Dx + v}$
17. a) $x = 4$
18. b) $18250 and $21900
19. b) $b = 36\frac{3}{4}$ and $c = 30\frac{5}{8}$
20. c) -2
21. b) $3\frac{3}{4}$ hours
22. d) 41 meters per minute
23. c) $z = 90$
24. d) $A = 1$
25. b) 497 miles

Name ______________________ Chapter 6 Form A Score ________

1. Find the ordered pair for each point shown in the coordinate plane.

1. 

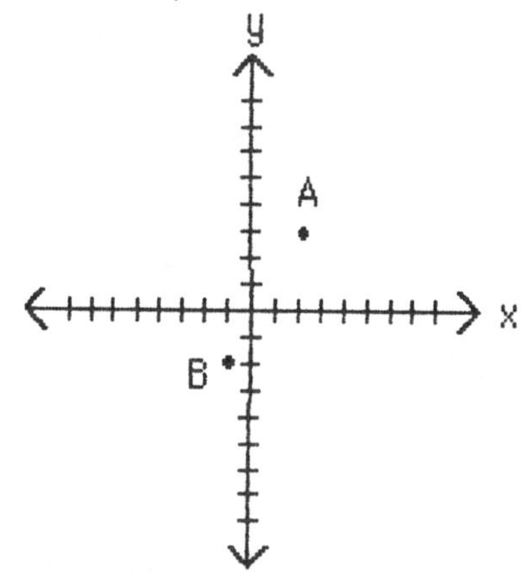

2. Refer to the graph. Name the point(s) with an x-coordinate of -3.

2. 

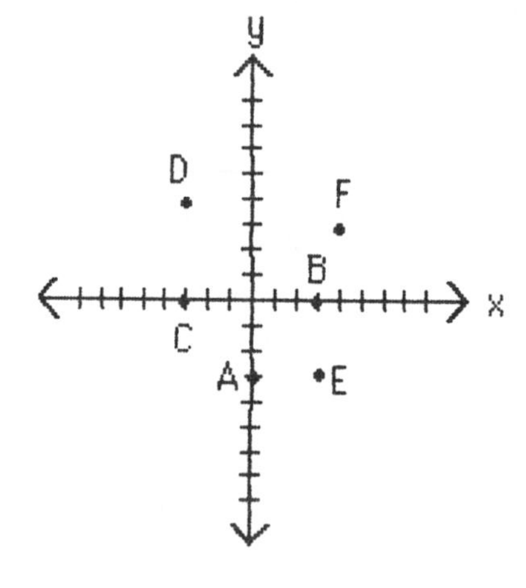

3. Plot four points (x,y) so that the sum of the coordinates is five.

3. 

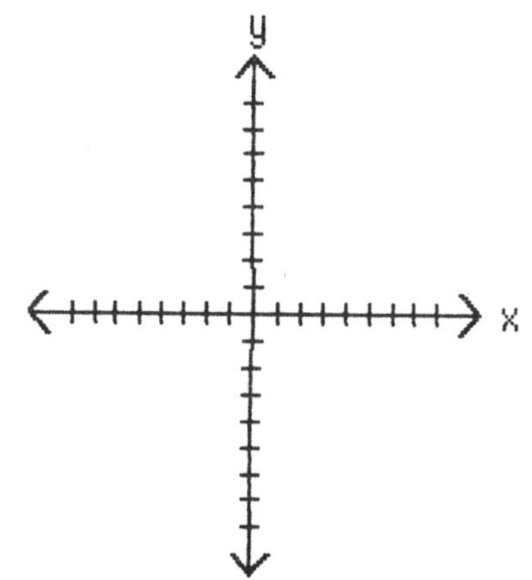

4. Graph the linear equation $x = -2y$.

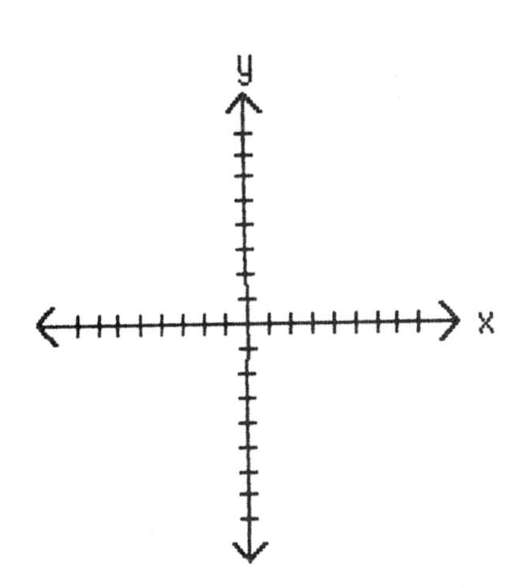

5. Write an equation from the given information, then graph the equation: "The sum of the y-coordinate and twice the x-coordinate is three".

5. ____________

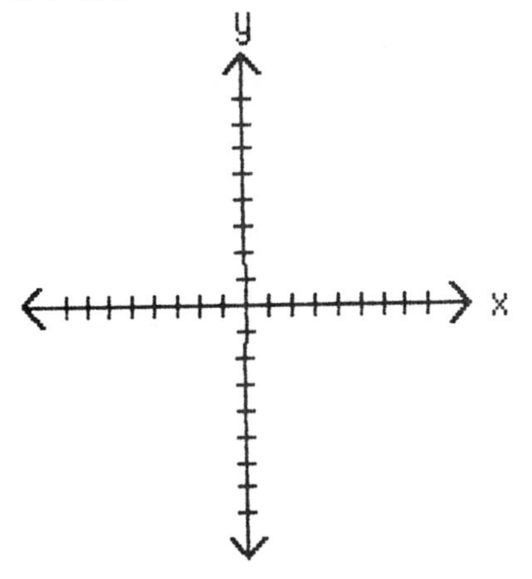

6. Find the slope, if it is defined, of the line passing through the points $(4, -1)$ and $(7, -3)$.

6. ____________

7. Find the slope, if it is defined, of the line.

7. ______________

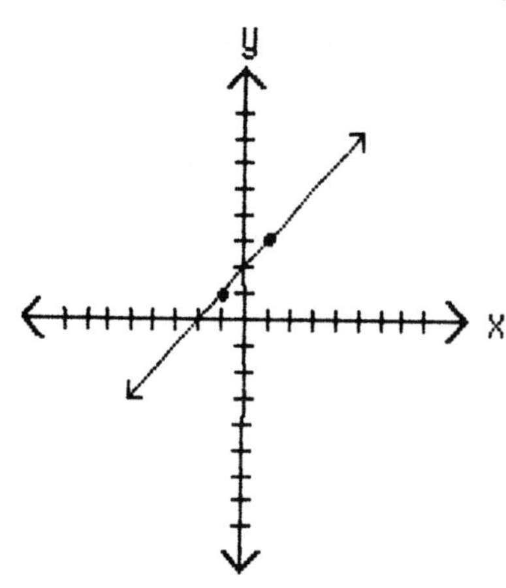

8. Determine if the line passing through the points (3, 2) and (2, 3) is parallel to the line passing through the points (1, 4) and (-1, -4).

8. ______________

9. Determine if the three points (-1, -1), (4, -11), and (-3, 3) are collinear.

9. ______________

10. In a coordinate plane, plot the point (2, -4). Then plot two other points so that all three points lie on a line with a slope of $-\frac{3}{4}$.

10. ______________

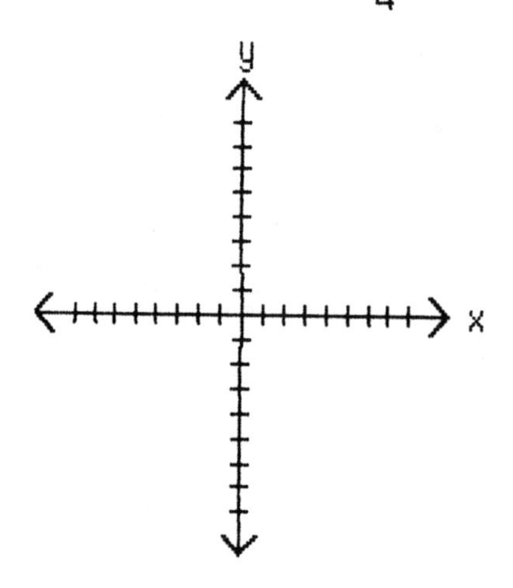

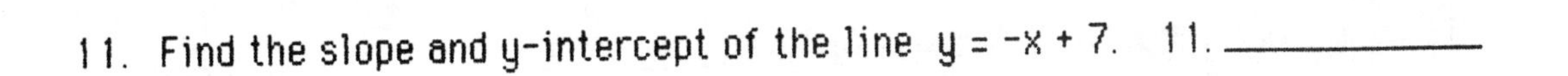

11. Find the slope and y-intercept of the line $y = -x + 7$. 11.

12. Draw the line and write an equation for a line with slope 2 and y-intercept 5. 12. 

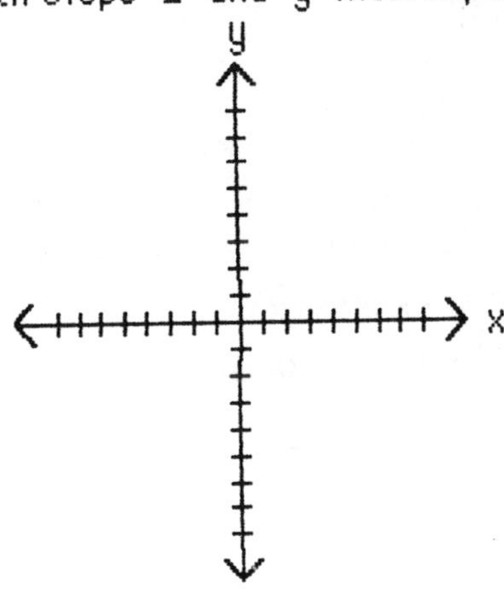

13. Find an equation of a line through the two points $P(3, -1)$ and $Q(-2, 4)$. 13. 

14. Find an equation of a line with x-intercept -2 if the line is parallel to the graph of $3x - 6y = 12$. 14. 

15. Graph the linear inequality given by $x + 2y \leq 6$. 15. 

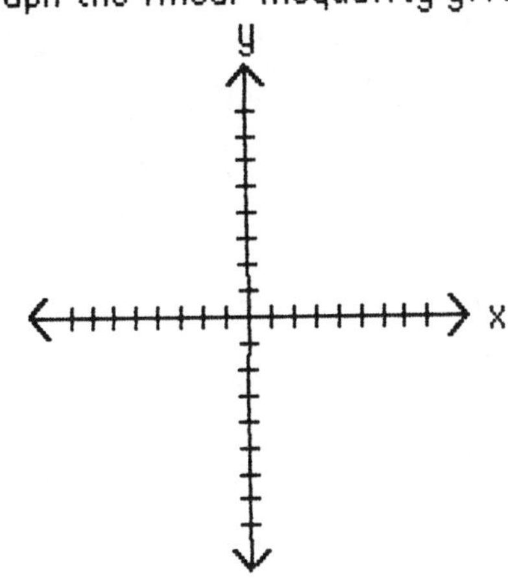

16. Write an inequality from the following information and graph it: "The sum of the x-coordinate and y-coordinate exceeds 3."

16. ____________

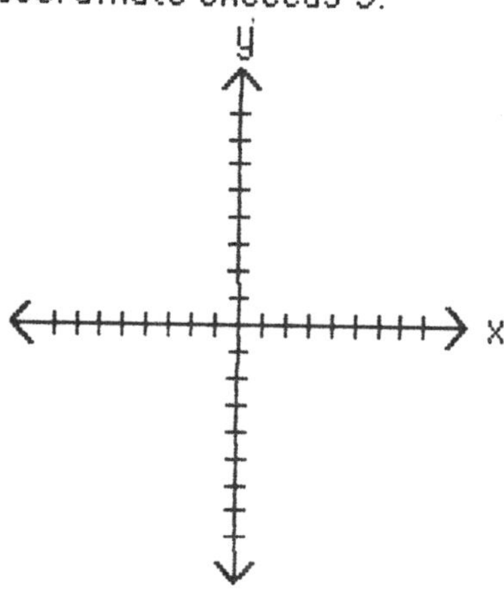

17. The U-Buy-It Department Store sells two brands of mixed chocolates. Brand x sells for \$3.20 a pound and Brand y sells for \$4.10 a pound. The store must sell at least \$815 worth of chocolates. Write an inequality to represent the combined sales.

17. 

18. Charlie buys a car for \$8000. The value of the car decreases with time. At the end of 8 years, the car has a resale value of \$1600. Assume that the value V of the car is linearly dependent upon the number of years after purchase. Write the linear equation that expresses V in terms of t, the number of years after purchase.

18. 

19. When the demand for oranges in Westville was 10,000 dozen, the price was \$2 per dozen. When the demand rose to 18,000 dozen, the price was \$1.50 per dozen. Assume that the price p per dozen is linearly dependent upon the demand x of oranges. Write the linear equation that expresses p in terms of x.

19. ____________

20. State the domain and range of the relation $\{(1, -1), (2, -2), (3, -3), (4, -4)\}$.

20. ____________

21. Write the relation S whose graph is given and determine if S is a function.

21. 

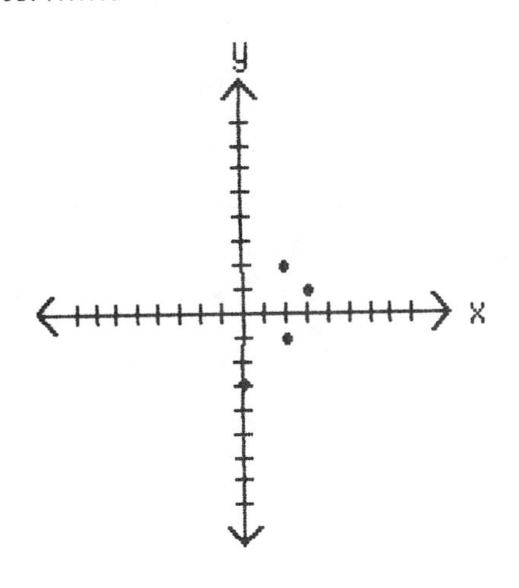

22. Suppose y is a function of x defined by $y = -\dfrac{1}{x + 1}$. State the domain of the function.

22. 

23. Suppose y is a function of x defined by $y = \dfrac{-4}{x^2 - 9}$. State the domain of the function.

23. ____________

24. Let $g(x) = 2x^2 - x + 3$. Find $g(-2)$.

24. ____________

25. Jim's Deli makes and sells sub sandwiches. The cost function C of making x subs is given by $C(x) = .25x + .40$. The revenue function R from selling x subs is given by $R(x) = -0.15x^2 + 1.95x$. Let P be the profit function from making x subs. Express $P(x)$ in terms of x.

25. ____________

Name ______________________ Chapter 6 Form B Score ________

1. Find the ordered pair for each point shown in the coordinate plane.

1. 

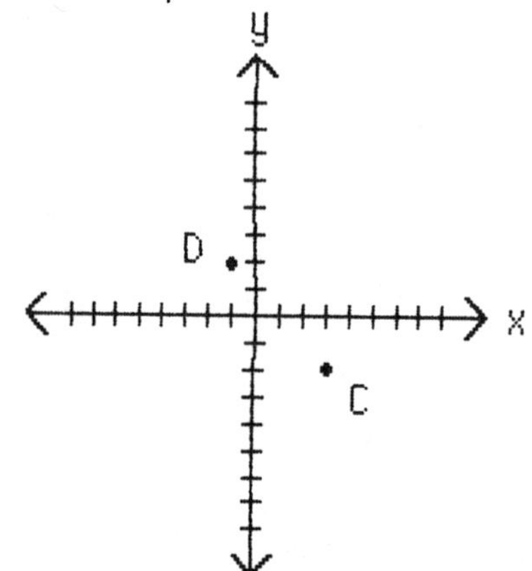

2. Refer to the graph. Name the point(s) with the y-coordinate twice the x-coordinate .

2. 

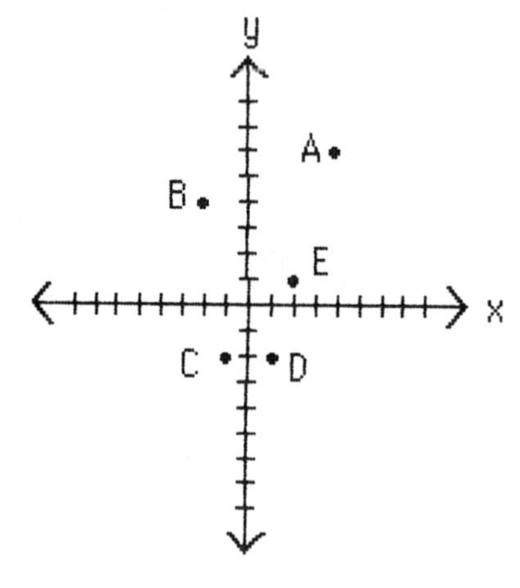

3. Plot four points (x,y) so that the y-coordinate is half the x-coordinate.

3. 

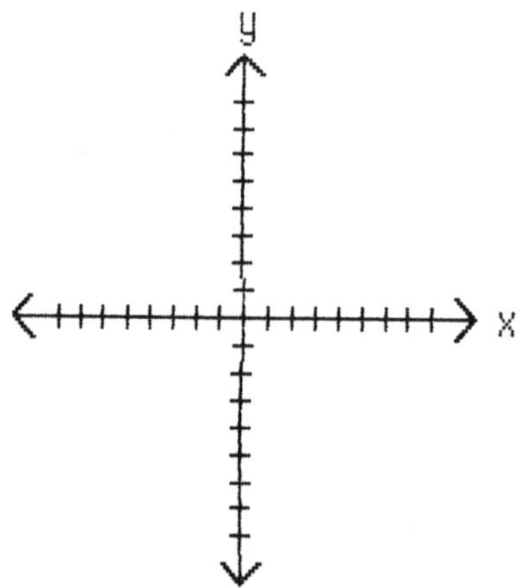

4. Graph the linear equation $y = 2x - 4$.

4. 

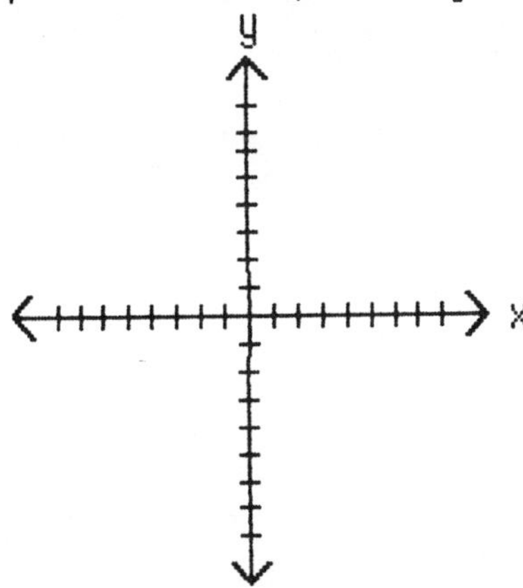

5. Write an equation from the given information, then graph the equation: "The y-coordinate is twice the difference of the x-coordinate and one".

5. 

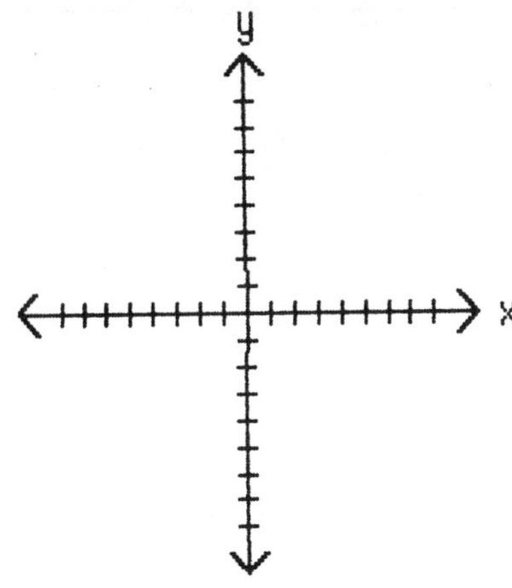

6. Find the slope, if it is defined, of the line passing through the points $(3, -5)$ and $(-1, -5)$.

6. 

7. Find the slope, if it is defined, of the line.

7. 

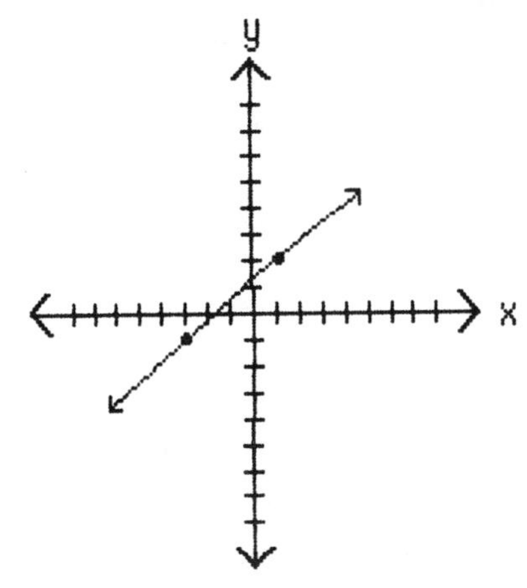

8. Determine if the line passing through the points (4, -3) and (6, -1) is parallel to the line passing through the points (-2, -1) and (-3, -2).

8. 

9. Determine if the three points (2, -4), (4, -1), and (8, 1) are collinear.

9. 

10. In a coordinate plane, plot the point (-1, -3). Then plot two other points so that all three points lie on a line with a slope of 3.

10. 

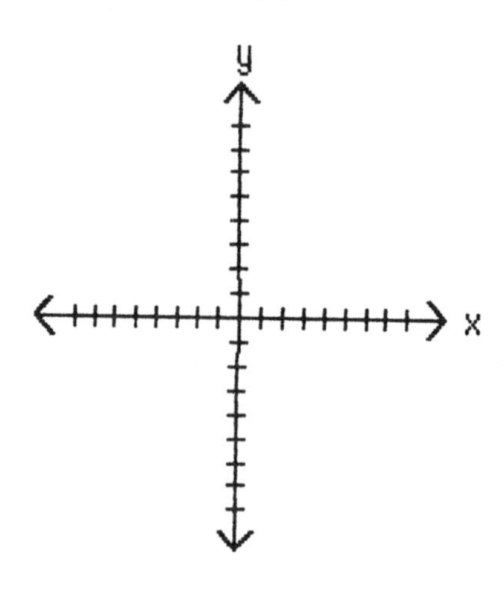

11. Find the slope and y-intercept of the line $6x - y = 9$.

11. ____________

12. Draw the line and write an equation for a line with slope $m = \frac{2}{5}$ and y-intercept $b = 3$.

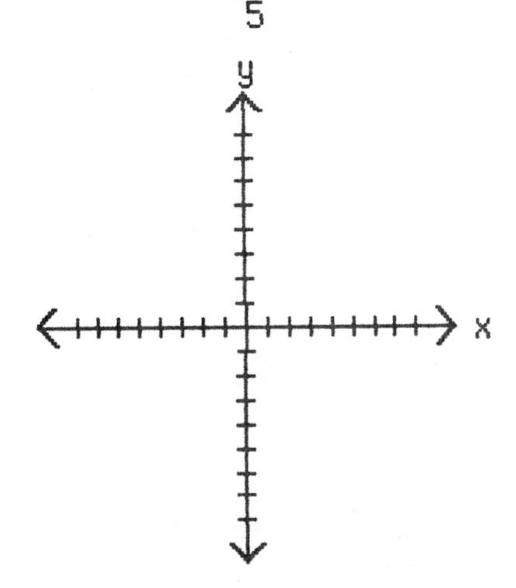

13. Find an equation of a line through the two points $P(0, 0)$ and $Q(-2, 5)$.

14. Find an equation of a line that contains the point $(4, -2)$ and is parallel to the graph of $4x - 3y = 12$.

15. Graph the linear inequality given by $2x - y > 4$.

15. ______________

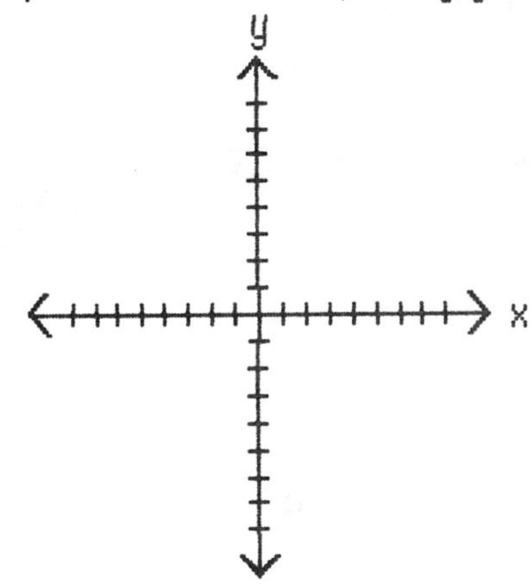

16. Write an inequality from the following information and graph it: "The difference of the x-coordinate and y-coordinate does not exceed 4."

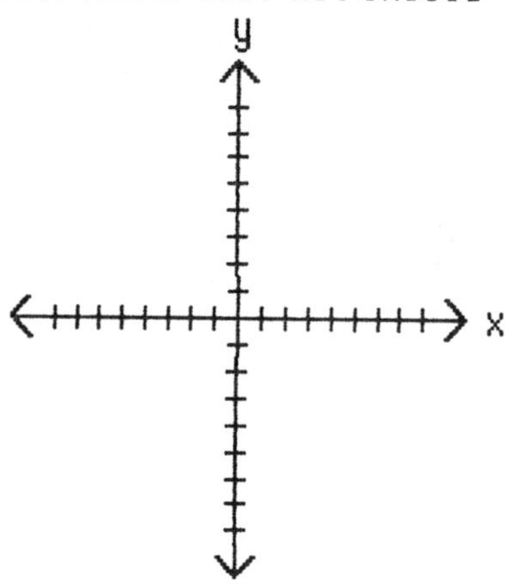

17. The Take-It-With-You Rental company rents two kinds of trailers. The x-type rents for $4.50 a day and the y-type rents for $8.00 a day. The rental company must make at least $85 a day in rentals. Write an inequality to represent the amount of rent taken in each day.

18. A company buys a large crane for $45,000. The value of the crane decreases with time. At the end of 15 years, the crane has a scrap value of $12,000. Assume that the value V of the crane is linearly dependent upon the number of years after purchase. Write the linear equation that expresses V in terms of t the number of years after purchase.

19. When the demand for sweaters was 14 dozen, the price was $95 per dozen. When the demand rose to 20 dozen, the price was $80 per dozen. Assume that the price P per dozen is linearly dependent upon the demand x of sweaters. Write the linear equation that expresses P in terms of x.

19. ______________

20. State the domain and range of the relation $\{(0, 4), (-2, 5), (3, 6), (-2, 3)\}$.

20. 

21. Write the relation S whose graph is given and determine if S is a function.

21. 

22. Suppose y is a function of x defined by $y = |x + 3|$. State the domain of the function.

22. ____________

23. Suppose y is a function of x defined by $y = \dfrac{x}{x^2 - 25}$. State the domain of the function.

23. ____________

24. Let $g(x) = 4 - 2x - x^2$. Find $g(3)$.

24. ____________

25. The tent company makes and sells pup tents. The cost function C of making x pup tents is given by $C(x) = 35x + 20$. The revenue function R from selling x tents is given by $R(x) = -5x^2 + 325$. Let P be the profit function from making x pup tents. Express $P(x)$ in terms of x.

25. ____________

Name ______________________ Chapter 6 Form C Score ________

1. Find the ordered pair for each point shown in the coordinate plane.

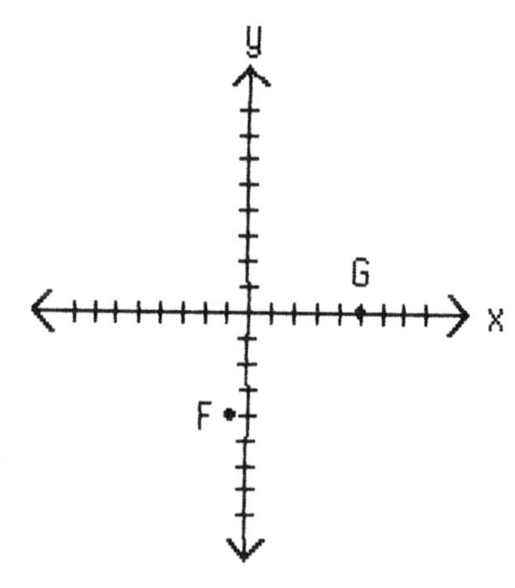

2. Refer to the graph. Name the point(s) (x, y) where $y = -\frac{1}{4}x + 2$.

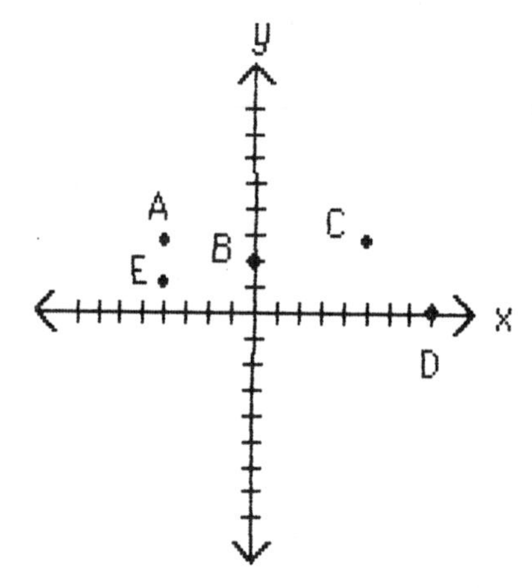

3. Plot the points (x,y) where the x-coordinate is the cube of the y-coordinate and $y \in \{-1, 0, 1, 2\}$.

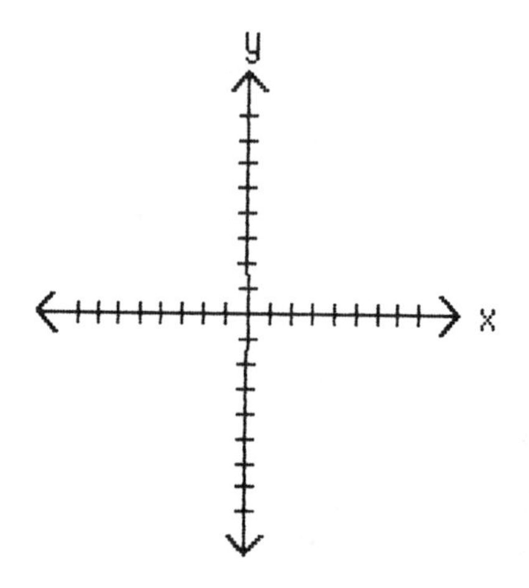

4. Graph the linear equation $3x - 4y = 12$.

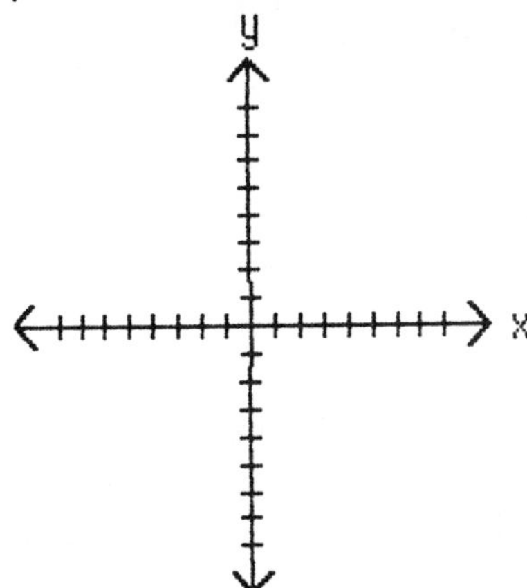

5. Write an equation from the given information, then graph the equation: "The difference of the x-coordinate and half the y-coordinate is two".

5. __________

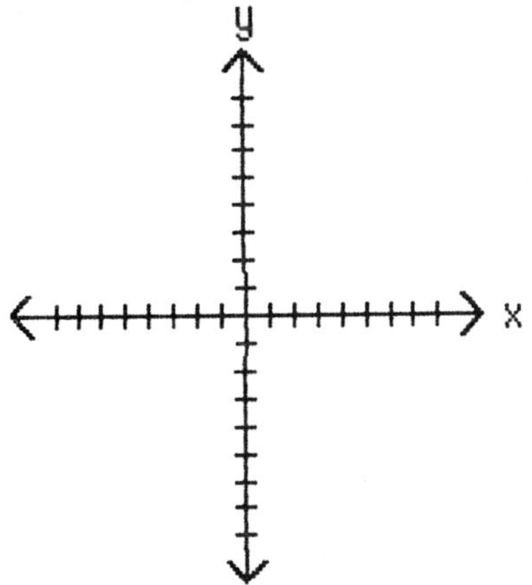

6. Find the slope, if it is defined, of the line passing through the points $\left(\frac{1}{2}, \frac{2}{3}\right)$ and $\left(2, -\frac{1}{3}\right)$.

7. Find the slope, if it is defined, of the line.

7. __________

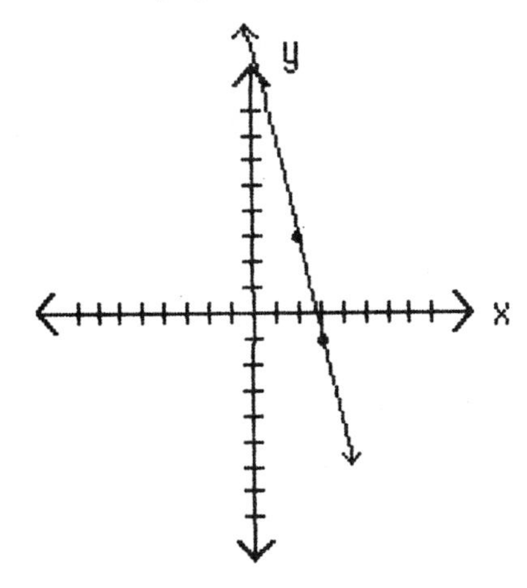

8. Determine if the line passing through the points $(-6, -2)$ and $(4, -1)$ is parallel to the line passing through the points $(-1, 3)$ and $(-9, 4)$.

8. ____________

9. Determine if the three points $(6, -7)$, $(1, -2)$, and $(-2, 1)$ are collinear.

9. ____________

10. In a coordinate plane, plot the point $(-4, 1)$. Then plot two other points so that all three points lie on a line with a slope of $\frac{5}{2}$.

10. ____________

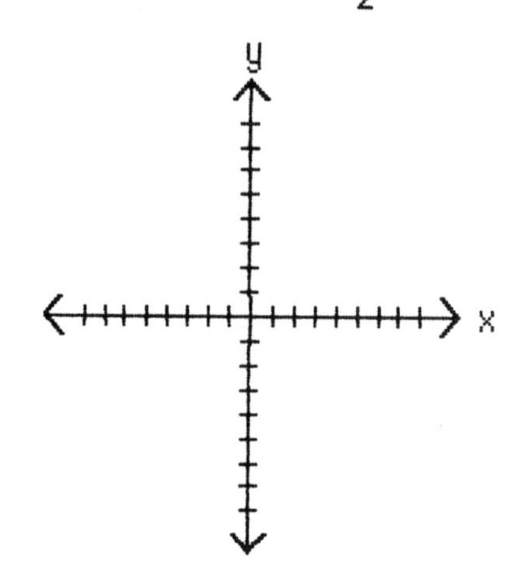

11. Find the slope and y-intercept of the line $x + \frac{2}{3}y = 0$.

11. ____________

12. Draw the line and write an equation for a line with slope $m = 0$ and y-intercept $b = -4$.

12. 

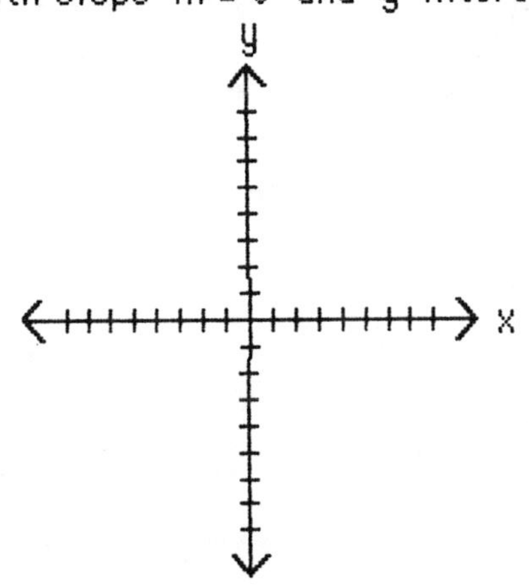

13. Find an equation of a line through the two points $P(8, -3)$ and $Q(3, -8)$.

13. 

14. Find an equation of a line with y-intercept -5 and parallel to the graph of $y - 4x + 3 = 0$.

14. 

15. Graph the linear inequality given by $2x - y > 6$.

15. 

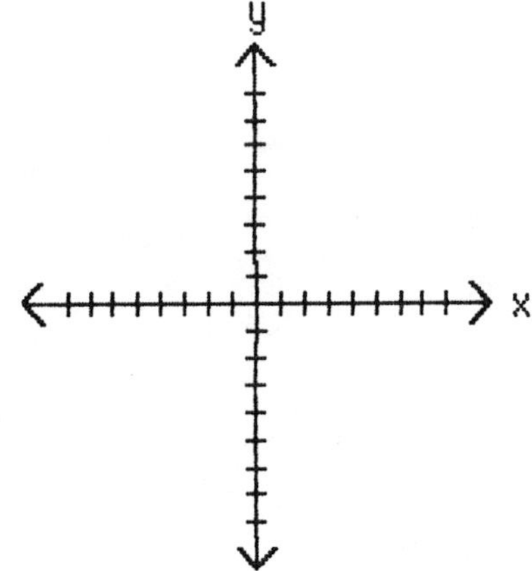

16. Write an inequality from the following information and graph it: "Four times the x-coordinate added to twice the y-coordinate is less than 12."

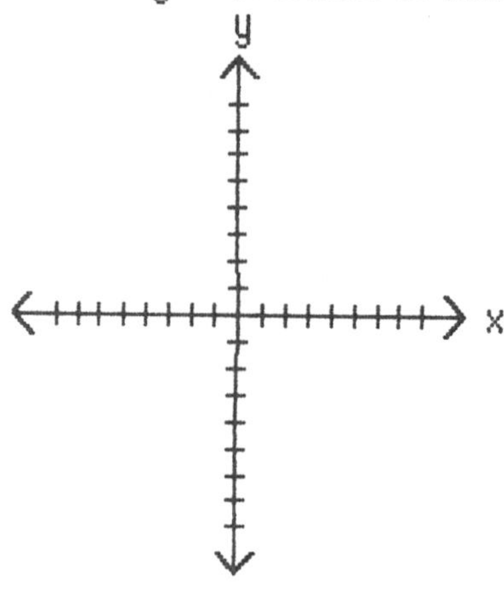

17. A chemical company mixes two different chemicals in a given process. Chemical A cost 35¢ an ounce, and Chemical B cost 25¢ an ounce. The combined cost cannot exceed $4.85. Write an inequality to represent the combined cost.

17. ____________

18. Kathy buys an antique plate for $125. The value of the plate increases with time. At the end of 10 years, the plate has a resale value of $355. Assume that the value V of the plate is linearly dependent upon the number of years after purchase. Write the linear equation that expresses V in terms of t, the number of years after purchase.

18. ____________

19. When the demand for strawberries was 500 quarts, the price was $1.00 per quart. When the demand rose to 800 quarts, the price was 85¢ per quart. Assume that the price P per quart is linearly dependent upon the demand x of strawberries. Write the linear equation that expresses P in terms of x.

19. ____________

20. State the domain and range of the relation $\{(3, 4), (7, -2), (11, -8), (-1, 10)\}$.

20. ____________

21. Write the relation S whose graph is given and determine if S is a function.

21. ____________

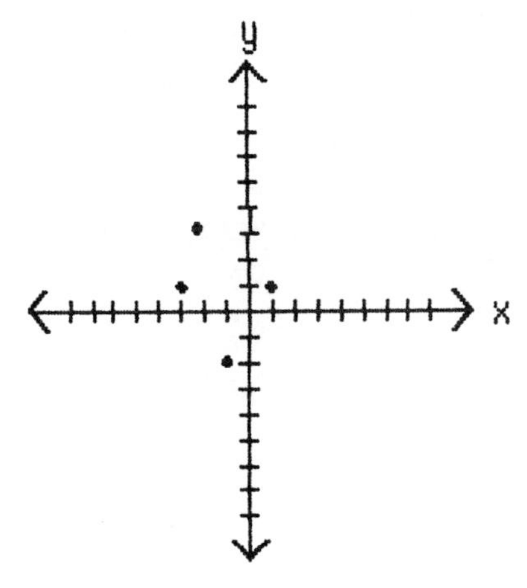

22. Suppose y is a function of x defined by $y = -\dfrac{3}{2 - x}$. State the domain of the function.

22. ____________

23. Suppose y is a function of x defined by $y = \dfrac{3}{x^2 - 3x + 2}$. State the domain of the function.

23. ____________

24. Let $h(x) = 5x^2 + 6x - 2$. Find $h(\frac{1}{2})$.

24. ____________

25. An awning company makes and sells window awnings. The profit function is given by $P(x) = 0.3x^2 - 64x$. How much profit was made on 325 awnings?

25. ____________

Name ______________________ Chapter 6 Form D Score ________

1. Find the ordered pair for each point shown in the coordinate plane.

1. ____________

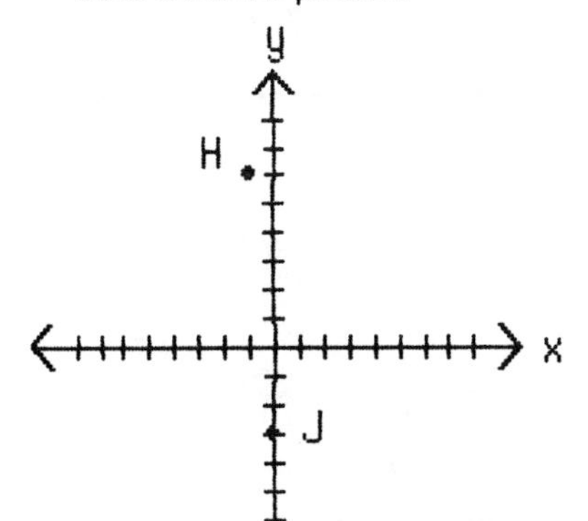

a. H (-1, 6) J (-3, 0)
b. H (-1, 6) J (0, -3)
c. H (6, -1) J (0, -3)
d. H (6, -1) J (-3, 0)
e. None of these

2. Refer to the graph. Name the point(s) with a y-coordinate of -4.

2. 

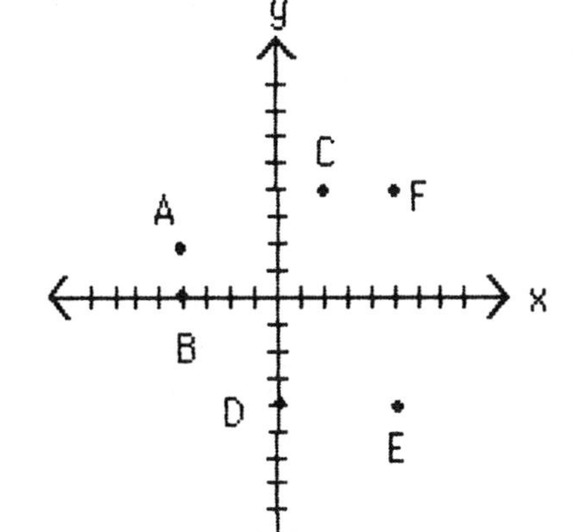

a. D
b. C and F
c. A and B
d. D and E
e. None of these

3. Plot four points (x, y) so that the sum of the coordinates is seven. What pattern do these points follow?

3. 

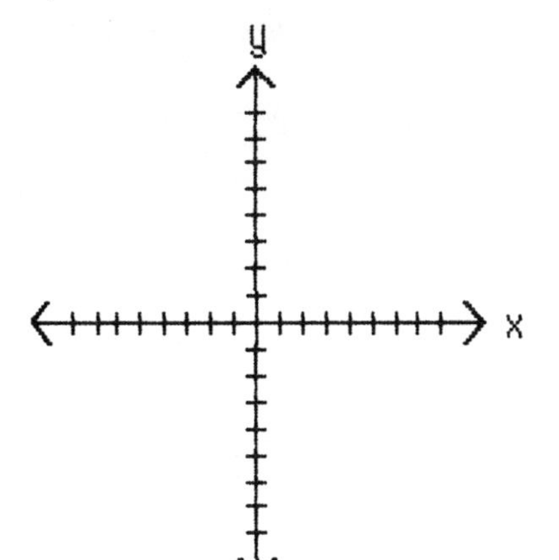

a. points lie on a line
b. points have the same y-value
c. points have no pattern
d. points lie on a circle
e. None of these

4. Graph the linear equation $x = -3y$.

4. ____________

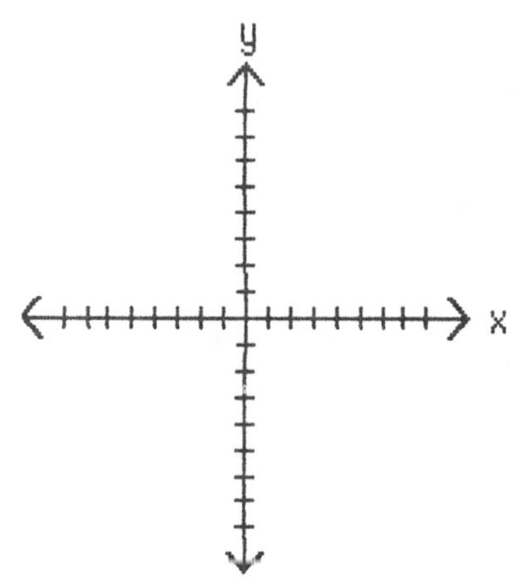

5. Write an equation from the given information, then graph the equation: "The sum of the y-coordinate and twice the x-coordinate is four".

5. ____________

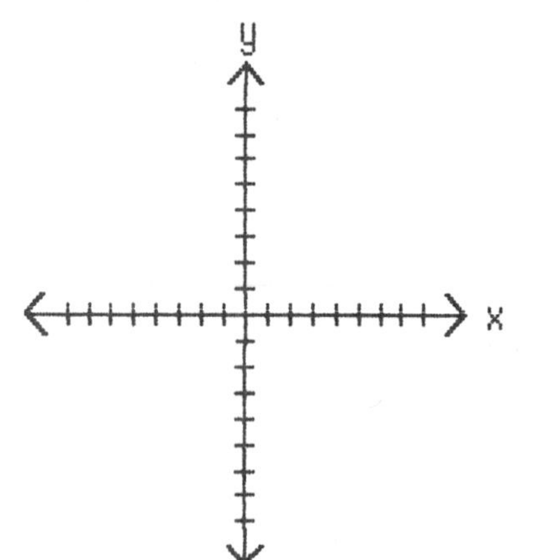

a. $2y + x = 4$
b. $2(y + x) = 4$
c. $y + 2x = 4$
d. $y + x + 2 = 4$
e. None of these

6. Find the slope, if it is defined, of the line passing through the points $(8, -3)$ and $(-2, 2)$.

6. ____________

a. $m = \frac{1}{2}$

b. $m = -\frac{1}{2}$

c. $m = \frac{1}{5}$

d. $m = -\frac{1}{5}$

e. None of these

7. Find the slope, if it is defined, of the line.

7. ______

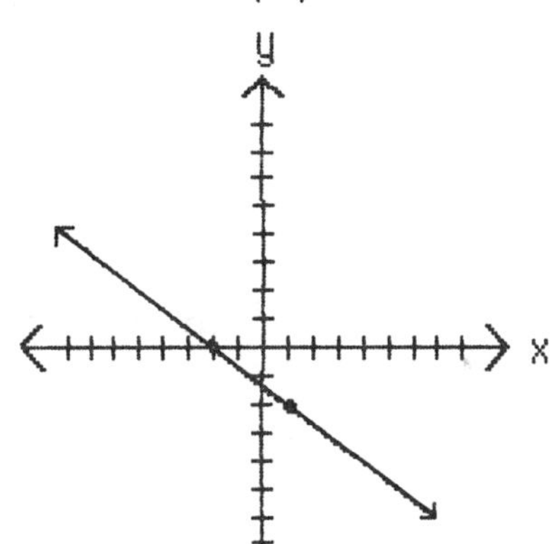

a. $m = -\frac{2}{3}$

b. $m = -\frac{3}{2}$

c. $m = \frac{2}{3}$

d. $m = 2$

e. None of these

8. Determine which of the following lines is parallel to the line passing through the points $(-1, 0)$ and $(3, 5)$.

8. ______

a. $4x - 5y + 1 = 0$
b. $4x + 5y + 1 = 0$
c. $5x + 4y + 1 = 0$
d. $-5x - 4y - 4 = 0$
e. None of these

9. Determine which of the following points is collinear with the points $(-2, -9)$ and $(3, 1)$.

9. 

a. $(-4, -7)$
b. $(2, 11)$
c. $(6, 7)$
d. $(5, 26)$
e. None of these

10. In a coordinate plane, plot the point $(3, 2)$. Then plot two other points so that all three points lie on a line with a slope of -4. Possible points are

10. 

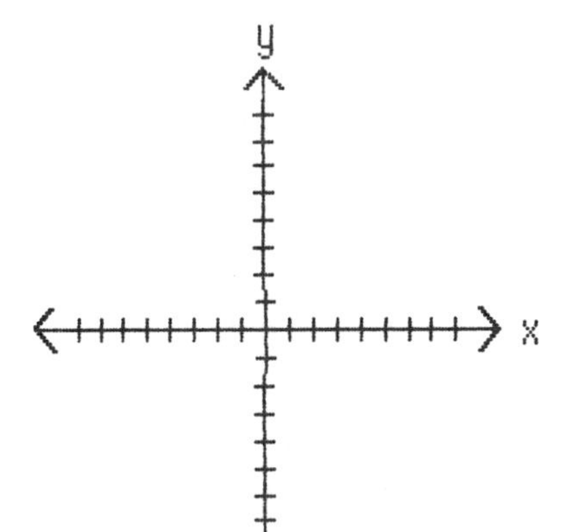

a. $(1, 7)$ and $(3, -1)$
b. $(2, -2)$ and $(4, 6)$
c. $(-1, 3)$ and $(7, 1)$
d. $(2, 6)$ and $(4, -2)$
e. None of these

11. Find the slope and y-intercept of the line $y = -x - 9$. 11. ______________

a. $m = 1, b = -9$
b. $m = -1, b = -9$
c. $m = -1, b = 9$
d. $m = -9, b = -1$
e. None of these

12. Draw the line and write an equation for a line with slope 3 and y-intercept -1.

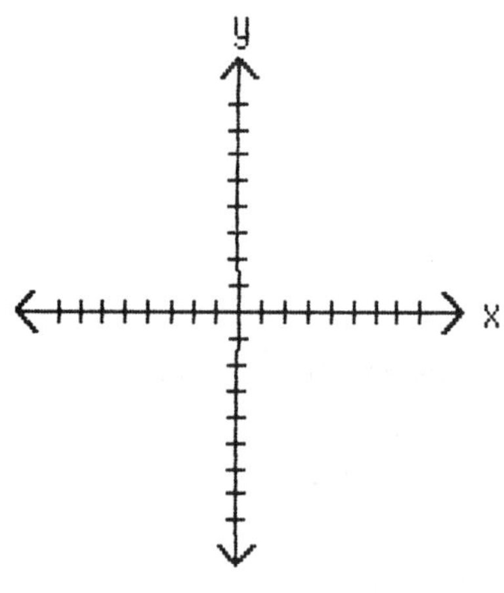

a. $y = 3x + 1$
b. $y = -x + 3$
c. $y = 3x - 1$
d. $y = -x - 3$
e. None of these

13. Find an equation of a line through the two points $P(4, 0)$ and $Q(0, -4)$. 13. ______________

a. $y = x - 4$
b. $y = -x - 4$
c. $y = x + 4$
d. $y = -x + 4$
e. None of these

14. Find an equation of a line with x-intercept 3 if the line is parallel to the graph of $4x - y = 1$. 14. ______________

a. $y = 4x + 3$
b. $y = 4x + 1$
c. $y = -4x + 12$
d. $y = 4x - 12$
e. None of these

15. The linear inequality graphed is 15. ______________

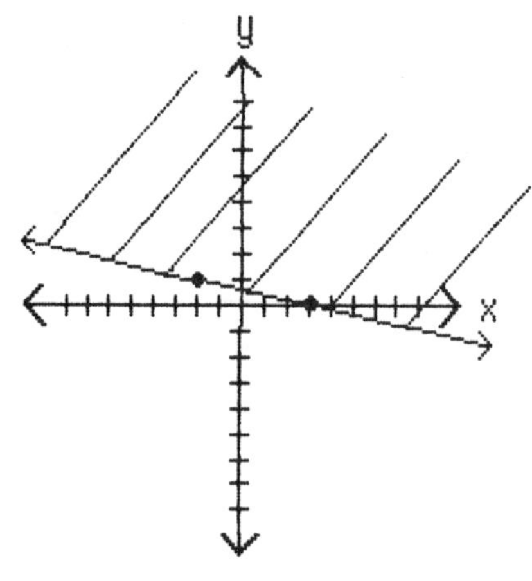

a. $x + 5y \leq 3$
b. $x + 5y < 3$
c. $x + 5y \geq 3$
d. $x + 5y > 3$
e. None of these

16. Write an inequality from the following information and graph it: "The sum of the x-coordinate and y-coordinate exceeds 4".

16. 

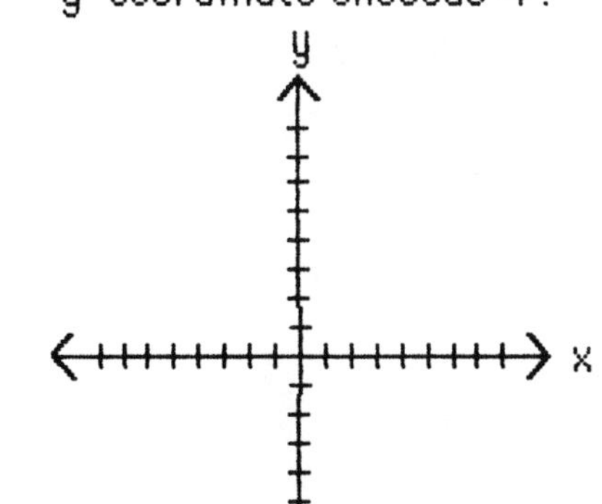

a. $x + y < 4$
b. $x + y > 4$
c. $x + y \geq 4$
d. $x + y \leq 4$
e. None of these

17. Jane is selling crafts at the flea market. She sells afghans for \$35 each, and baby layettes for \$25 each. She must sell at least \$325 worth of crafts to buy a TV she wants. If she sells x afghans and y layettes, write an inequality to represent the desired sales.

17. ____________

a. $35x + 25y > 325$
b. $35x + 25y < 325$
c. $25x + 35y \geq 325$
d. $25x + 35y \leq 325$
e. None of these

18. The Jones family buys a van for \$11,000. The value of the van decreases with time. At the end of 9 years, the van has a resale value of \$4,700. Assume that the value V of the van is linearly dependent upon the number of years after purchase. Write the linear equation that expresses V in terms of t, the number of years after purchase.

18. ____________

a. $V = -700t + 11000$
b. $V = -\frac{1}{700}t + 11000$
c. $V = -\frac{1}{700}t + 4700$
d. $V = -700t + 4700$
e. None of these

19. When the demand for potatoes was 150 bushels, the price was \$50 per bushel. When the demand rose to 200 bushels, the price was \$40 per bushel. Assume that the price P per bushel is linearly dependent upon the demand x of potatoes. Write the linear equation that expresses P in terms of x. 19. ____________

a. $P = \frac{1}{5}x + 20$

b. $P = -\frac{1}{5}x + 20$

c. $P = \frac{1}{5}x + 80$

d. $P = -\frac{1}{5}x + 80$

e. None of these

20. State the domain and range of the relation $\{(3, -1), (5, -4), (0, 6), (2, -6)\}$. 20. ____________

a. $\{-6, -4, -1, 6\}$
b. $\{0, 2, 3, 5\}$
c. $\{-6, -4, -1, 0, 2, 3, 5, 6\}$
d. $\{2, 3, 5\}$
e. None of these

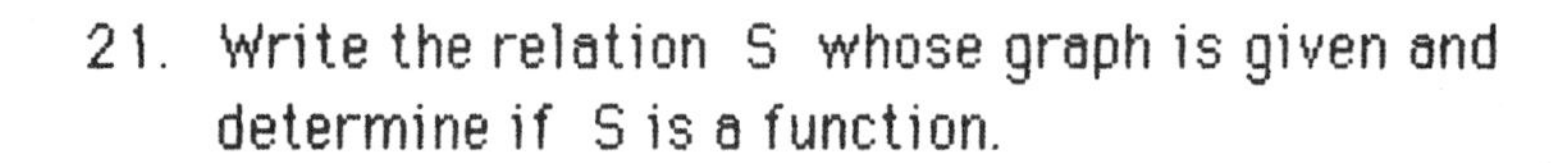

21. Write the relation S whose graph is given and determine if S is a function. 21. ____________

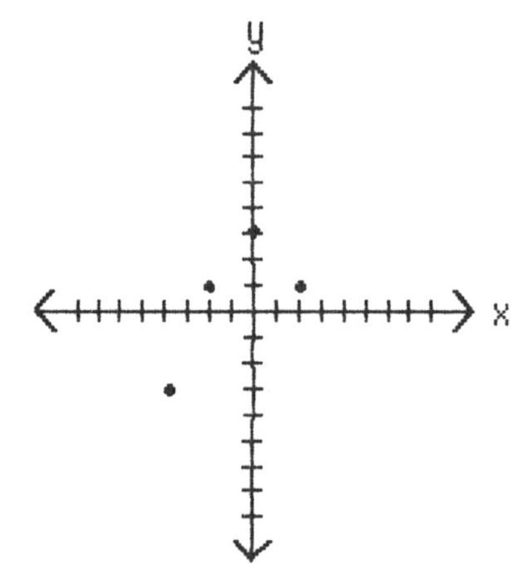

a. $\{(-4, -3), (-2, 1), (0, 3), (2, 1)\}$
not a function
b. $\{(-3, -4), (1, -2), (3, 0), (1, 2)\}$
function
c. $\{(-4, -3), (-2, 1), (0, 3), (2, 1)\}$
function
d. $\{(-3, -4), (1, -2), (0, 3), (1, 2)\}$
not a function
e. None of these

22. Suppose y is a function of x defined by $y = -\dfrac{3}{x+5}$. State the domain of the function.

22. ________

a. $\{x \mid x \neq -5\}$
b. $\{x \mid x \neq 3\}$
c. $\{x \mid x \neq 0\}$
d. $\{x \mid x \neq 5\}$
e. None of these

23. Suppose y is a function of x defined by $y = \dfrac{-5}{x^2 - 25}$. State the domain of the function.

23. ________

a. $\{x \mid x \neq 5\}$
b. $\{x \mid x \neq 0\}$
c. $\{x \mid x \neq 25\}$
d. $\{x \mid x \neq 5, x \neq -5\}$
e. None of these

24. Let $g(x) = 4x^2 - x + 1$. Find $g(-3)$.

24. ________

a. $g(-3) = 34$
b. $g(-3) = 40$
c. $g(-3) = 148$
d. $g(-3) = 32$
e. None of these

25. The Green Pickle Deli makes and sells sub sandwiches. The cost function C of making x subs is given by $C(x) = .35x + .30$. The revenue function R from selling x subs is given by $R(x) = -0.15x^2 + 1.85x$. Let P be the profit function from making x subs. Express $P(x)$ in terms of x.

25. ________

a. $P(x) = 0.15x^2 - 1.5x + 0.30$
b. $P(x) = -0.15x^2 + 1.5x + 0.30$
c. $P(x) = -0.15x^2 + 2.2x + 0.30$
d. $P(x) = -0.15x^2 + 1.5x - 0.30$
e. None of these

Name ______________________ Chapter 6 Form E Score 

1. Find the ordered pair for each point shown in the coordinate plane. 1. ____________

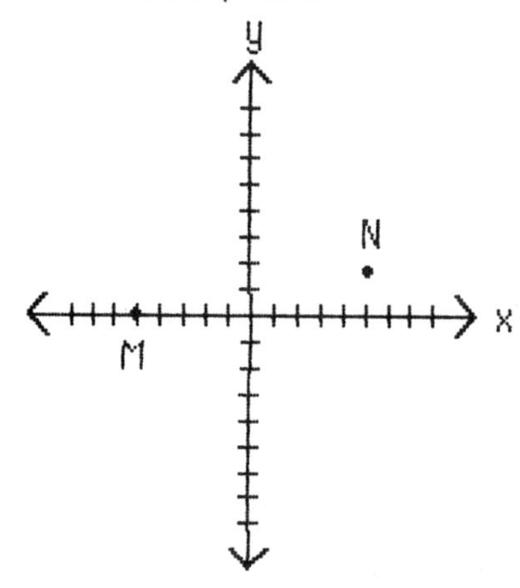

2. Refer to the graph. Name the point(s) with x-coordinate twice the y-coordinate. 2. 

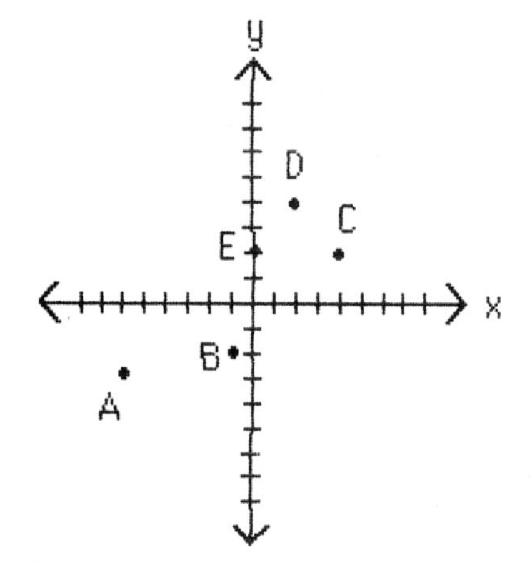

a. A and C
b. E
c. B and D
d. A, C, and E
e. None of these

3. Plot four points (x,y) so that the y-coordinate is one-third the x-coordinate. What pattern do these points follow? 3. 

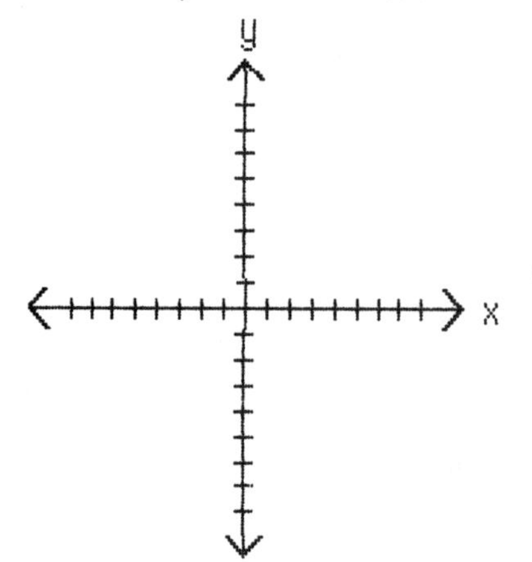

a. points have the same y value
b. points lie on a line
c. points have no pattern
d. points lie on a circle
e. None of these

4. Graph the linear equation $y = 4x - 1$.

4. 

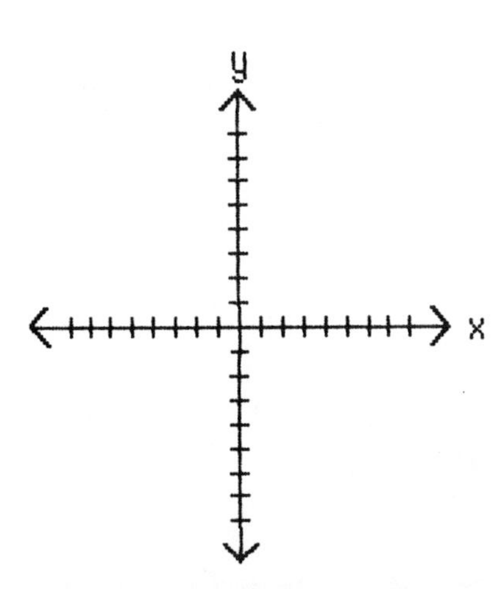

5. Write an equation from the given information, then graph the equation: "The y-coordinate is twice the difference of the x-coordinate and four".

5. 

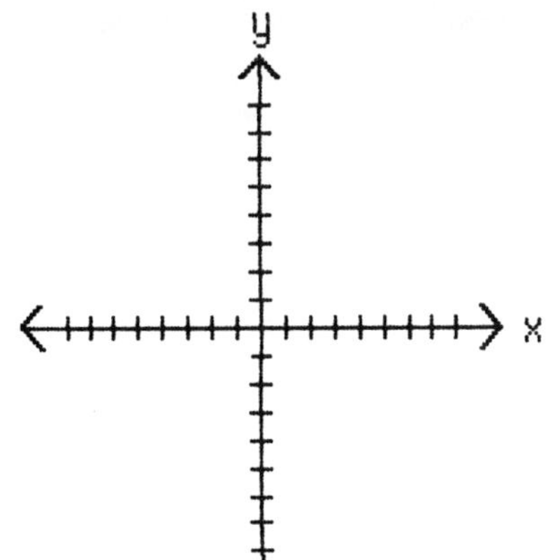

a. $y = 2x - 4$
b. $y = 2(4 - x)$
c. $y = 4 - 2x$
d. $y = 2(x - 4)$
e. None of these

6. Find the slope, if it is defined, of the line passing through the points (-2, 6) and (-2, -2).

6. 

a. $m = -1$
b. $m = 0$
c. $m = 1$
d. $m = -2$
e. None of these

7. Find the slope, if it is defined, of the line.

7. ____________

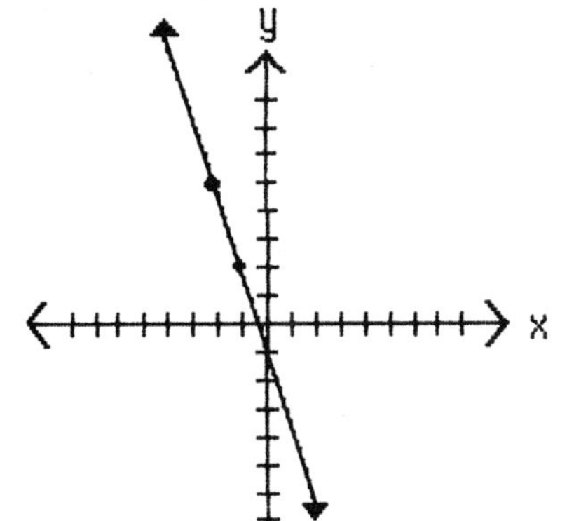

a. $m = -1$

b. $m = -3$

c. $m = -\frac{1}{3}$

d. $m = 3$

e. None of these

8. Determine which of the following lines is parallel to the line passing through the points (2, -3) and (-6, 15). 8. ______

a. $4y + 9x - 4 = 0$
b. $9x - 4y + 4 = 0$
c. $4x + 9y - 1 = 0$
d. $9y - 4x + 1 = 0$
e. None of these

9. Determine which of the following points is collinear with the points $(-2, \frac{1}{2})$ and (8, 8). 9. 

a. (-4, 5)
b. (0, -2)
c. (4, 7)
d. (4, 5)
e. None of these

10. In a coordinate plane, plot the point (4, -2). Then plot two other points so that all three points lie on a line with a slope of $-\frac{1}{6}$. Possible points are 10. 

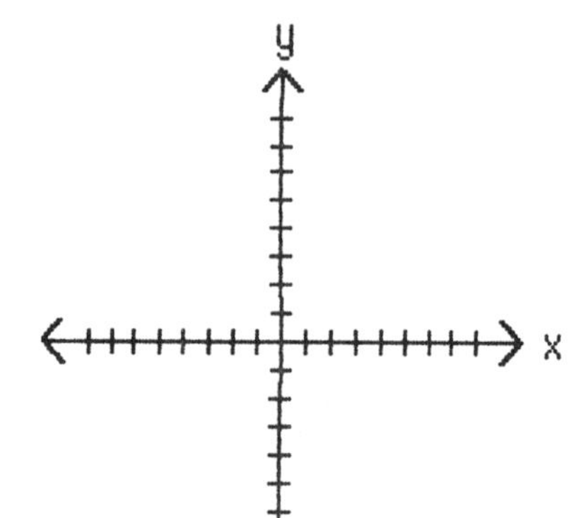

a. (10, -1) and (-2, -3)
b. (3, 4) and (5, -8)
c. (-3, 2) and (1, 10)
d. (2, -3) and (-10, 1)
e. None of these

11. Find the slope and y-intercept of the line 11. 

$$4x - y = 10.$$

a. $m = 4, b = 10$
b. $m = -4, b = 10$
c. $m = 4, b = -10$
d. $m = -4, b = -10$
e. None of these

12. Draw the line and write an equation for a line with slope $m = -\frac{3}{4}$ and y-intercept $b = 2$.

12. ____________

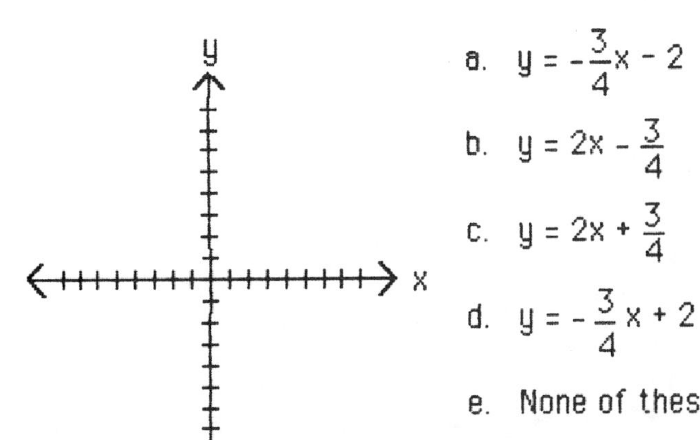

a. $y = -\frac{3}{4}x - 2$

b. $y = 2x - \frac{3}{4}$

c. $y = 2x + \frac{3}{4}$

d. $y = -\frac{3}{4}x + 2$

e. None of these

13. Find an equation of a line through the two points P(0, 0) and Q(-3, -2).

13. ____________

a. $y = -\frac{2}{3}x$

b. $y = \frac{2}{3}x$

c. $y = \frac{3}{2}x$

d. $y = -\frac{3}{2}x$

e. None of these

14. Find an equation of a line that contains the point (-3, 6) and is parallel to the graph of $5x - 2y = 6$.

14. ____________

a. $y = \frac{5}{2}x + \frac{27}{2}$

b. $y = -3x - 3$

c. $y = \frac{5}{2}x - \frac{3}{2}$

d. $y = -\frac{5}{2}x - \frac{3}{2}$

e. None of these

15. The linear inequality graphed is

15. ______________

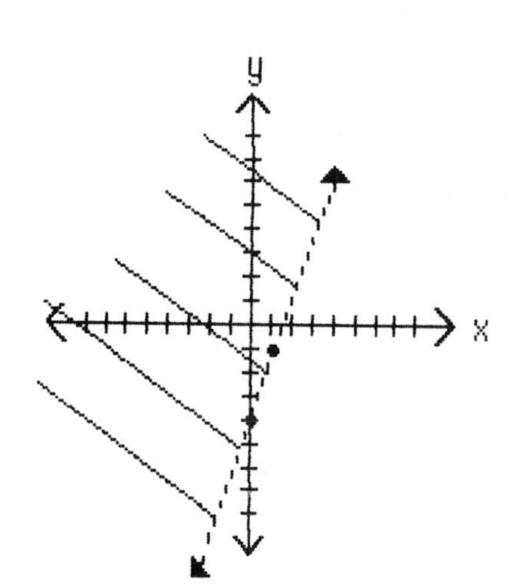

a. $3x - y \leq 4$
b. $3x - y > 4$
c. $3x - y \geq 4$
d. $3x - y < 4$
e. None of these

16. Write an inequality from the following information and graph it: "The difference of the y-coordinate and x-coordinate does not exceed 5".

16. ______________

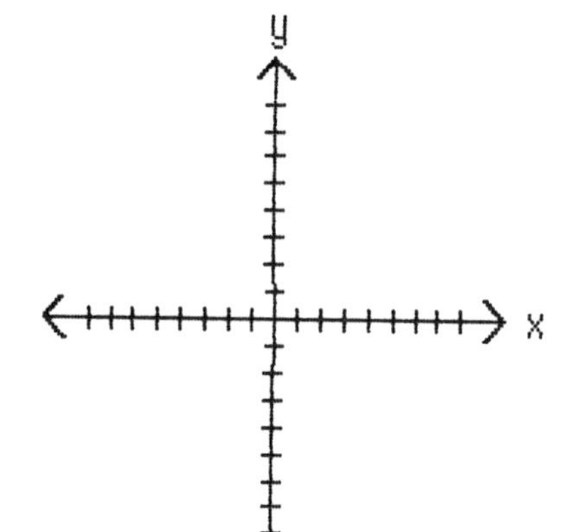

a. $y - x \geq 5$
b. $y - x < 5$
c. $y - x \leq 5$
d. $y - x > 5$
e. None of these

17. The Take-It-With-You Rental Company rents two kinds of trailers. The x-type rents for $6.00 a day and the y-type rents for $9.00 a day. The rental company must make at least $95 a day in rentals. Write an inequality to represent the amount of rent taken in each day.

17. ______________

a. $6x + 9y \geq 95$
b. $6x + 9y \leq 95$
c. $6x + 9y > 95$
d. $6x + 9y < 95$
e. None of these

18. A company buys a large piece of machinery for $50,000. The value of the machine decreases with time. At the end of 12 years, the machine has a scrap value of $14,000. Assume that the value V of the machine is linearly dependent upon the number of years after purchase. Write the linear equation that expresses V in terms of t, the number of years after purchase.

18. ____________

a. $V = -\frac{1}{3000}t + 50000$

b. $V = -3000t + 50000$

c. $V = -3000t + 14000$

d. $V = -\frac{1}{3000}t + 14000$

e. None of these

19. When the demand for sweaters was 25 dozen, the price was $96 per dozen. When the demand rose to 50 dozen, the price was $80 per dozen. Assume that the price P per dozen is linearly dependent upon the demand x of sweaters. Write the linear equation that expresses P in terms of x.

19. ____________

a. $P = -\frac{16}{25}x + 112$

b. $P = -\frac{16}{25}x + 30$

c. $P = -\frac{16}{25}x - 80$

d. $P = -\frac{16}{25}x + 71$

e. None of these

20. State the domain and range of the relation $\{(1, 5), (-3, 4), (5, 6), (-3, 3)\}$.

20. ____________

a. $\{3, 4, 5, 6\}$

b. $\{-3\}$

c. $\{-3, 1, 5\}$

d. $\{-3, 1, 3, 4, 5, 6\}$

e. None of these

21. Write the relation S whose graph is given and determine if S is a function. 21. ______

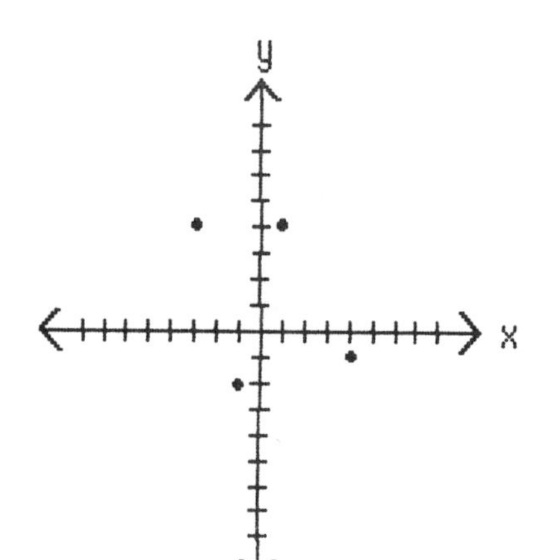

a. {(-3, 4), (-1, -2), (1, 4), (4, -1)} not a function
b. {(-3, 4), (-1, -2), (1, 4), (4, -1)} function
c. {(4, -3), (-2, -1), (4, 1), (-1, 4)} function
d. {(4, -3), (-2, -1), (4, 1), (-1, 4)} not a function
e. None of these

22. Suppose y is a function of x defined by $y = |2 - x|$ State the domain of the function. 22. ______

a. $\{x \mid x > 2\}$
b. $\{x \mid x \text{ is Real}\}$
c. $\{x \mid x \neq 2\}$
d. $\{x \mid x > 0\}$
e. None of these

23. Suppose y is a function of x defined by $y = \frac{x}{x^2 + 36}$. State the domain of the function. 23. ______

a. $\{x \mid x \neq 6\}$
b. $\{x \mid x \neq 6, x \neq -6\}$
c. $\{x \mid x \text{ is Real}\}$
d. $\{x \mid x \neq 0\}$
e. None of these

24. Let $g(x) = 7 - 3x - x^2$. Find $g(-2)$. 24. ______

a. $g(-2) = -3$
b. $g(-2) = 17$
c. $g(-2) = 9$
d. $g(-2) = 5$
e. None of these

25. The Tent Company makes and sells pup tents. The cost function C of making x pup tents is given by $C(x) = 25x + 30$. The revenue function R from selling x tents is given by $R(x) = -3x^2 + 285$. Let P be the profit function from making x pup tents. Express $P(x)$ in terms of x.

25. ______________

a. $P(x) = -3x^2 - 25x + 255$
b. $P(x) = -3x^2 + 25x + 315$
c. $P(x) = 3x^2 + 25x - 255$
d. $P(x) = -3x^2 - 25x + 315$
e. None of these

Name ____________________ Chapter 6 Form F Score ______

1. Find the ordered pair for each point shown in the coordinate plane. 1. ____________

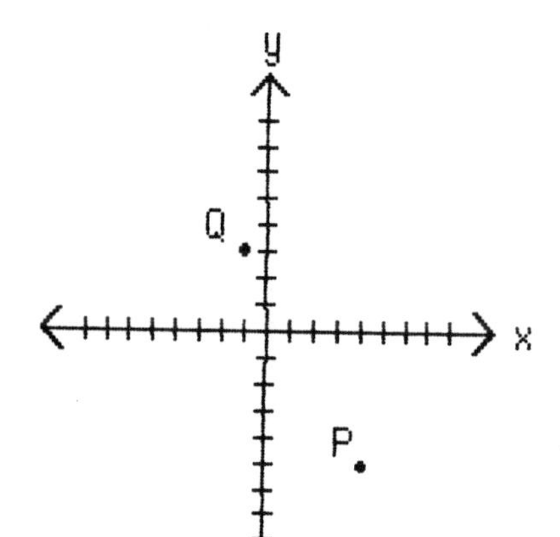

a. P(−5, 4), Q(3, −1)
b. P(−5, 4), Q(−1, 3)
c. P(4, −5), Q(3, −1)
d. P(4, −5), Q(−1, 3)
e. None of these

2. Refer to the graph. Name the point(s) (x,y) such that $y = 2x - 1$.

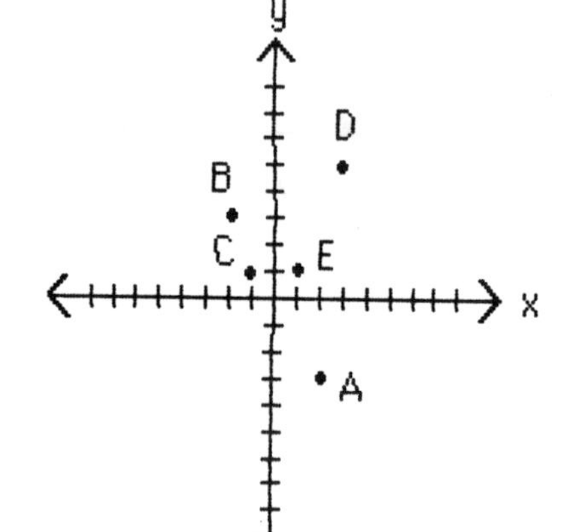

a. A and C
b. D and E
c. C
d. E
e. None of these

3. Plot the points (x,y) where the y-coordinate is the square of the x-coordinate and $y \in \{-2, -1, 0, 1\}$. What pattern do these points follow?

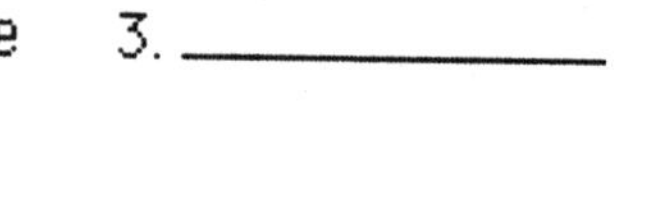

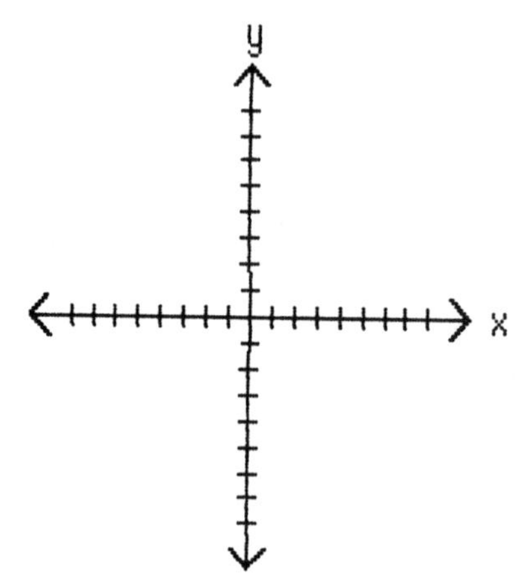

a. points lie on a circle
b. points lie on a line
c. points have the same x-value
d. points are all in quadrant IV
e. None of these

4. Graph the linear equation $2x - 5y = 10$.

4. ____________

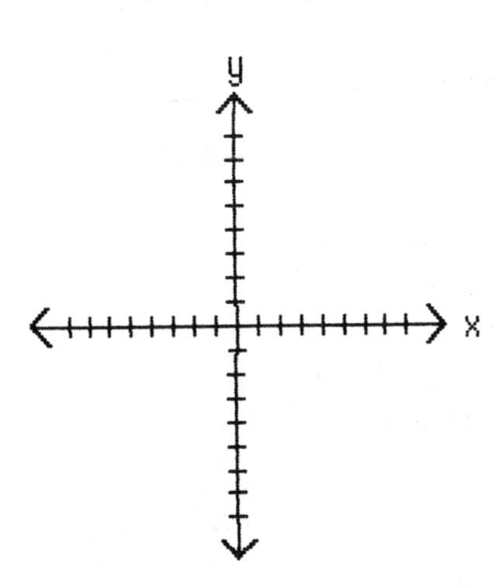

5. Write an equation from the given information, then graph the equation: "The difference of the x-coordinate and half the y-coordinate is four".

5. ____________

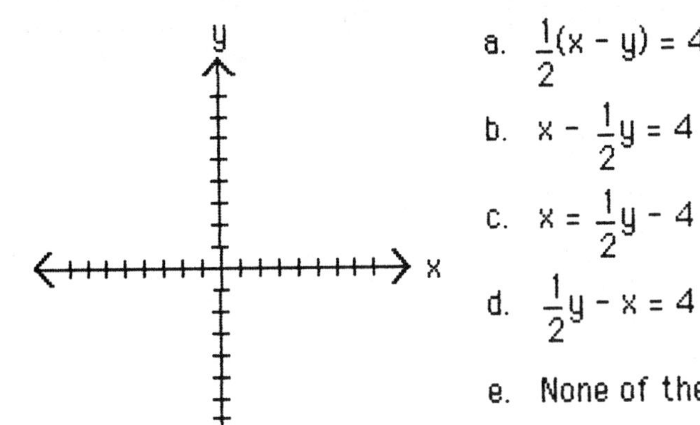

a. $\frac{1}{2}(x - y) = 4$

b. $x - \frac{1}{2}y = 4$

c. $x = \frac{1}{2}y - 4$

d. $\frac{1}{2}y - x = 4$

e. None of these

6. Find the slope, if it is defined, of the line passing through the points $(\frac{1}{4}, -\frac{1}{2})$ and $(\frac{5}{4}, 3)$.

6. ____________

a. $m = \frac{5}{2}$

b. $m = \frac{2}{7}$

c. $m = \frac{7}{2}$

d. $m = \frac{2}{5}$

e. None of these

7. Find the slope, if it is defined, of the line.

7. ______

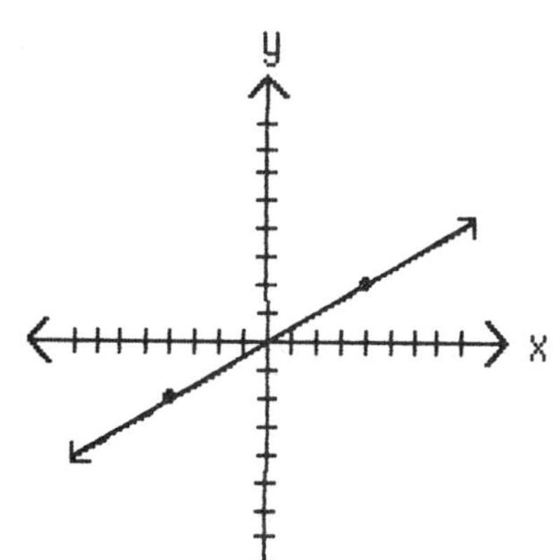

a. $m = \frac{1}{4}$

b. $m = 2$

c. $m = \frac{1}{2}$

d. $m = 0$

e. None of these

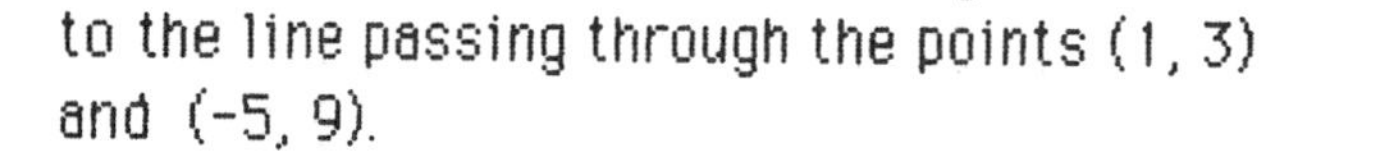
8. Determine which of the following lines is parallel to the line passing through the points (1, 3) and (-5, 9).

8. ______

a. $x - y = 3$
b. $x + y = 3$
c. $y - x = 3$
d. $3x + 2y = 6$
e. None of these

9. Determine which of the following points is collinear with the points $(-2, -\frac{5}{3})$ and $(6, -7)$.

9. ______

a. (-3, -1)
b. (3, -9)
c. (3, -6)
d. (9, -5)
e. None of these

10. In a coordinate plane, plot the point (-2, -5). Then plot two other points so that all three points lie on a line with a slope of $\frac{5}{7}$. Possible points are

10. ______

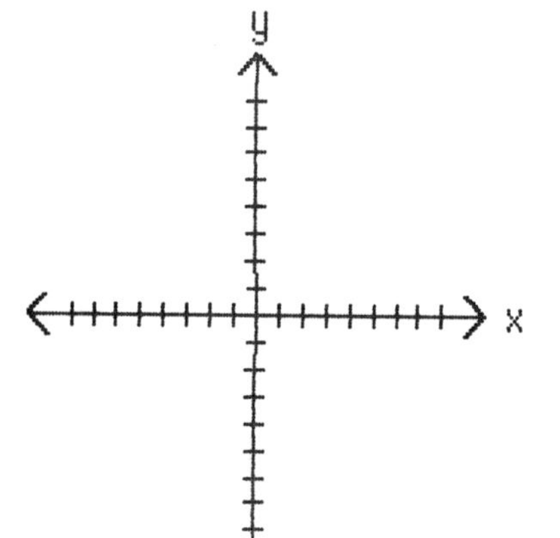

a. (3, 2) and (-7, -12)
b. (2, 3) and (-12, -7)
c. (5, 0) and (-9, -10)
d. (-9, 0) and (5, -10)
e. None of these

11. Find the slope and y-intercept of the line 11. ____________

$$x - \frac{3}{5}y = 2.$$

a. $m = \frac{5}{3}, b = \frac{10}{3}$

b. $m = \frac{3}{5}, b = 2$

c. $m = -\frac{5}{3}, b = \frac{10}{3}$

d. $m = \frac{5}{3}, b = -\frac{10}{3}$

e. None of these

12. Draw the line and write an equation for a line with slope $m = -4$ and y-intercept $b = -1$. 12. ____________

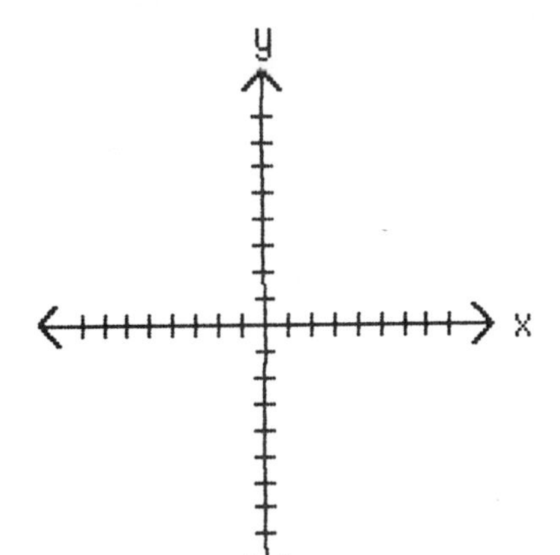

a. $y = -4x - 1$
b. $y = -4x + 1$
c. $y = -x - 4$
d. $y = x + 4$
e. None of these

13. Find an equation of a line through the two points P(2, 4) and Q(-2, 8). 13. ____________

a. $y = -x - 2$
b. $y = -x + 10$
c. $y = -x + 2$
d. $y = -x + 6$
e. None of these

14. Find an equation of a line with y-intercept -6 and parallel to the graph of $y - 5x + 1 = 0$. 14. ____________

a. $y + 5x = 6$
b. $y + 5x = -6$
c. $y = -6x + 1$
d. $y = 5x - 1$
e. None of these

15. The linear inequality graphed is 15. ________

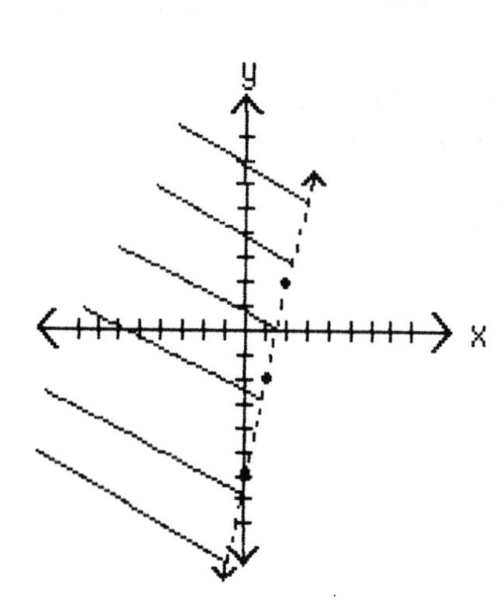

a. $4x - y \geq 6$
b. $4x - y < 6$
c. $4x - y > 6$
d. $4x - y \leq 6$
e. None of these

16. Write an inequality from the following information and graph it: "Three times the x-coordinate added to twice the y-coordinate is less than 6." 16. 

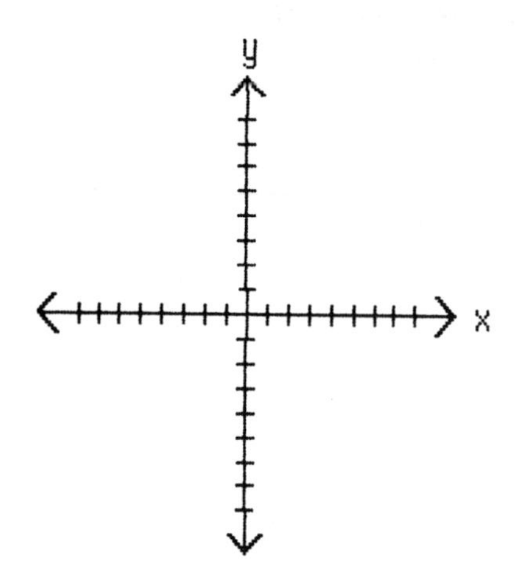

a. $3(x + 2y) < 6$
b. $3x + 2 + y < 6$
c. $3x + 2y > 6$
d. $3x + 2y < 6$
e. None of these

17. A chemical company mixes two different chemicals in a given process. Chemical X costs 45¢ per cc., and chemical Y costs 40¢ per cc. The combined cost cannot exceed \$3.65. Write an inequality to represent the combined cost. 17. ________

a. $.45x + .40y \geq 3.65$
b. $.45x + .40y > 3.65$
c. $.45x + .40y \leq 3.65$
d. $.45x + .40y < 3.65$
e. None of these

18. Connie buys an antique doll for \$155. The value of the doll increases with time. At the end of 8 years, the doll has a resale value of \$315. Assume that the value V of the doll is linearly dependent upon the number of years after purchase. Write the linear equation that expresses V in terms of t, the number of years after purchase.

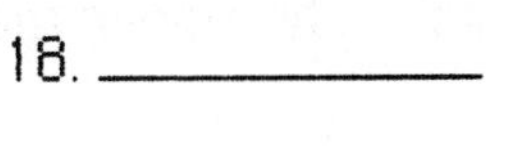

a. $V = 20t + 315$
b. $V = \frac{1}{20}t + 315$
c. $V = 20t + 155$
d. $V = \frac{1}{20}t + 155$
e. None of these

19. When the demand for strawberries was 300 pounds, the price was 99¢ per pound. When the demand rose to 500 pounds, the price was 74¢ per pound. Assume that the price P per pound is linearly dependent upon the demand x of strawberries. Write the linear equation that expresses P in terms of x in hundred pounds.

19. ____________

a. $P = -.125x - 4.26$
b. $P = -.125x + 13.65$
c. $P = -.125x - 2.01$
d. $P = -.125x - 6.15$
e. None of these

20. State the domain and range of the relation $\{(6, -1), (7, -3), (9, -8), (11, -10)\}$.

20. ____________

a. $\{6, 7, 9, 11\}$
b. $\{-1, -3, -8, -10\}$
c. $\{(6, -1), (7, -3), (9, -8), (11, -10)\}$
d. $\{-10, -8, -3, -1, 6, 7, 9, 11\}$
e. None of these

21. Write the relation S whose graph is given and determine if S is a function.

21. 

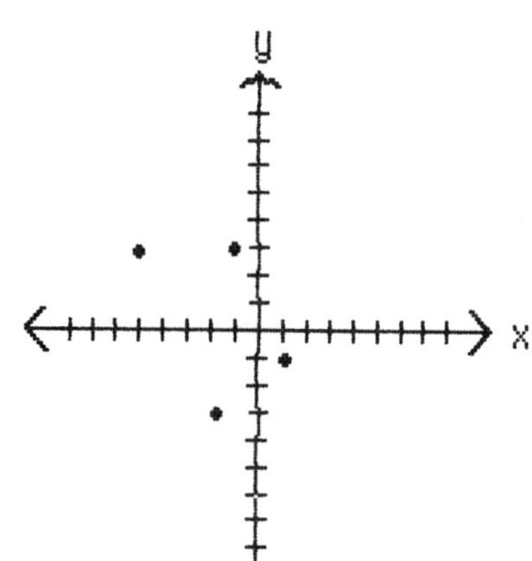

a. $\{(-5, 3), (-2, -3), (-1, 3), (1, -1)\}$ not a function
b. $\{(3, -5), (-3, -2), (3, -1), (-1, 1)\}$ function
c. $\{(3, -5), (-3, -2), (3, -1), (-1, 1)\}$ not a function
d. $\{(-5, 3), (-2, -3), (-1, 3), (1, -1)\}$ function
e. None of these

22. Suppose y is a function of x defined by $y = -\dfrac{3}{6 - x}$ State the domain of the function.

22. ____________

a. $\{x \mid x \neq -6\}$
b. $\{x \mid x \neq 0\}$
c. $\{x \mid x \neq 6\}$
d. $\{x \mid x \neq 3, x \neq 6\}$
e. None of these

23. Suppose y is a function of x defined by $y = \dfrac{5}{x^2 - 4x - 5}$. State the domain of the function.

23. 

a. $\{x \mid x \neq -1, x \neq 5\}$
b. $\{x \mid x \neq 0\}$
c. $\{x \mid x \neq -1\}$
d. $\{x \mid x \neq 1, x \neq -5\}$
e. None of these

24. Let $h(x) = 8x^2 + 2x - 4$. Find $h(\frac{1}{2})$.

24. ____________

a. $h(\frac{1}{2}) = 13$
b. $h(\frac{1}{2}) = 14$
c. $h(\frac{1}{2}) = 1$
d. $h(\frac{1}{2}) = -1$
e. None of these

25. An Awning Company makes and sells window awnings. The profit function is given by $P(x) = 0.4x^2 + 80x$. How much profit was made on 200 awnings?

25. ____________

a. $P(200) = 16160$
b. $P(200) = 32000$
c. $P(200) = 22400$
d. $P(200) = 22000$
e. None of these

CHAPTER # 6 TEST KEYS

Form A

1. A (2, 3) B (-1, -2)
2. C and D
3. any points on the line $x + y = 5$

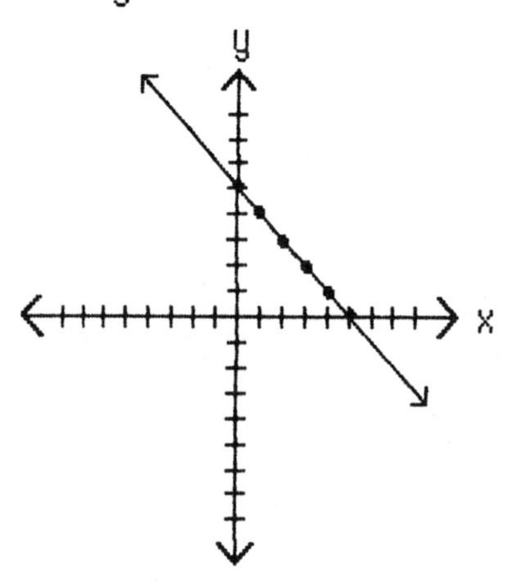

4. Answer:

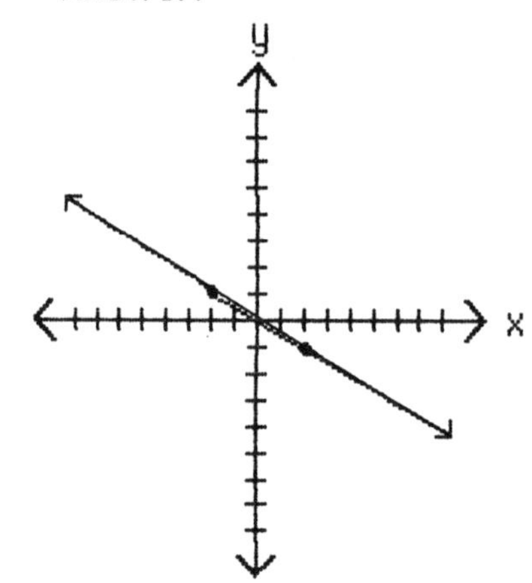

5. $y + 2x = 3$

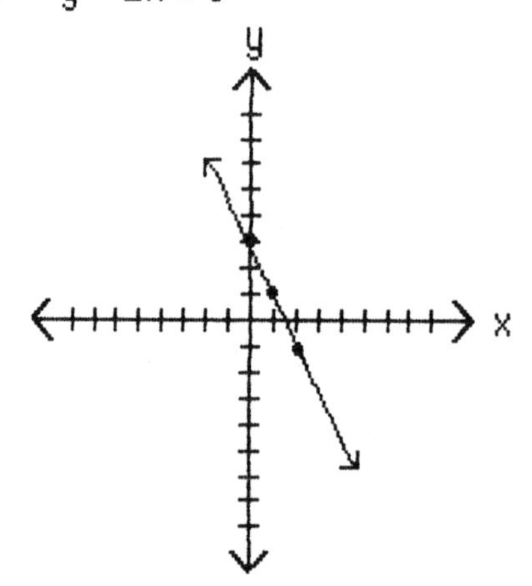

6. $-\frac{2}{3}$

Form B

1. C (3, -2) D (-1, 2)
2. C
3. any 4 points on $y = \frac{1}{2}x$

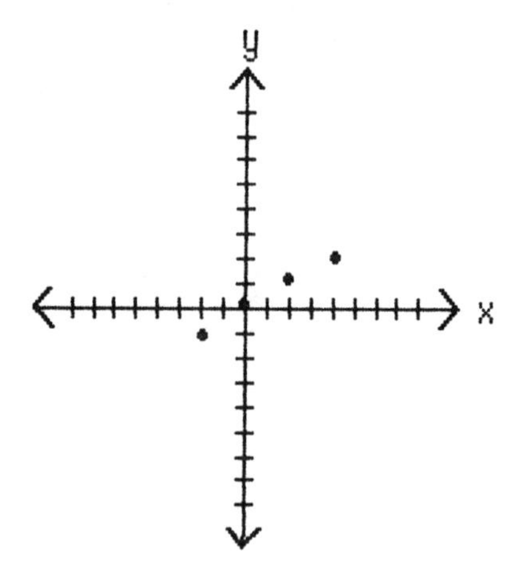

4. Answer:

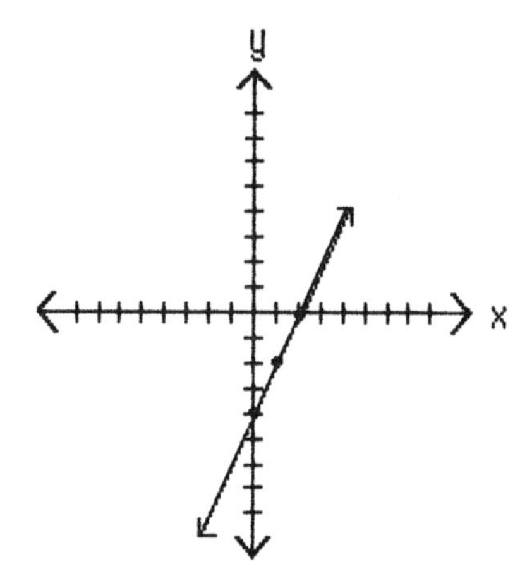

5. $y = 2(x - 1)$

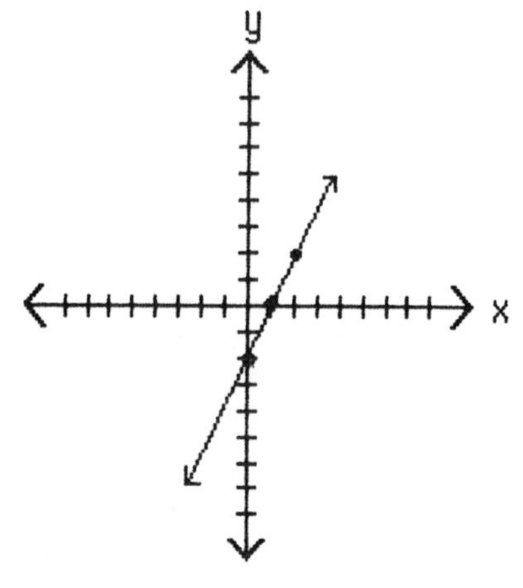

6. 0

7. 1

8. No

9. Yes

10. Answer:

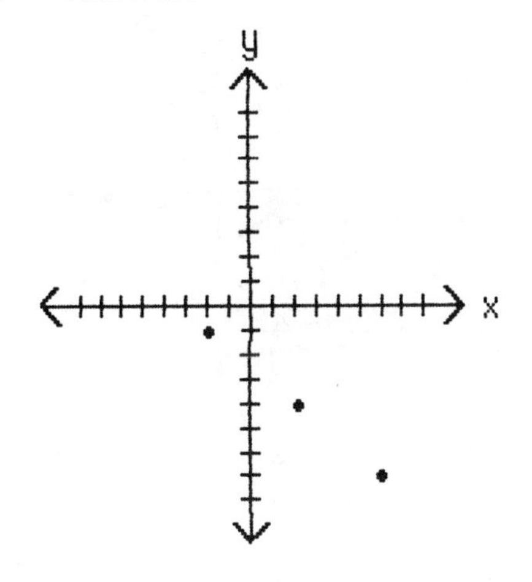

11. $m = -1$ y-intercept $= 7$

12. $y = 2x + 5$

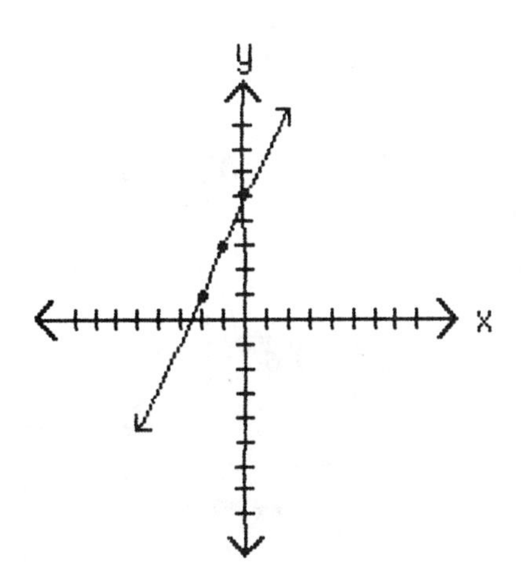

13. $y = -x + 2$

14. $x - 2y + 2 = 0$

7. $\frac{3}{4}$

8. Yes

9. NO

10. Answer:

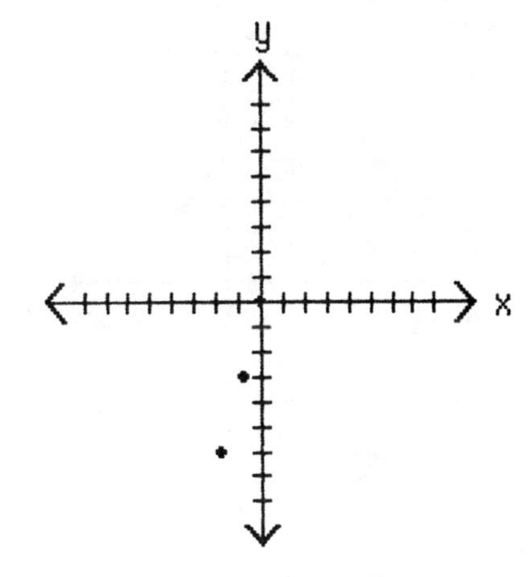

11. $m = 6$ $b = -9$

12. $y = \frac{2}{5}x + 3$

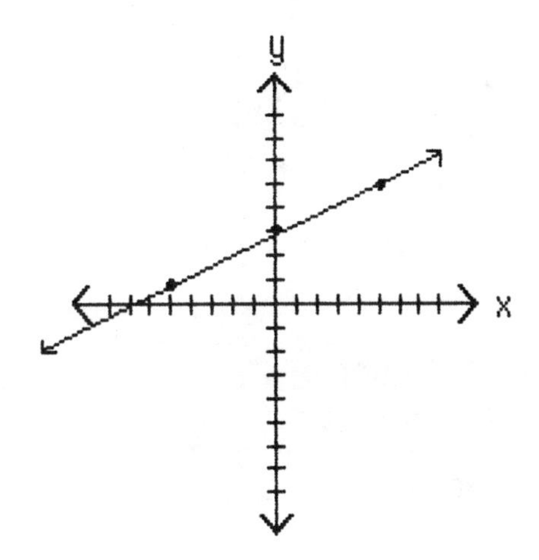

13. $y = -\frac{5}{2}x$

14. $4x - 3y = 22$

15. Answer:

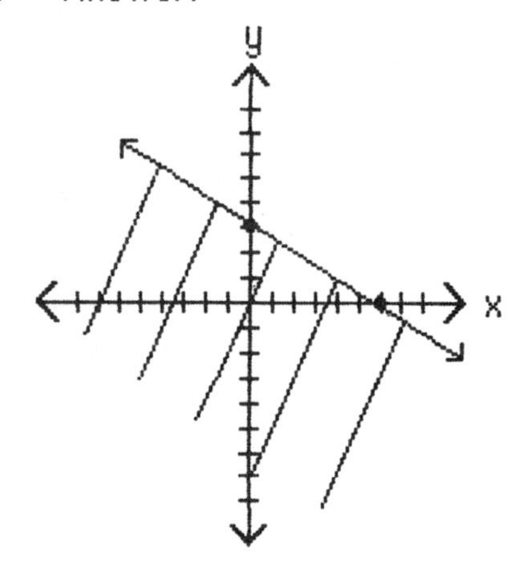

16. $x + y > 3$

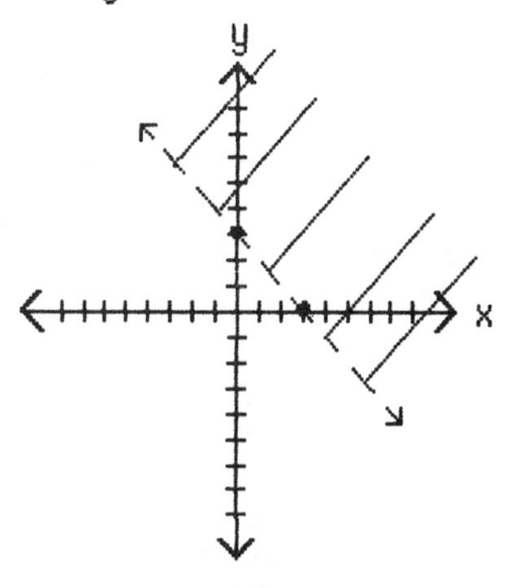

17. $3.20x + 4.10y \geq 815$

18. $V = -800t + 8000$

19. $y = \frac{1}{16000}x + \frac{11}{8}$

20. Domain {1, 2, 3, 4}
Range {-1, -2, -3, -4}

21. S = {(0, -3), (2, -1), (2, 2), (3, 1)} S is not a function

22. $\{x \mid x \neq -1\}$

23. $\{x \mid x \neq -3,\ x \neq 3\}$

24. $g(-2) = 13$

25. $P(x) = -0.15x^2 + 1.7x - 0.40$

15. Answer:

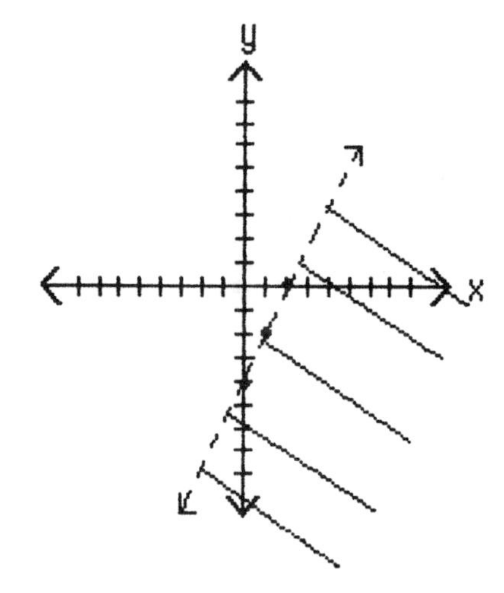

16. $x - y \leq 4$

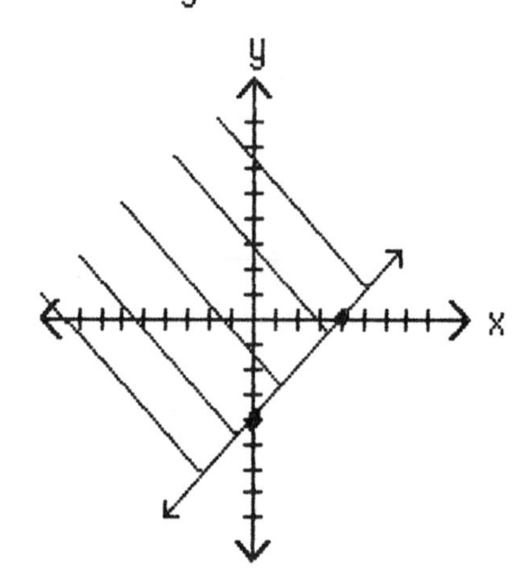

17. $4.50x + 8.00y \geq 85$

18. $y = -2200x + 45000$

19. $y = -\frac{5}{2}x + 130$

20. Domain {-2, 0, 3}
Range {3, 4, 5, 6}

21. S = {(-2, 0), (1, 2), (2, -3), (3, -1)} S is a function

22. $\{x \mid x \text{ is Real}\}$

23. $\{x \mid x \neq 5,\ x \neq -5\}$

24. $g(3) = -11$

25. $P(x) = -5x^2 - 35x + 305$

CHAPTER # 6 TEST KEYS

Form C

1. F(-1, -4), G(5, 0)
2. A, B, and D
3. Answer:

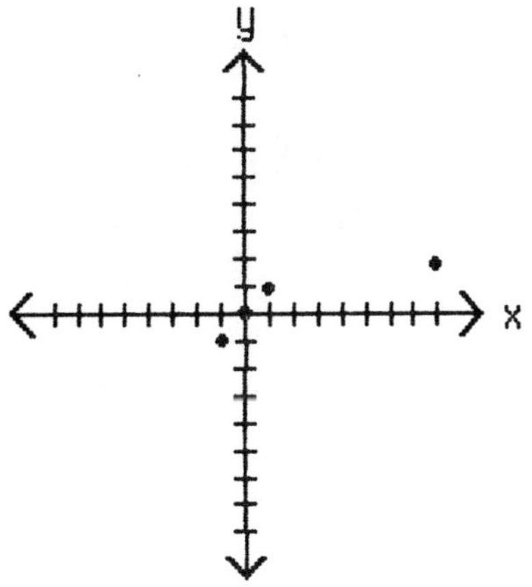

4. Answer:

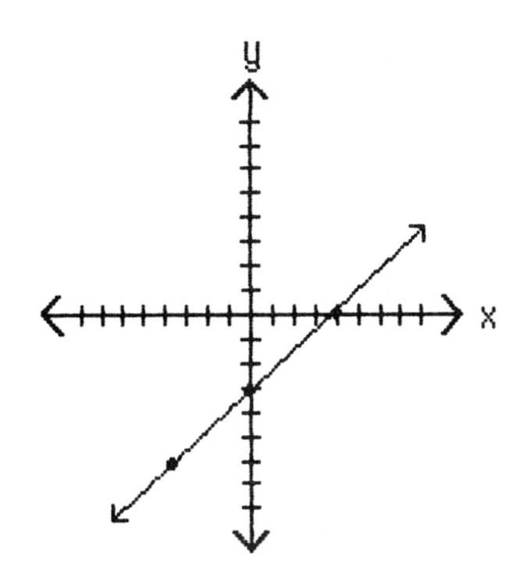

5. $x - \frac{1}{2}y = 2$

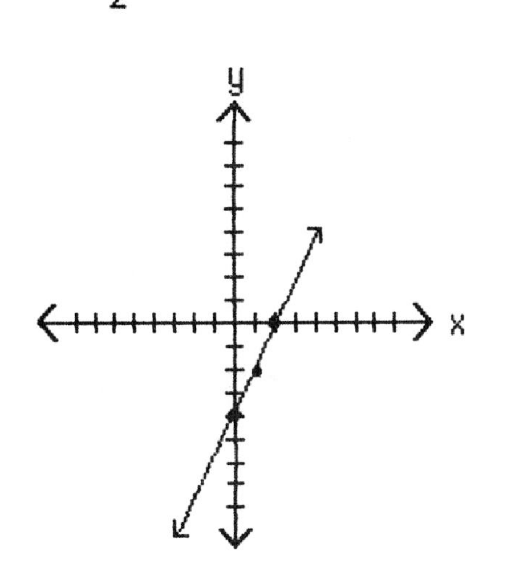

Form D

1. b) H(-1, 6), J(0, -3)
2. d) D and E
3. a) points lie on a line

4. Answer:

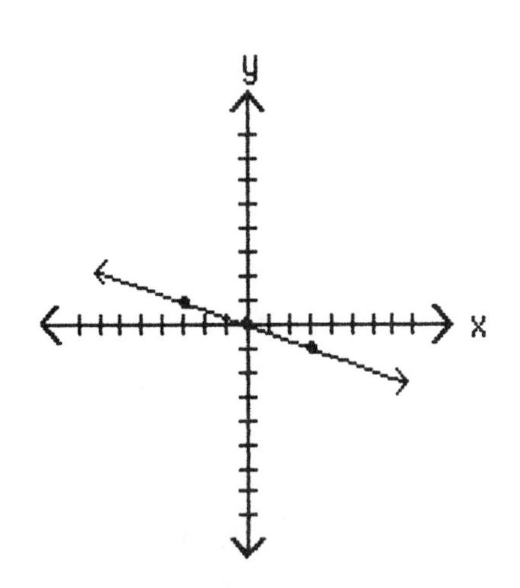

5. c) $y + 2x = 4$

6. $m = -\frac{2}{3}$

7. $m = -4$

8. Yes

9. Yes

10. Answer:

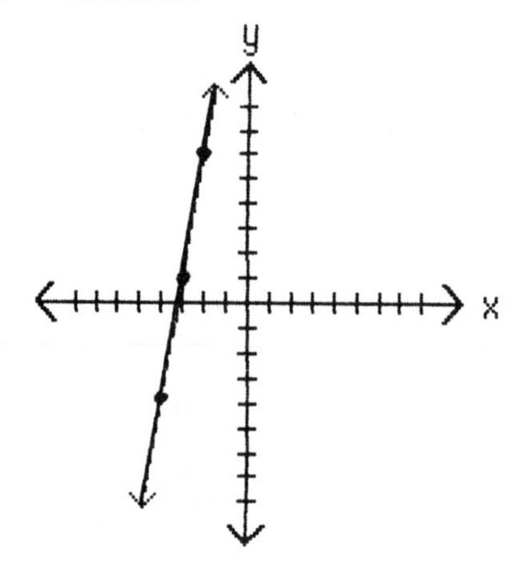

11. $m = -\frac{3}{2}$, $b = 0$

12. $y = -4$

y
x

13. $y = x - 11$

14. $y = 4x - 5$

6. b) $m = -\frac{1}{2}$

7. a) $m = -\frac{2}{3}$

8. e) None of these

9. c) (6, 7)

10. 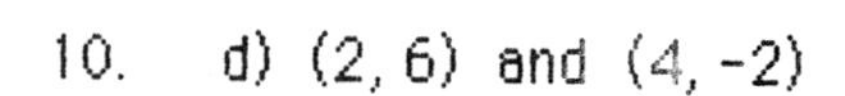
d) (2, 6) and (4, -2)

11. b) $m = -1$, $b = -9$

12. c) $y = 3x - 1$

13. a) $y = x - 4$

14. d) $y = 4x - 12$

15. Answer:

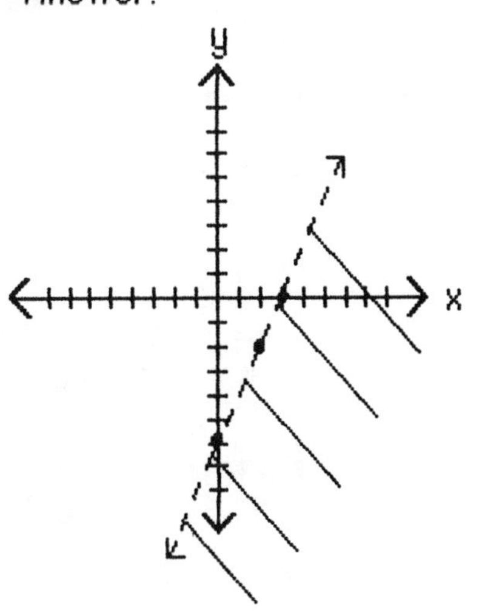

15. c) $x + 5y \geq 3$

16. $4x + 2y < 12$

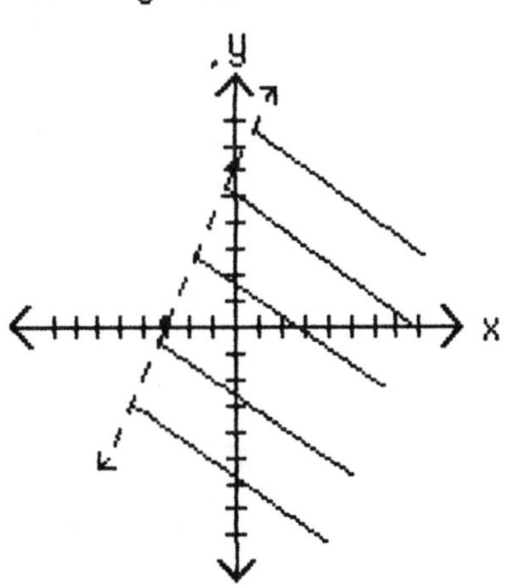

16. b) $x + y > 4$

17. $.35A + .25B \leq 4.85$

17. e) None of these

18. $V = 23x + 125$

18. a) $V = -700t + 11000$

19. $P = -\frac{1}{20}x + 125$

19. d) $P = -\frac{1}{5}x + 80$

20. Domain {-1,3, 7, 11}
Range {-8, -2, 4, 10}

20. b) {0, 2, 3, 5}

21. S = {(-3, 1), (-2, 3), (-1, -2), (1, 1)} S is a function

21. c) {(-4, -3), (-2, 1), (0, 3), (2, 1)} S is a function

22. $\{x \mid x \neq 2\}$

22. a) $\{x \mid x \neq -5\}$

23. $\{x \mid x \neq 2,\ x \neq 1\}$

23. d) $\{x \mid x \neq 5,\ x \neq -5\}$

24. $h(\frac{1}{2}) = \frac{9}{4}$

24. b) $g(-3) = 40$

25. $10887.50

25. d) $P(x) = -0.15x^2 + 1.5x - 0.30$

CHAPTER # 6 TEST KEYS

Form E

1. c) $M(-5, 0)$ $N(5, 2)$
2. a) A and C
3. b) points lie on a line
4. Answer:

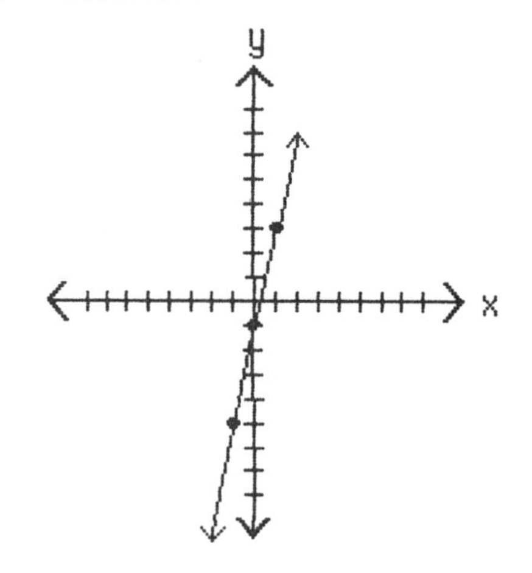

5. d) $y = 2(x - 4)$
6. e) None of these
7. b) $m = -3$
8. a) $4y + 9x - 4 = 0$
9. d) $(4, 5)$
10. e) None of these
11. c) $m = 4,\ b = -10$
12. d) $y = -\frac{3}{4}x + 2$
13. b) $y = \frac{2}{3}x$
14. a) $y = \frac{5}{2}x + \frac{27}{2}$
15. d) $3x - y < 4$
16. c) $y - x \leq 5$

Form F

1. d) $P(4, -5)$ $Q(-1, 3)$
2. b) D and E
3. e) None of these
4. Answer:

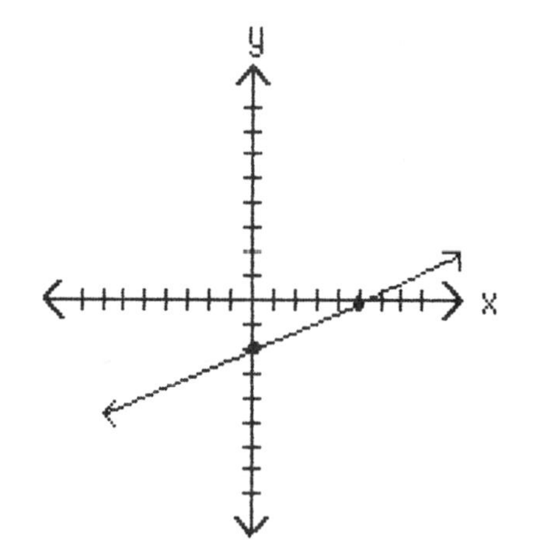

5. b) $x - \frac{1}{2}y = 4$
6. c) $m = \frac{5}{2}$
7. c) $m = \frac{1}{2}$
8. b) $x + y = 3$
9. a) $(-3, -1)$
10. c) $(5, 0)$ and $(-9, -10)$
11. d) $m = \frac{5}{3},\ b = -\frac{10}{3}$
12. a) $y = -4x - 1$
13. d) $y = -x + 6$
14. e) None of these
15. b) $4x - y < 6$
16. d) $3x + 2y < 6$

17. a) $6x + 9y \geq 95$

18. b) $V = -3000t + 50000$

19. a) $P = -\frac{16}{25}x + 112$

20. c) $\{-3, 1, 5\}$

21. b) $\{(-3, 4), (-1, -2), (1, 4)$ $(4, -1)\}$ function

22. b) $\{x \mid x \text{ is Real}\}$

23. c) $\{x \mid x \text{ is Real}\}$

24. c) $g(-2) = 9$

25. a) $P(x) = -3x^2 - 25x + 255$

17. c) $.45x + .40y \leq 3.65$

18. c) $V = 20t + 155$

19 b) $P = -.125x + 13.65$

20. a) $\{6, 7, 9, 11\}$

21. d) $\{(-5, 3), (-2, -3), (-1, 3)$ $(1, -1)\}$ function

22. c) $\{x \mid x \neq 6\}$

23. a) $\{x \mid x \neq -1,\ x \neq 5\}$

24. d) $h(\frac{1}{2}) = -1$

25. b) $P(200) = 32000$

Name ______________________ Chapter 7 Form A Score ______

1. Determine if (3, 2) is a solution of the system of equations

$$4x - 3y = 6$$
$$3x + 2y = 12$$

1. 

2. If a system of equations is inconsistent, there are ______________ solutions.

2. 

3. Solve the following system using the graphing method:

$$y - 3x = 5$$
$$y + 3x = -1$$

3. 

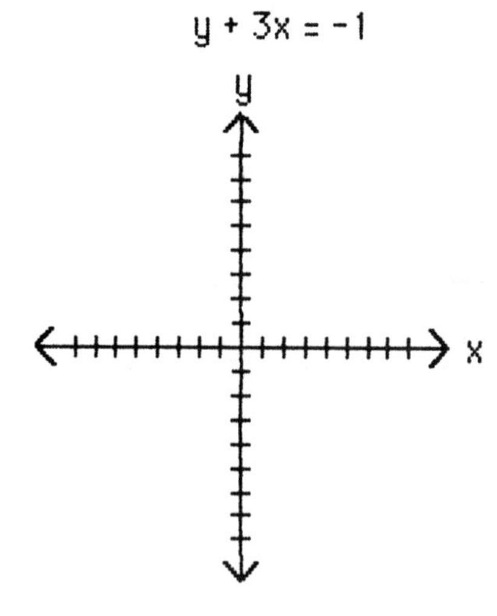

4. Solve the following system using the graphing method:

$$y = x + 3$$
$$y = x - 1$$

4. ______________

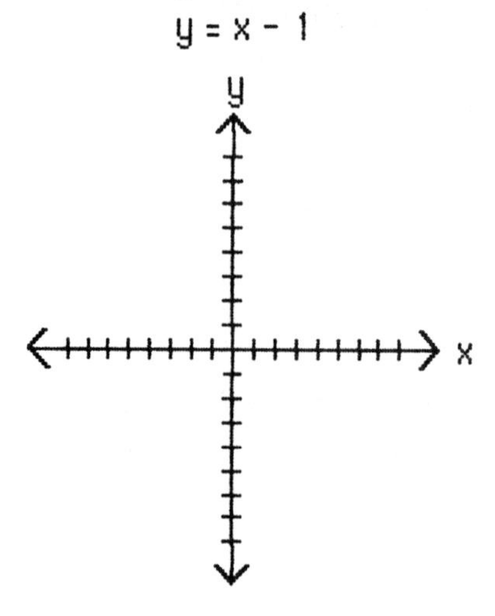

5. Solve the system by the elimination method: 5. ____________

$$4x - y = 11$$
$$2x + y = 7$$

6. Solve the system by the elimination method: 6. ____________

$$8x + 3y = -1$$
$$3x - 2y = -16$$

7. Solve the system by the elimination method: 7. ____________

$$\frac{3}{5}x + \frac{2}{5}y = \frac{19}{8}$$
$$\frac{4}{5}x - \frac{2}{5}y = -\frac{3}{2}$$

8. Solve the system by the elimination method: 8. ____________

$$2(x + 1) - 3(2 - y) = -15$$
$$3(x - 4) - 5y = 0$$

9. Twice a number is one less than three times another number. Five times the first number is one more than seven times the second. Find the two numbers. 9. ____________

10. Solve the system using the substitution method: 10. ____________

$$x = y + 5$$
$$3x - 5y = 5$$

11. Solve the system using the substitution method: 11. ____________

$$2x + 3y = 8$$
$$3x - y = 1$$

12. One number is three fourths of another number. The sum of the two numbers is −14. Find the two numbers. 12. ____________

13. Solve the system of equations: $3a + 6b = 4$, $2a - b = 1$ 13. ____________

14. The length of a rectangular swimming pool is to be 30 feet greater than the width. If the perimeter must be 160 feet, what dimensions must the pool have? 14. ____________

15. A fraction reduces to $\frac{2}{9}$. One half the numerator plus $\frac{1}{6}$ of the denominator is −10. 15. ____________

Find the numerator and denominator.

16. The manager of a supermarket ordered two types of flour. Some of it was sold before he checked how many bags of each type were actually received. The per-bag cost was $1.05 for type A and $0.85 for type B. The total order of 400 bags cost $370.00. How many bags of each type were received?

16. ____________

17. A certain alloy contains 8% silver. Another alloy contains 16% silver. How many kilograms of each alloy must be mixed to make 10 kilograms of an alloy that is 12% silver?

17. ____________

18. Graph the system of linear inequalities: $x + y \leq 4$
$2x - y > 1$

18. ____________

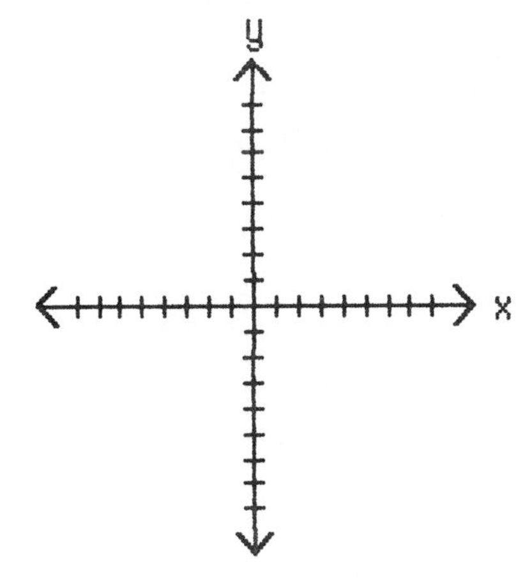

19. Graph the system of linear inequalities: $3x + 2y \le 6$ 19. ______

$x \ge 0$

$y \ge 0$

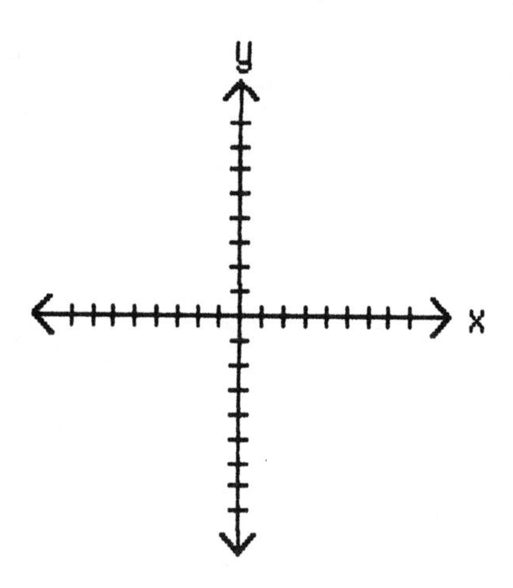

20. Graph the system of linear inequalities: $1 \le x \le 5$ 20. ______

$1 \le y \le 6$

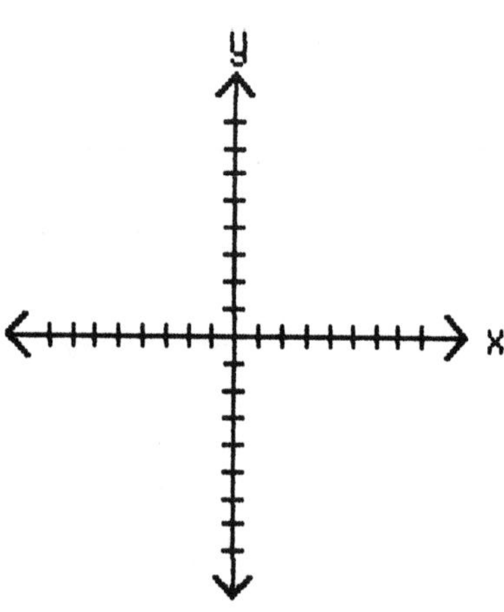

Name ______________________ Chapter 7 Form B Score ______

1. Determine if $(-2, 4)$ is a solution of the system of equations $5x - 2y = -2$
$3x + y = -10$

1. ______________

2. If a system of equations is dependent, there are ______________ solutions.

2. ______________

3. Solve the following system using the graphing method: $y - 2x = -1$
$y + 2x = -5$

3. ______________

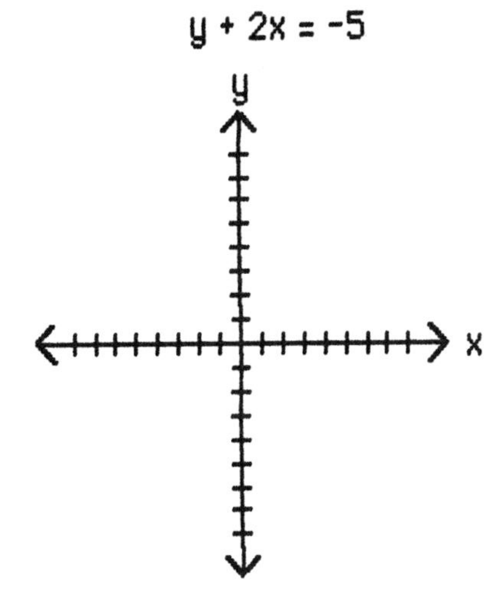

4. Solve the following system using the graphing method: $y = x - 2$
$y = 4 - x$

4. ______________

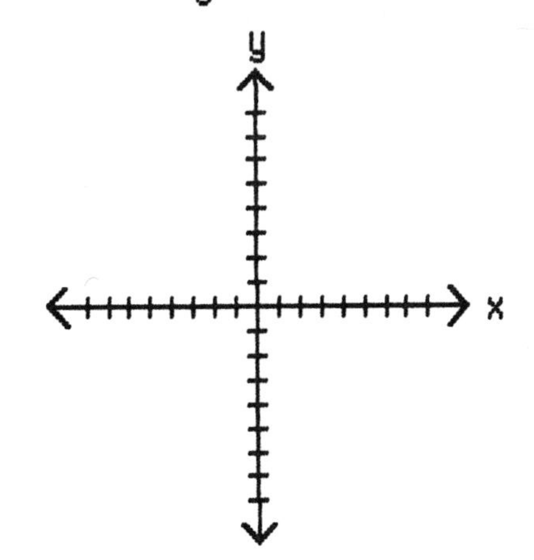

5. Solve the system by the elimination method: 5. ____________

$$9x - 2y = -10$$
$$3x + 2y = -2$$

6. Solve the system by the elimination method: 6. ____________

$$5x - 3y = 27$$
$$4x - 2y = 20$$

7. Solve the system by the elimination method: 7. ____________

$$\frac{5}{6}x + \frac{1}{4}y = \frac{23}{9}$$
$$\frac{1}{2}x - \frac{3}{8}y = -\frac{8}{3}$$

8. Solve the system by the elimination method: 8. ____________

$$3(2 - x) - 4(y + 3) = 11$$
$$5(x + 3) - 2(y - 1) = 6$$

9. Twice a number is one more than three times another number. Five times the first number is five less than nine times the second. Find the two numbers. 9. ____________

10. Solve the system using the substitution method: 10. ____________

$$x = y - 6$$
$$7x - 3y = 6$$

11. Solve the system using the substitution method: 11. ______

$$5x + 2y = -16$$
$$x - 4y = 10$$

12. One number is two thirds of another number. The sum of the two numbers is -20. Find the two numbers. 12. 

13. Solve the system of equations: $4x - 8y = 0$, $x + 2y = 1$ 13. 

14. Two angles are complementary. The measure of one angle is 5 degrees less than twice the measure of the other angle. Find the measures of the two angles. 14. ______

15. A bookstore shelves books vertically. A 2-foot shelf holds 12 copies of a dictionary and 3 copies of an encyclopedia. A 3-foot shelf holds 4 copies of the dictionary and 15 copies of the encyclopedia. How thick is each book? 15. ______

16. Kelly has half as many quarters as dimes. If she has a total of \$4.05, how many of each type does she have?

16. ____________

17. One solution is 18% insecticide and another solution is 28% insecticide. How much of each solution is needed to form 28 pints of a solution which is 25% insecticide?

17. 

18. Graph the system of linear inequalities: $y + 2x \le 6$
$2y + 3x \ge 4$

18. ____________

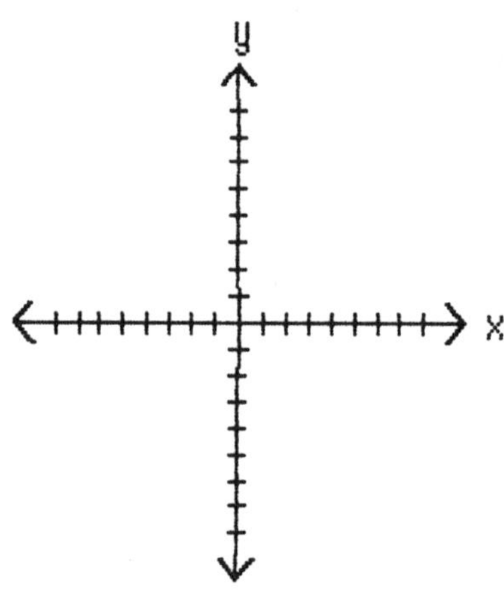

19. Graph the system of linear inequalities: $y \geq 3$
$x \leq -2$
$y > x$

19. ____________

20. Graph the system of linear inequalities:
$-2 \leq x \leq 3$
$-3 < y < 4$

20. ____________

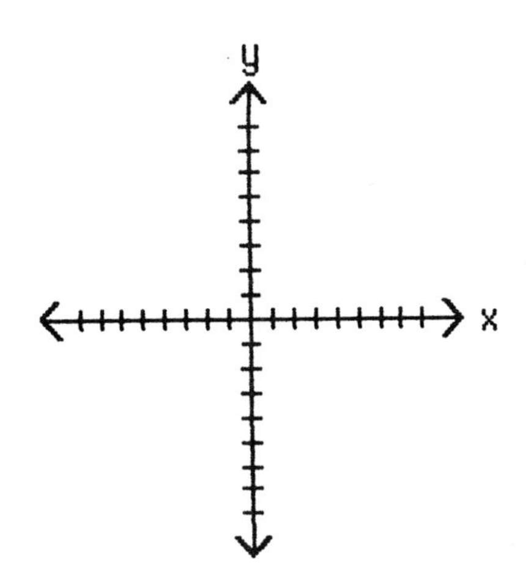

Name ______________________ Chapter 7 Form C Score ______

1. Determine if (7, 3) is a solution of the system of equations $2x - 3y = 5$
$3x - 4y = 9$

1. ____________

2. If a system of equations contains two parallel lines, the system is ________________ .

2. ____________

3. Solve the following system using the graphing method: $2y + x = 1$
$3y - x = 4$

3. ____________

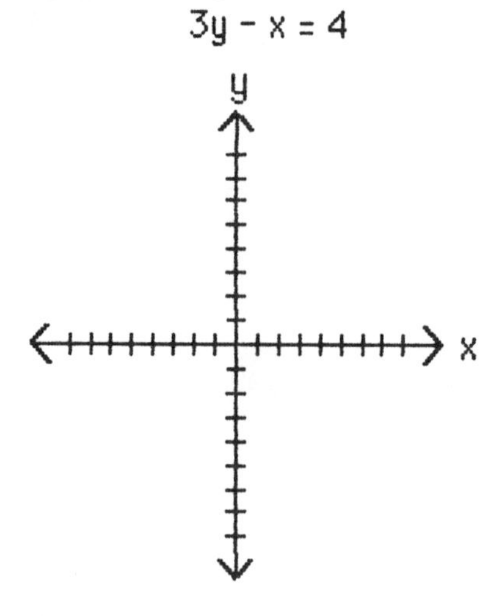

4. Solve the following system using the graphing method: $x - y = 1$
$2y = 2x - 2$

4. ____________

5. Solve the system by the elimination method: 5. ____________

$$3a - b = 1$$
$$3a + b = -5$$

6. Solve the system by the elimination method: 6. ____________

$$7x - 3y = 2$$
$$2x + 7y = 32$$

7. Solve the system by the elimination method: 7. ____________

$$\frac{1}{4}x + \frac{1}{5}y = 6$$
$$\frac{1}{3}x + \frac{1}{6}y = 2$$

8. Solve the system by the elimination method: 8. ____________

$$4(x - 1) - 3(y + 2) = 17$$
$$6(x + 1) + 2(y - 1) = 12$$

9. The sum of four times the first number and five times the second number is 27. The difference of the first number and the second number, divided by 3 is 3. Find the two numbers. 9. ____________

10. Solve the system using the substitution method: 10. ____________

$$2x + y = 3$$
$$x = y + 3$$

11. Solve the system using the substitution method: 11. ____________

$3y - x = 15$
$2x + y = 5$

12. One number is three fourths of another number. The sum of the two numbers is -28. Find the two numbers. 12. ____________

13. Solve the system of equations: $4x + 2y = 3$ 13. ____________

$9x - 5y = 3\frac{3}{8}$

14. Two angles are supplementary. The measure of one angle is 15 degrees less than twice the measure of the other angle. Find the measure of the two angles. 14.

15. In a Federal game preserve, a herd of antelope contains two species. One species is known to increase its population by 5% per year. The other species increases by 10% per year. An aerial survey by helicopter determines that the total number in the herd is 1200 and the total number of new offspring is 75. How many of each species are in the herd? 15. ____________

16. At a skating rink, students pay \$0.75 admission and adults pay \$1.25. For one night, the receipts were \$85.00 and 100 people paid admission. How many of these people were students and how many were adults?

16. ____________

17. A jet airplane, cruising with a tailwind, made a trip of 1200 kilometers in 2.4 hours. The airplane required 3 hours to make the return trip, cruising against the same wind. Find the speeds of the airplane and the wind.

17. ____________

18. Graph the system of linear inequalities: $x + 2y < 6$
$x - 3y > 3$

18. ____________

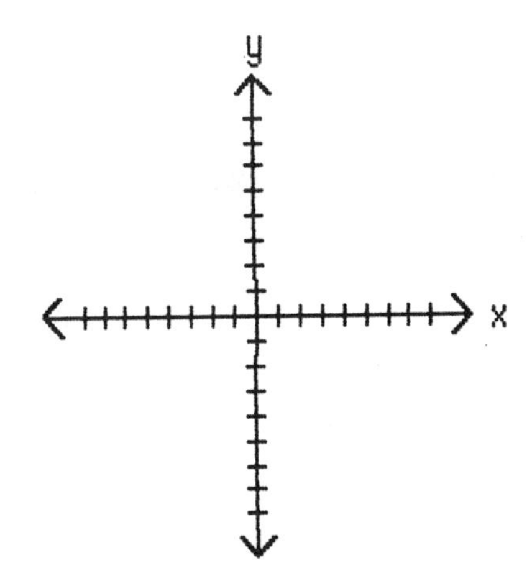

19. Graph the system of linear inequalities: $y < 2x - 2$ 19. ____________

$y \leq 1$

$x \geq -2$

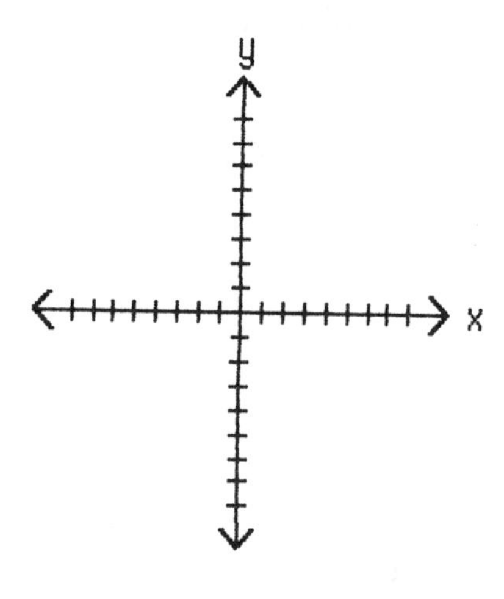

20. Graph the system of linear inequalities: $-3 < x < 2$ 20. ____________

$2 \leq y \leq 6$

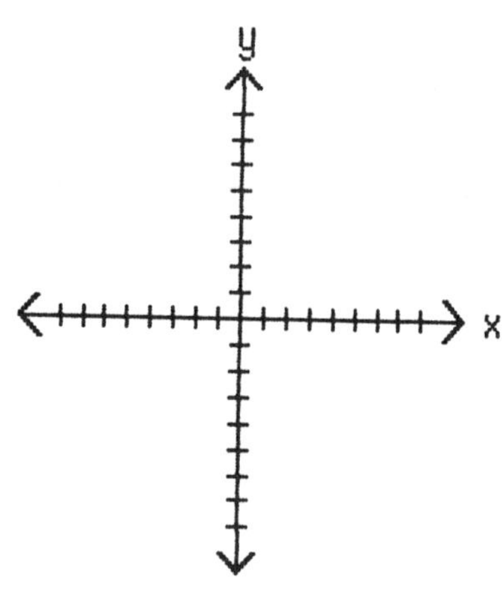

Name ______________________ Chapter 7 Form D Score ________

1. Which of the following points is a solution of the system of equations $6x - 4y = 10$
$3x - 5y = -1$

1. ____________

a. $x = \frac{9}{7}, y = -\frac{4}{7}$

b. $x = 2, y = 1$

c. $x = 3, y = 2$

d. $x = \frac{18}{3}, y = 6$

e. None of these

2. If a system of equations has exactly one solution, it is

2. 

a. inconsistent
b. dependent
c. two parallel lines
d. two coinciding lines
e. None of these

3. Solve the following system using the graphing method: $x - y = 2$
$2x + y = -5$

3. ____________

The solution is

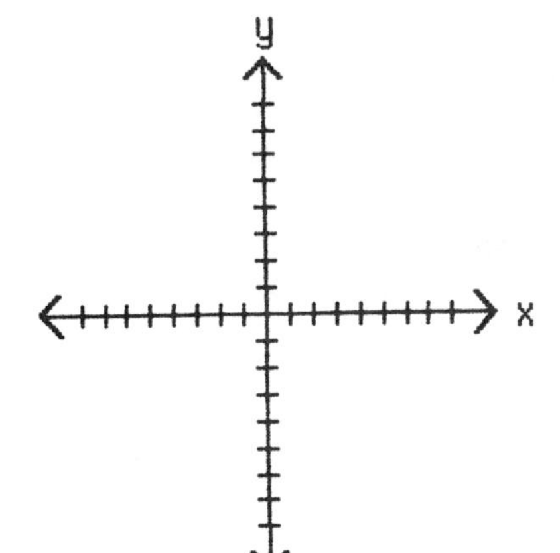

a. $x = 7, \quad y = 9$
b. $x = -1, \quad y = -3$
c. $x = -1, \quad y = 1$
d. $x = -3, \quad y = -1$
e. None of these

4. Solve the following system using the graphing method: $y = x - 7$
$y = -3x + 1$
The solution is

4. ______________

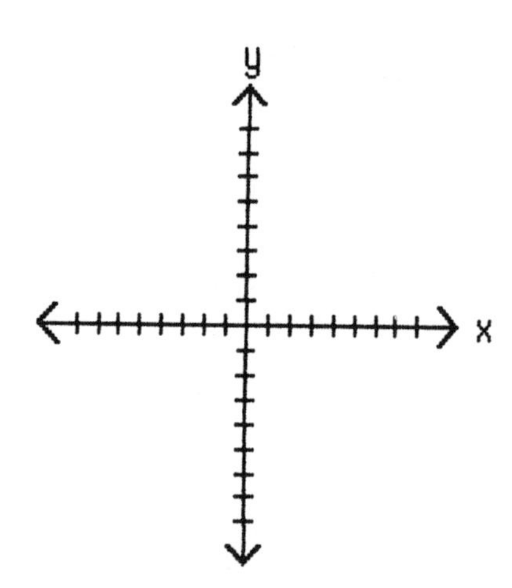

a. $x = 2, \quad y = -5$
b. $x = 3, \quad y = -4$
c. $x = -5, \quad y = 2$
d. $x = 4, \quad y = -3$
e. None of these

5. Solve the system by the elimination method:

5. ______________

$$2x + 3y = -3$$
$$x - 3y = -6$$

a. $x = -6, \quad y = 0$
b. $x = 3, \quad y = -3$
c. $x = 3, \quad y = 3$
d. $x = -3, \quad y = 1$
e. None of these

6. Solve the system by the elimination method:

6. ______________

$$2x - 3y = 5$$
$$3x - 4y = 9$$

a. $x = -\frac{1}{2}, \quad y = -2$
b. $x = 7, \quad y = 3$
c. $x = -2, \quad y = 3$
d. $x = 1, \quad y = -3$
e. None of these

7. Solve the system by the elimination method:

7. ______________

$$\frac{1}{4}x + \frac{1}{2}y = 10$$
$$\frac{1}{4}x - \frac{1}{2}y = 0$$

a. $x = 10, \quad y = 20$
b. $x = 20, \quad y = 30$
c. $x = 20, \quad y = 10$
d. $x = 5, \quad y = \frac{5}{2}$
e. None of these

8. Solve the system by the elimination method: 8. ______________

$$4(x + 3) - 2(1 - y) = 14$$
$$3(2 - x) + 5(y - 3) = 14$$

a. $x = -1, \quad y = 4$
b. $x = 1, \quad y = 3$
c. $x = 4, \quad y = 3$
d. $x = 2, \quad y = 4$
e. None of these

9. Three times a number is one less than seven times another number. Twice the first number is two more than four times the second. Find the two numbers. 9. ______________

a. -1 and 1
b. -2 and -1
c. 2 and 5
d. 2 and $\frac{1}{2}$
e. None of these

10. Solve the system using the substitution method: 10. ______________

$$x = y + 6$$
$$4x - 2y = 8$$

a. $x = 7, \quad y = 1$
b. $x = 22, \quad y = 16$
c. $x = -2, \quad y = -8$
d. $x = 14, \quad y = 8$
e. None of these

11. Solve the system using the substitution method: 11. ______________

$$2x - y = -9$$
$$5x - 3y = -22$$

a. $x = -5, \quad y = 1$
b. $x = -5, \quad y = -1$
c. $x = -\frac{49}{11}, \quad y = -\frac{1}{11}$
d. $x = 31, \quad y = 71$
e. None of these

12. One number is three fourths of another number. The sum of the two numbers is -21. Find the two numbers. 12. ______________

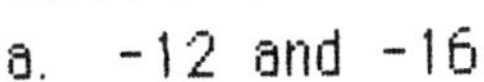

a. -12 and -16
b. -84 and 63
c. 9 and 12
d. -9 and -12
e. None of these

13. Solve the system of equations: $4a + 8b = 7$ 13. ____________

$7a - b = 1$

a. $a = 4, \quad b = 27$
b. $a = \frac{8}{11}, \quad b = \frac{45}{11}$
c. $a = \frac{2}{15}, \quad b = \frac{4}{5}$
d. $a = \frac{1}{4}, \quad b = \frac{3}{4}$
e. None of these

14. The length of a rectangular garden is to be 25 feet greater than the width. If the perimeter must be 130 feet, how long is the garden to be? 14. 

a. 45 feet
b. 20 feet
c. 70 feet
d. 32.5 feet
e. None of these

15. A fraction reduces to $\frac{3}{8}$. One half the numerator added to $\frac{1}{3}$ the denominator is 25. Find the denominator. 15. ____________

a. 18
b. 48
c. 1
d. 15
e. None of these

16. The manager of a supermarket ordered two types of flour. Some of it was sold before he checked how many bags of each type were actually received. The per-bag cost was \$1.15 for type A and \$0.95 for type B. The total order of 400 bags cost \$410. How many bags of type A were received? 16. ____________

a. 150 bags
b. 250 bags
c. 50 bags
d. 180 bags
e. None of these

17. A certain alloy contains 9% silver. Another alloy contains 18% silver. Determine how many kilograms of each alloy must be mixed to make 18 kilograms of an alloy that is 14% silver? How much of the 18% alloy must be used?

17. ____________

a. 8 kilograms
b. 9 kilograms
c. 10 kilograms
d. 12 kilograms
e. None of these

18. Graph the system of linear inequalities: $x + y \leq 3$
$2x + y > 2$

18. ____________

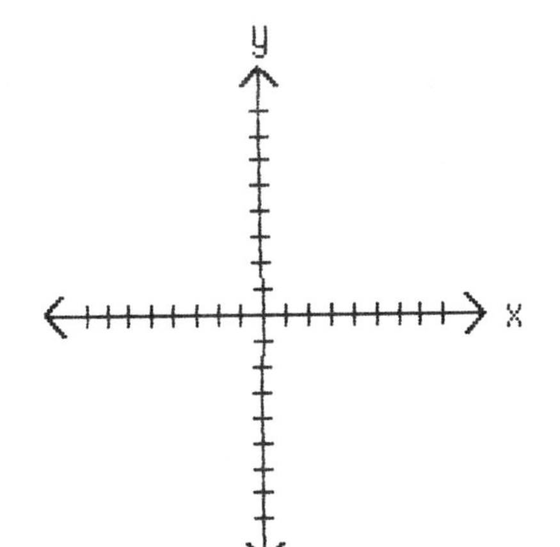

Which of the following points is a solution to both inequalities?

a. (1, 0)
b. (-1, 3)
c. (3, -1)
d. (2, 2)
e. None of these

19. Graph the system of linear inequalities:

$2x + 5y \leq 10$
$x \geq 0$
$y \geq 0$

19. 

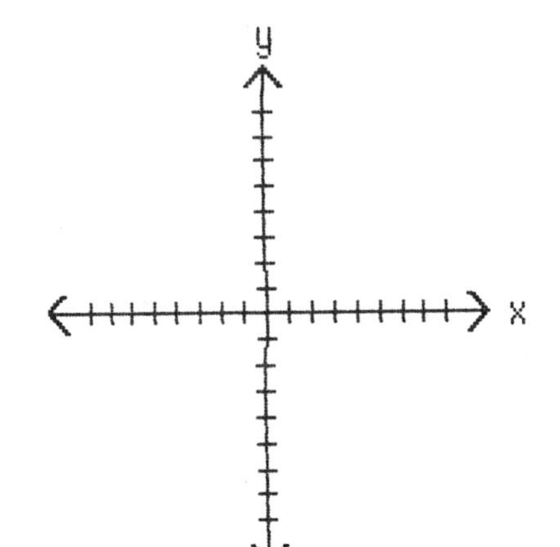

Those points which satisfy all three linear inequalities lie

a. in the first quadrant
b. in the second quadrant
c. in the third quadrant
d. in the fourth quadrant
e. None of these

20. Graph the system of linear inequalities:

$$-4 \le x \le -1$$
$$-3 < y < 0$$

20. ____________

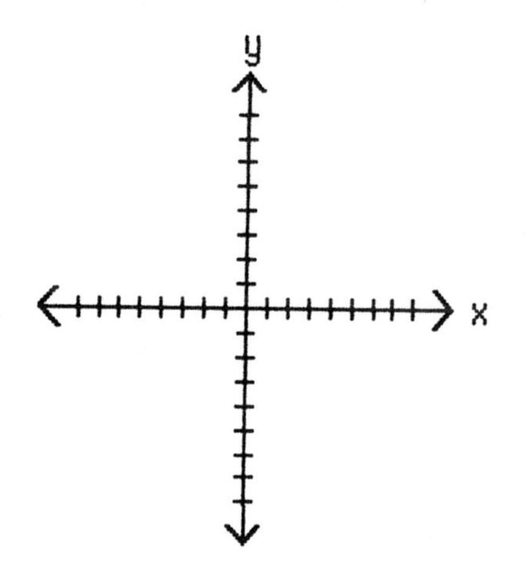

The solution set of the system is:

a. in the first quadrant
b. in the fourth quadrant
c. in the second quadrant
d. in the third quadrant
e. None of these

Name ______________________ Chapter 7 Form E Score ______

1. Which of the following points is a solution of the system of equations: $9x - 3y = 30$
   $3x + 2y = -2$ 1. ____________

   a. $x = \frac{4}{3}, y = -3$
   b. $x = 2, y = -4$
   c. $x = 3, y = -1$
   d. $x = 2, y = 4$
   e. None of these

2. If a system of equations has infinitely many solutions, it is 2. 

   a. inconsistent
   b. two parallel lines
   c. independent
   d. dependent
   e. None of these

3. Solve the following system of equations using the graphing method: $x - y = 4$
   $2x + y = 5$ 3. ____________

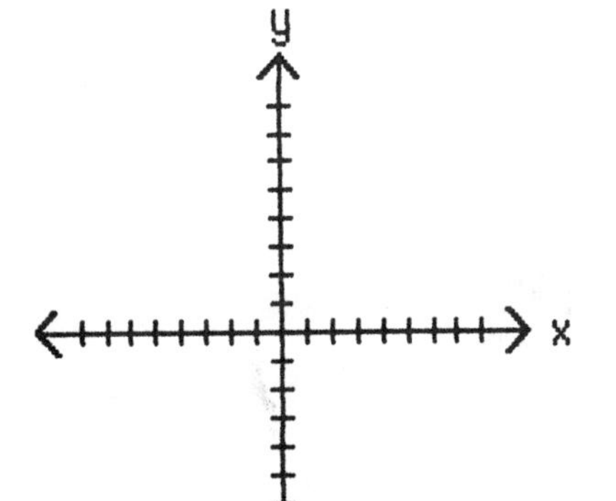

The solution is

   a. $x = 3, \; y = -1$
   b. $x = 9, \; y = 5$
   c. $x = 9, \; y = -5$
   d. $x = 3, \; y = 1$
   e. None of these

4. Solve the following system using the graphing method: $y = x - 4$
$y = -4x + 1$

4. ______________

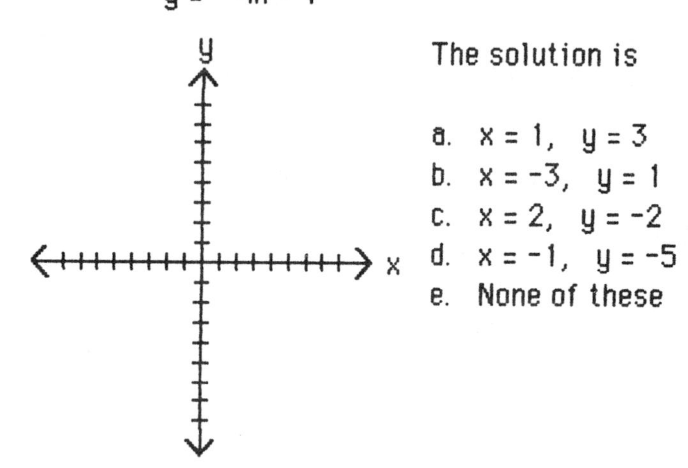

The solution is

a. $x = 1, \quad y = 3$
b. $x = -3, \quad y = 1$
c. $x = 2, \quad y = -2$
d. $x = -1, \quad y = -5$
e. None of these

5. Solve the system by the elimination method:

5. ______________

$4x - 3y = 32$
$8x + 3y = 28$

a. $x = -1, \quad y = -12$
b. $x = 5, \quad y = 4$
c. $x = 5, \quad y = -4$
d. $x = -1, \quad y = 12$
e. None of these

6. Solve the system by the elimination method:

6. ______________

$5x - 3y = 6$
$4x - 2y = 2$

a. $x = -3, \quad y = -7$
b. $x = -3, \quad y = 3$
c. $x = 4, \quad y = 7$
d. $x = 9, \quad y = 13$
e. None of these

7. Solve the system by the elimination method:

7. ______________

$\frac{5}{6}x + \frac{1}{4}y = 1$

$\frac{1}{2}x - \frac{3}{8}y = \frac{-3}{16}$

a. $x = \frac{4}{3}, \quad y = -\frac{4}{9}$

b. $x = \frac{3}{4}, \quad y = \frac{3}{2}$

c. $x = \frac{3}{4}, \quad y = -\frac{3}{16}$

d. $x = \frac{1}{2}, \quad y = \frac{7}{3}$

e. None of these

8. Solve the system by the elimination method:

$$3(2 - x) - 4(y + 3) = 16$$
$$5(x + 3) - 2(y - 1) = 15$$

8. ____________

a. $x = -3, \quad y = \frac{1}{2}$
b. $x = -\frac{14}{13}, \quad y = -\frac{22}{13}$
c. $x = 2, \quad y = -7$
d. $x = -2, \quad y = -4$
e. None of these

9. Twice a number is four more than twice another number. Six times the first number is three less than nine times the second. Find the larger of the two numbers.

9. ____________

a. 5
b. $\frac{7}{5}$
c. $\frac{5}{3}$
d. 7
e. None of these

10. Solve the system using the substitution method:

$$x = y - 6$$
$$7x - 4y = 6$$

10. ____________

a. $x = -18, \quad y = -12$
b. $x = 10, \quad y = 16$
c. $x = -6, \quad y = 0$
d. $x = -2, \quad y = 4$
e. None of these

11. Solve the system using the substitution method:

$$5x + 2y = -22$$
$$x - 4y = 22$$

11. ____________

a. $x = -2, \quad y = -6$
b. $x = -\frac{22}{3}, \quad y = \frac{22}{3}$
c. $x = 14, \quad y = -2$
d. $x = 38, \quad y = 4$
e. None of these

12. One number is two thirds of another number. The sum of the two numbers is -35. Find the smaller number.

12. 

a. -70

b. -14

c. -21

d. $-26\frac{1}{4}$

e. None of these

13. Solve the system of equations: $4x + 8y = 4$
$x + 2y = -2$

13. ____________

a. $x = \frac{5}{2}$, $y = -\frac{3}{4}$

b. $x = \frac{1}{2}$, $y = \frac{1}{4}$

c. $x = -\frac{1}{2}$, $y = -\frac{3}{4}$

d. $x = -\frac{7}{5}$, $y = -\frac{6}{5}$

e. None of these

14. Two angles are complementary. The measure of one angle is 6 degrees more than twice the measure of the other angle. Find the measure of the larger angle.

14. ____________

a. 122 degrees

b. 58 degrees

c. 70 degrees

d. 56 degrees

e. None of these

15. A bookstore shelves books vertically. A 2-foot shelf holds 4 copies of a dictionary and 12 copies of an encyclopedia. A 3-foot shelf holds 11 copies of a dictionary and 9 copies of an encyclopedia. How thick is a dictionary?

15. ____________

a. $2\frac{1}{4}$ inches

b. $1\frac{1}{4}$ inches

c. $\frac{3}{16}$ inches

d. $4\frac{1}{4}$ inches

e. None of these

16. Jenny has half as many quarters as dimes. If she has a total of $3.15, how many quarters does she have? 16. ________

a. 14 quarters
b. 6 quarters
c. 10 quarters
d. 7 quarters
e. None of these

17. One solution is 16% insecticide and another solution is 26% insecticide. How much of each solution is needed to form 24 pints of solution which is 22% insecticide? 17. ________

a. 9.6 pints 26%, 14.4 pints 16%
b. 9.6 pints 16%, 14.4 pints 26%
c. 16.4 pints 26%, 7.6 pints 16%
d. 7.6 pints 26%, 16.4 pints 16%
e. None of these

18. Graph the system of linear inequalities: 18. ________

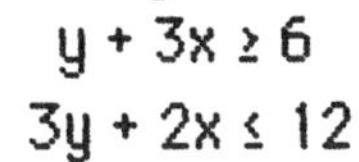

$$y + 3x \geq 6$$
$$3y + 2x \leq 12$$

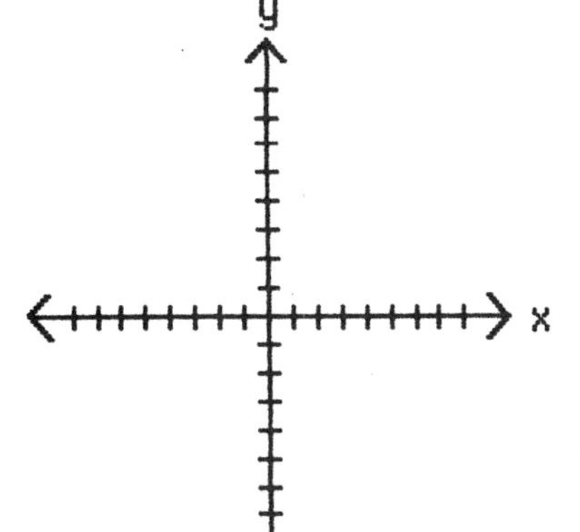

Which of the following points is a solution to both inequalities ?

a. (1, 4)
b. (5, -1)
c. (0, 4)
d. (3, -4)
e. None of these

19. Graph the system of linear inequalities: 19. ____________

$y \geq 2$

$x \leq -3$

$y > x$

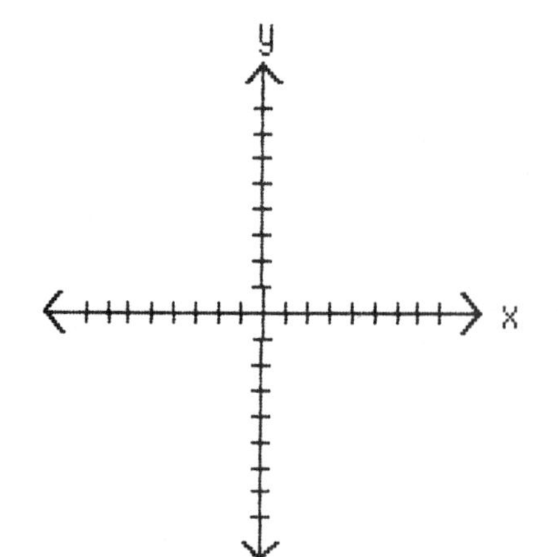

Those points which satisfy all three inequalities lie in:

a. the first quadrant
b. the fourth quadrant
c. the third quadrant
d. the second quadrant
e. None of these

20. Graph the system of linear inequalities: 20. ____________

$-5 < x < -1$

$-4 < y < 0$

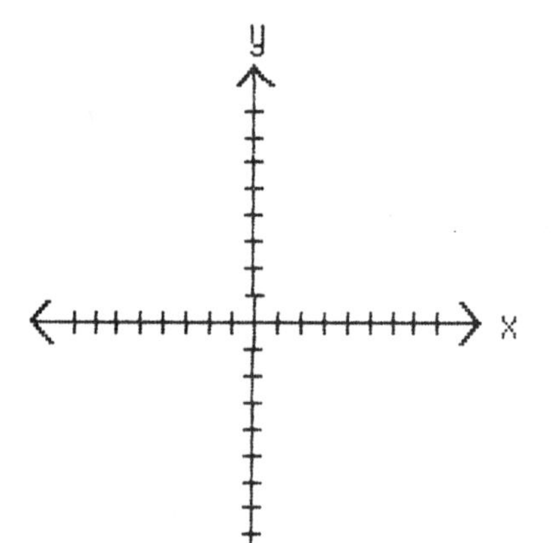

The solution set of the system lies in:

a. the first quadrant
b. the second quadrant
c. the third quadrant
d. the fourth quadrant
e. None of these

Name ______________________ Chapter 7 Form F Score ________

1. Which of the following points is a solution of the system of equations: 1. ____________

$$3x - 8y = 28$$
$$4x - 2y = -6$$

a. $x = -4, \quad y = -5$
b. $x = 4, \quad y = -2$
c. $x = -4, \quad y = -2$
d. $x = 4, \quad y = 11$
e. None of these

2. If a system of equations is dependent it has 2. ____________

a. two parallel lines
b. no solution
c. infinitely many solutions
d. exactly one solution
e. None of these

3. Solve the following system of equations using the graphing method: 3. 

$$2y + x = -8$$
$$3y - x = -7$$

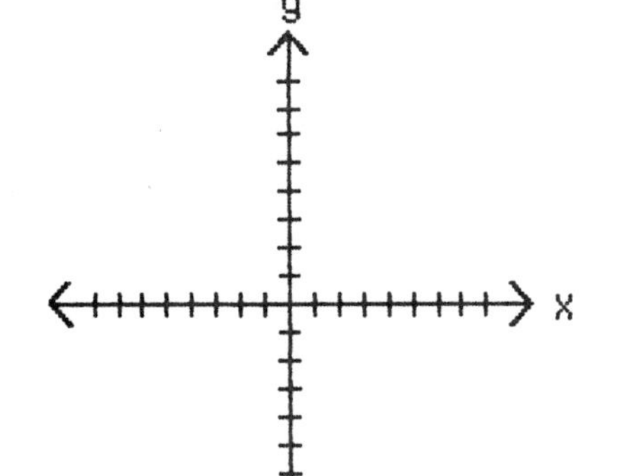

The solution is:

a. $x = -3, \quad y = -2$
b. $x = -6, \quad y = -1$
c. $x = 2, \quad y = -3$
d. $x = -1, \quad y = -3$
e. None of these

4. Solve the following system of equations using the graphing method: 4. 

$$x - y = 7$$
$$2y = -2 - 2x$$

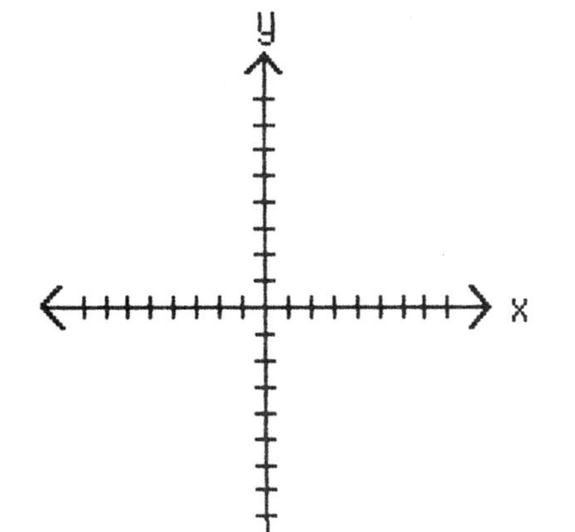

The solution is:

a. $x = -4, \quad y = 3$
b. $x = -4, \quad y = -3$
c. $x = 2, \quad y = -5$
d. $x = 3, \quad y = -4$
e. None of these

5. Solve the system of equations by the elimination method: $3a - b = 6$
$3a + b = -2$

5. ______________

a. $a = \frac{2}{3}$, $b = 4$

b. $a = \frac{2}{3}$, $b = -4$

c. $a = \frac{10}{3}$, $b = -4$

d. $a = -2$, $b = -12$

e. None of these

6. Solve the system by the elimination method:

$6x - 5y = 20$
$4x + 7y = 34$

6. ______________

a. $x = -5$, $y = 2$

b. $x = 5$, $y = -10$

c. $x = \frac{5}{3}$, $y = 2$

d. $x = 5$, $y = 2$

e. None of these

7. Solve the system by the elimination method:

$\frac{3}{4}x + \frac{2}{5}y = 3$

$\frac{1}{2}x - \frac{1}{3}y = -7$

7. ______________

a. $x = -4$, $y = 15$

b. $x = -2$, $y = 18$

c. $x = -4$, $y = 0$

d. $x = -\frac{4}{27}$, $y = 20\frac{7}{9}$

e. None of these

8. Solve the system by the elimination method:

$3(x - 2) - 4(y + 1) = 16$
$2(x - 1) + 5(y + 3) = 15$

8. ______________

a. $x = 6$, $y = -\frac{3}{4}$

b. $x = 8\frac{2}{3}$, $y = 0$

c. $x = 6$, $y = -2$

d. $x = 8\frac{22}{23}$, $y = \frac{5}{23}$

e. None of these

9. The sum of four times the first number and five times the second number is 4. The difference of the first number and the second number, divided by 2 is 5. Find the two numbers.

9. ______________

a. 4 and -4
b. $3\frac{6}{7}$ and $-2\frac{2}{7}$
c. 6 and -4
d. 6 and 4
e. None of these

10. Solve the system using the substitution method:

10. ______________

$$2x + y = 3$$
$$x = 5 - y$$

a. $x = -2, \quad y = 7$
b. $x = \frac{8}{3}, \quad y = \frac{7}{3}$
c. $x = 18, \quad y = -13$
d. $x = 12, \quad y = -7$
e. None of these

11. Solve the system using the substitution method:

11. ______________

$$4y - 3x = 5$$
$$2x + y = -7$$

a. $x = 6\frac{3}{5}, \quad y = 6\frac{1}{5}$
b. $x = -\frac{8}{5}, \quad y = -\frac{19}{5}$
c. $x = -3, \quad y = -13$
d. $x = -\frac{12}{11}, \quad y = -\frac{53}{11}$
e. None of these

12. One number is two thirds of another number. The sum of the two numbers is 30. Find the larger number.

12. ______________

a. 12
b. 18
c. $22\frac{1}{2}$
d. 20
e. None of these

13. Solve the system of equations: $2x + 4y = 1$
$3x - 14y = -6$

13. ____________

a. $x = -\frac{1}{4}$, $y = \frac{3}{8}$

b. $x = \frac{5}{4}$, $y = \frac{3}{8}$

c. $x = \frac{3}{4}$, $y = -\frac{1}{8}$

d. $x = -\frac{1}{4}$, $y = \frac{1}{8}$

e. None of these

14. Two angles are supplementary. The measure of one angle is 20 degrees less than three times the measure of the other angle. Find the measure of the larger angle.

14. 

a. 50 degrees
b. 100 degrees
c. 62.5 degrees
d. 130 degrees
e. None of these

15. In a Federal game preserve, a herd of antelope contains two species. One species is known to increase its population by 5% per year. The other species increases by 10% per year. An aerial survey by helicopter determines that the total number in the herd is 1500 and the total number of new offspring is 120. How many of each species are in the herd?

15. ____________

a. 1300 and 200
b. 1100 and 400
c. 900 and 600
d. 750 of each
e. None of these

16. At a skating rink, students pay $0.75 admission and adults pay $1.25. For one night, the receipts were $79.00 and 100 people paid admission. How many of these people were adults?

16. 

a. 23
b. 8
c. 10
d. 15
e. None of these

17. A jet airplane, cruising with a tailwind, made a trip of 1792 kilometers in 2.8 hours. The airplane required 3.2 hours to make the return trip, cruising against the same wind. Find the speed of the airplane.

17. 

a. 600 km. per hour
b. $597\frac{1}{3}$ km. per hour
c. 640 km. per hour
d. 560 km. per hour
e. None of these

18. Graph the system of linear inequalities: $x + 4y < 8$, $2x - 3y < 6$ 18. ______

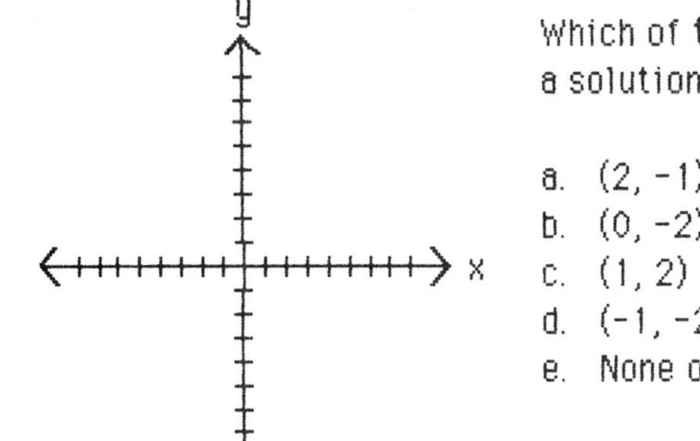

Which of the following points is a solution to both inequalities?

a. (2, -1)
b. (0, -2)
c. (1, 2)
d. (-1, -2)
e. None of these

19. Graph the system of linear inequalities: $y < \frac{1}{3}x - 3$ 19. ______

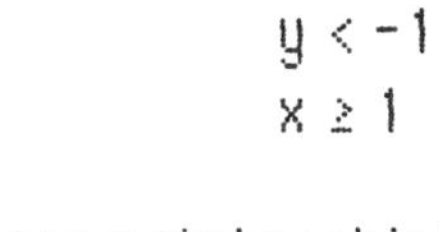

$y < -1$
$x \geq 1$

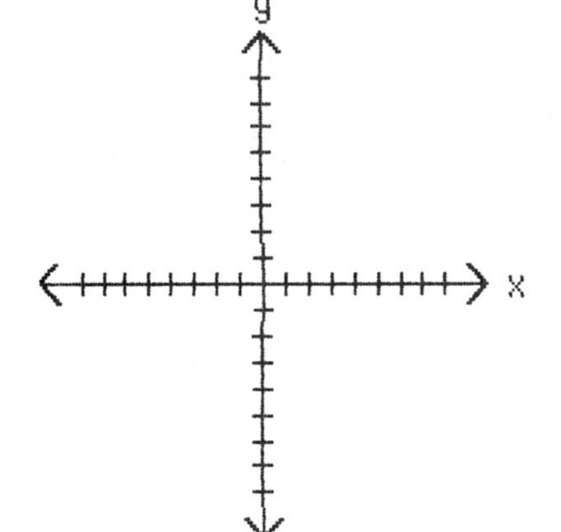

Those points which satisfy all three inequalities lie in

a. the first quadrant
b. the third quadrant
c. the fourth quadrant
d. the second quadrant
e. None of these

20. Graph the system of linear inequalities: $-7 < x < 0$ 20. ____________

$2 < y < 6$

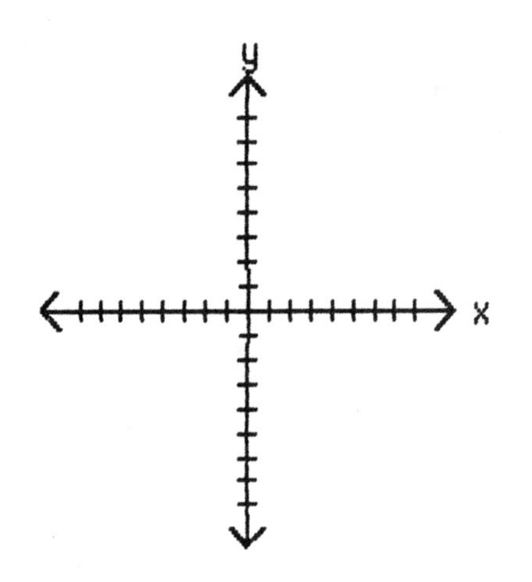

The solution set of the system lies in

a. the first quadrant
b. the second quadrant
c. the third quadrant
d. the fourth quadrant
e. None of these

CHAPTER # 7 TEST KEYS

Form A

1. No

2. No

3. $x = -1, \quad y = 2$

4. No solution

5. $x = 3, \quad y = 1$

6. $x = -2, \quad y = 5$

7. $x = \frac{5}{8}, \quad y = 5$

8. $x = -1, \quad y = -3$

9. First number is 10,
   Second number is 7.

10. $x = 10, \quad y = 5$

11. $x = 1, \quad y = 2$

12. -8 and -6

13. $a = \frac{2}{3}, \quad b = \frac{1}{3}$

14. 25 ft. by 55 ft.

15. numerator is -8,
    denominator is -36

16. type A: 150 bags
    type B: 250 bags

17. 5 kilograms of each

Form B

1. No

2. infinitely many

3. $x = -1, \quad y = -3$

4. $x = 3, \quad y = 1$

5. $x = -1, \quad y = \frac{1}{2}$

6. $x = 3, \quad y = -4$

7. $x = \frac{2}{3}, \quad y = 8$

8. $x = -3, \quad y = -2$

9. First number is 8,
   Second number is 5.

10. $x = 6, \quad y = 12$

11. $x = -2, \quad y = -3$

12. -5 and -15

13. $x = \frac{1}{2}, \quad y = \frac{1}{4}$

14. 35° and 65°

15. dictionary is $1\frac{1}{2}$ inches thick
    encyclopedia is 2 inches thick

16. 18 dimes, 9 quarters

17. 8.4 pints of 18% and
    19.6 pints of 20%

18. Answer:

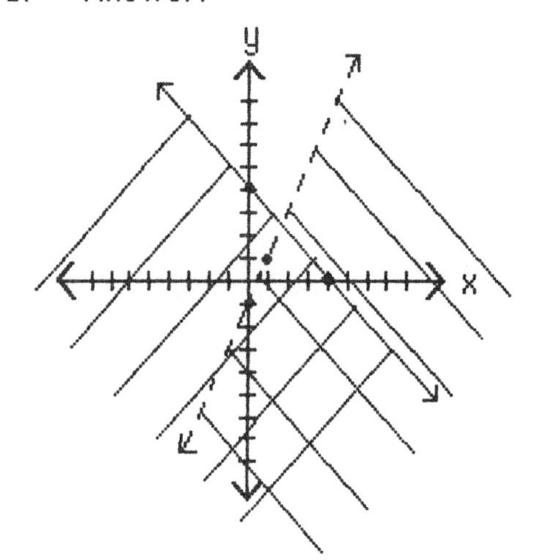

18. Answer:

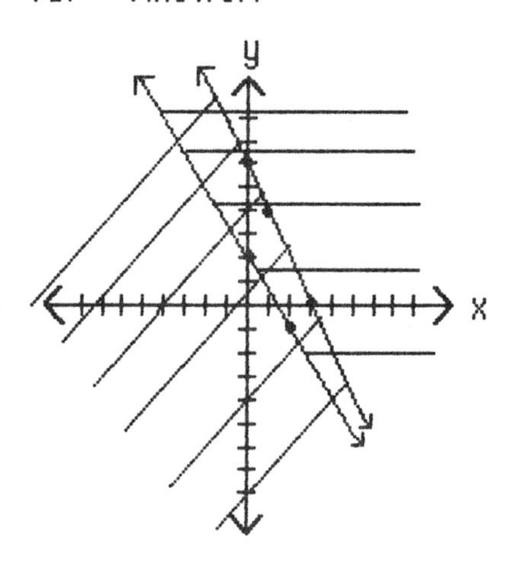

19. Answer:

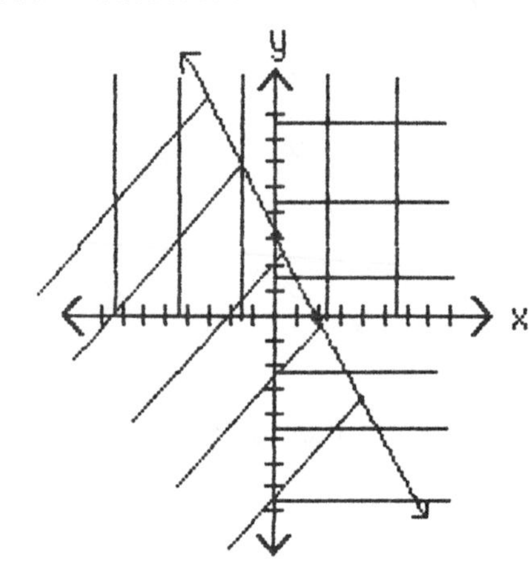

19. Answer:

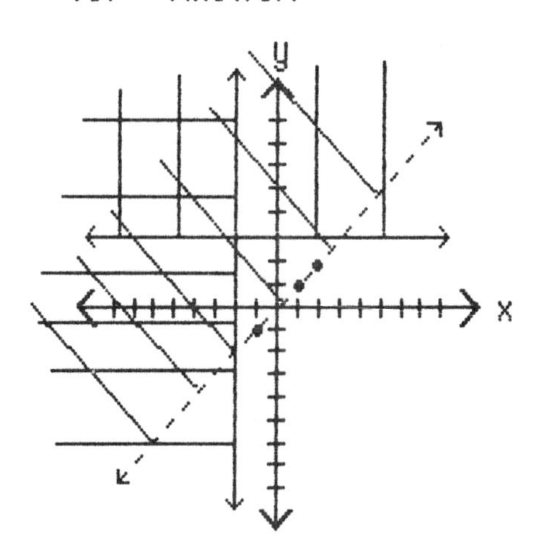

20 Answer:

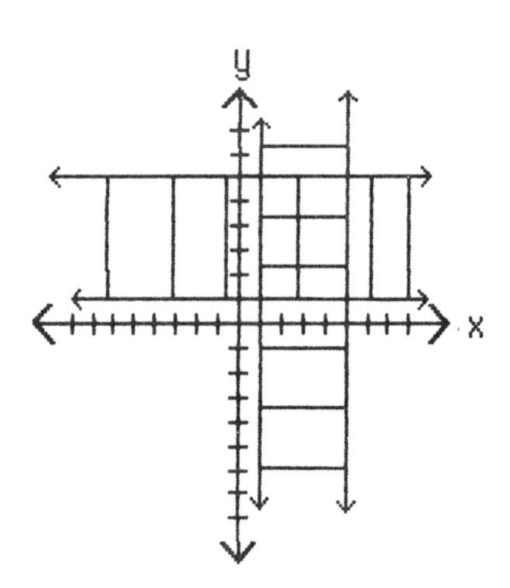

20 Answer:

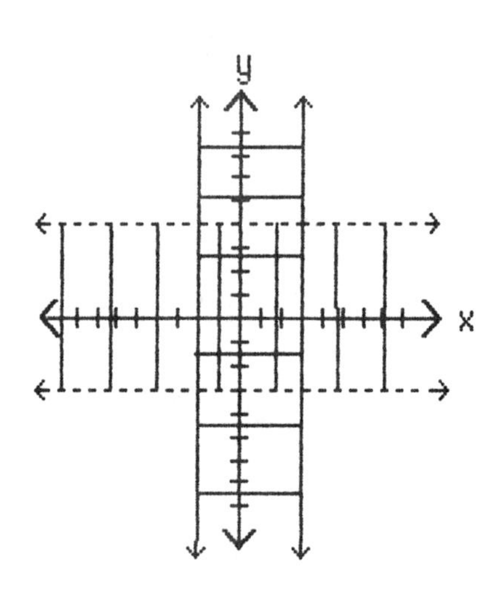

CHAPTER # 7 TEST KEYS

Form C		Form D	
1.	Yes	1.	c) $x = 3, \quad y = 2$
2.	inconsistent	2.	e) None of these
3.	$x = -1, \quad y = 1$	3.	b) $x = -1, \quad y = -3$
4.	same line	4.	a) $x = 2, \quad y = -5$
5.	$a = -\frac{2}{3}, \quad b = -3$	5.	d) $x = -3, \quad y = 1$
6.	$x = 2, \quad y = 4$	6.	b) $x = 7, \quad y = 3$
7.	$x = -24, \quad y = 60$	7.	c) $x = 20, \quad y = 10$
8.	$x = 3, \quad y = -5$	8.	a) $x = -1, \quad y = 4$
9.	first number is 8 second number is -1	9.	e) None of these
10.	$x = 2, \quad y = -1$	10.	c) $x = -2, \quad y = -8$
11.	$x = 0, \quad y = 5$	11.	b) $x = -5, \quad y = -1$
12.	-16 and -12	12.	d) -9 and -12
13.	$x = \frac{5}{8}, \quad y = \frac{1}{4}$	13.	d) $a = \frac{1}{4}, \quad b = \frac{3}{4}$
14.	65° and 115°	14.	a) 45 feet
15.	5% species 900 10% species 300	15.	b) 48
16.	80 students 20 adults	16.	a) 150 bags
17.	airplane 450 km. per hour wind 50 km. per hour	17.	c) 10 kilograms

18. Answer:

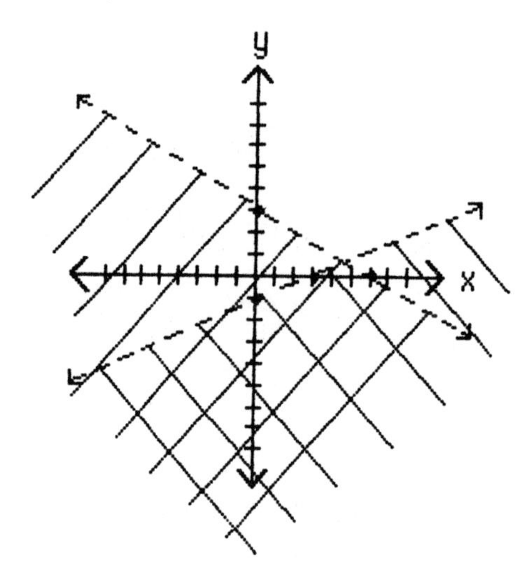

18. c) (3, -1)

19. Answer:

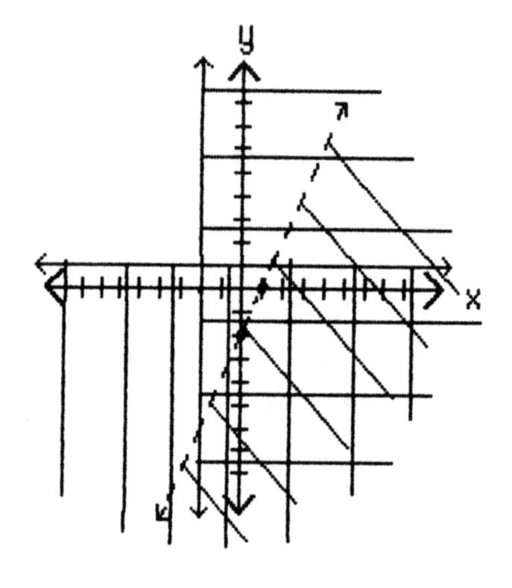

19. a) in the first quadrant

20. Answer:

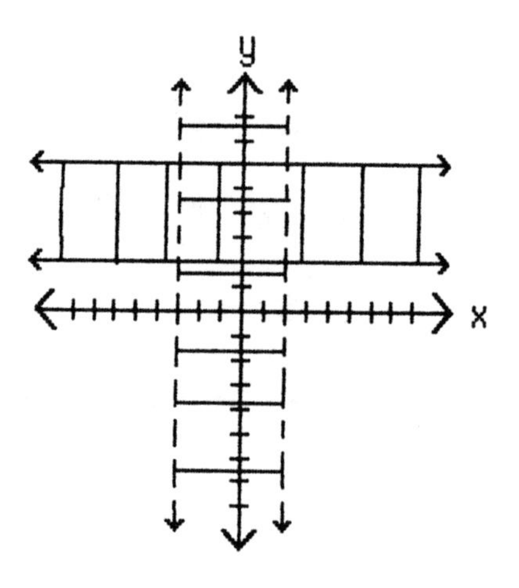

20. d) in the third quadrant

CHAPTER # 7 TEST KEYS

Form E

1. b) $x = 2$, $y = -4$
2. d) dependent
3. a) $x = 3$, $y = -1$
4. e) None of these
5. c) $x = 5$, $y = -4$
6. a) $x = -3$, $y = -7$
7. b) $x = \frac{3}{4}$, $y = \frac{3}{2}$
8. d) $x = -2$, $y = -4$
9. d) 7
10. b) $x = 10$, $y = 16$
11. a) $x = -2$, $y = -6$
12. c) -21
13. c) $x = -\frac{1}{2}$, $y = -\frac{3}{4}$
14. e) None of these
15. a) $2\frac{1}{4}$ inches
16. d) 7 quarters
17. b) 9.6 pints 16%
    14.4 pints 26%
18. b) $(5, -1)$
19. d) the second quadrant
20. c) the third quadrant

Form F

1. a) $x = -4$, $y = -5$
2. c) infinitely many solutions
3. e) None of these
4. d) $x = 3$, $y = -4$
5. b) $a = \frac{2}{3}$, $b = -4$
6. d) $x = 5$, $y = 2$
7. a) $x = -4$, $y = 15$
8. c) $x = 6$, $y = -2$
9. c) 6 and -4
10. a) $x = -2$, $y = 7$
11. e) None of these
12. b) 18
13. a) $x = -\frac{1}{4}$, $y = \frac{3}{8}$
14. d) 130 degrees
15. c) 900 and 600
16. b) 8
17. a) 600 km. per hour
18. d) $(-1, -2)$
19. c) the fourth quadrant
20. b) the second quadrant

Name ____________________ Chapter 8 Form A Score ________

1. Find the two square roots of 81. 1. ____________

2. Find the value of $\sqrt[3]{-125}$ if it exists. 2. ____________

3. Simplify the expression $\sqrt[3]{8a^{12}b^{6}c^{15}}$. 3. ____________

4. Multiply and simplify: $\sqrt{8}\ \sqrt{32}$. 4. ____________

5. Simplify: $\sqrt{\dfrac{2}{16}}$ 5. ____________

6. Simplify: $\sqrt{108}$ 6. ____________

7. Simplify: $\sqrt{\dfrac{9t^5}{2r}}$ 7. ____________

8. Simplify by rationalizing the denominator $\frac{x^2}{\sqrt{8x}}$. 8. ____________

9. Simplify by combining like radicals. 9. ____________

$$2\sqrt{32} - \sqrt{18} + \sqrt{8}$$

10. Simplify: $\frac{\sqrt{18}}{4} + \frac{\sqrt{48}}{6}$ 10. ____________

11. Multiply and simplify: $(4\sqrt{6})(3\sqrt{2})$ 11. ____________

12. Multiply and simplify: $3\sqrt{h}\,(\sqrt{h^3} + 4\sqrt{h})$ 12. ____________

13. Multiply and simplify: $(\sqrt{wt} - 3)(3\sqrt{wt} + 4)$ 13. ____________

14. Multiply $\sqrt{8} - 6$ by its conjugate and simplify the result. 14. ____________

15. Rationalize the denominator and simplify: $\frac{x}{\sqrt{x}+3}$. 15. ____________

16. Solve the radical equation: $\sqrt{z-1} = \frac{1}{2}$ 16. ____________

17. Solve the radical equation: $12 + 3\sqrt{x} = 18$. 17. ____________

18. Solve the radical equation: $3 - w = \sqrt{w^2 - 1}$. 18. ____________

19. The sum of the square root of a number and 3 is 9. Find the number. 19. ____________

20. Evaluate the expression: $\left(\frac{64}{81}\right)^{3/2}$ 20. ____________

21. Use properties of exponents to simplify: $\left(\frac{x^{1/2}}{x^{3/4}}\right)^3$ 21. ____________

22. Replace radicals with rational exponents and simplify: $\sqrt[4]{t^7}$ 22. ____________

23. Write $\sqrt{-49}$ as an imaginary number.

23. ____________

24. Perform the indicated operations and write the answer in the form $a + bi$.

$$-2i + (3 + 2i) + (6 - 5i)$$

24. ____________

25. Perform the indicated operations and write the answer in the form $a + bi$.

$$\frac{6 - 4i}{i}$$

25. ____________

Name ____________________ Chapter 8 Form B Score ________

1. Find the two square roots of $\frac{36}{121}$. 1. ____________

2. Find the value, if it exists of 2. ____________

$\sqrt[4]{256}$

3. Simplify the expression $\sqrt{36w^{12}x^{8}y^{4}}$. 3. ____________

4. Multiply and simplify: $\sqrt[3]{81}\ \sqrt[3]{24}$. 4. ____________

5. Simplify: $\sqrt[3]{\frac{9}{27}}$ 5. ____________

6. Simplify: $\sqrt[3]{16u^{16}}$ 6. ____________

7. Simplify: $\sqrt[3]{\frac{6m}{4n^{4}}}$ 7. ____________

8. Simplify by rationalizing the denominator 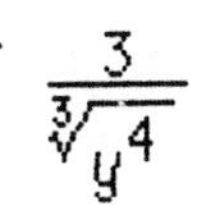 $\frac{3}{\sqrt[3]{y^4}}$.

8. ______________

9. Simplify by combining like radicals.

$\sqrt[3]{54} - 4\sqrt[3]{128} + 5\sqrt[3]{16}$

9. ______________

10. Simplify: $\frac{m^4\sqrt{p}}{4\sqrt{m^2p}} - \frac{m\sqrt{p^3}}{4\sqrt{mp^2}}$

10. ______________

11. Multiply and simplify: $(-8\sqrt{w})(-4\sqrt{w})$

11. ______________

12. Multiply and simplify: $10\sqrt[3]{x^2}\,(3\sqrt[3]{x^2} - 6)$

12. ______________

13. Multiply and simplify: $(5\sqrt{r} - 4\sqrt{t})^2$

13. ______________

14. Multiply $4\sqrt{mn} - 8\sqrt{p}$ by its conjugate and simplify the result.

14. ______________

15. Rationalize the denominator and simplify: $\frac{5\sqrt{3}}{\sqrt{3} + \sqrt{6}}$

15. ______________

16. Solve the radical equation: $\sqrt{2x + 3} = -1$ 16. ____________

17. Solve the radical equation: $2\sqrt{5w} + 3 = 9$. 17. ____________

18. Solve the radical equation: $\sqrt{4x + 17} - 3 = x$ 18. ____________

19. The product of the square root of a number and the square root of the sum of the number and 7 is 12. Find the number. 19. ____________

20. Evaluate the expression: $\left(-\frac{81}{16}\right)^{-1/4}$ 20. ____________

21. Use properties of exponents to simplify: 21. ____________

$(-3x^{2/3}y^{3/2})^6$

22. Replace radicals with rational exponents and 22. ____________

simplify: $\frac{\sqrt[3]{y^5}}{\sqrt[5]{y^3}}$

23. Write $-\sqrt{-121}$ as an imaginary number.

23. ____________

24. Perform the indicated operations and write the answer in the form $a + bi$.

$$18i - (2 + 3i) + (4 + i)$$

24. ____________

25. Perform the indicated operations and write the answer in the form $a + bi$.

$$\frac{6 + 12i}{3i}$$

25. ____________

Name ____________________ Chapter 8 Form C Score ________

1. Find the two square roots of 0.04 . 1. ____________

2. Find the value, if it exists of 2. ____________

$-\sqrt[3]{-\frac{27}{64}}$

3. Simplify the expression: 3. ____________

$\sqrt[4]{16x^{12}y^{16}z^{8}}$

4. Multiply and simplify: 4. ____________

$\sqrt[4]{4x^5} \quad \sqrt[4]{4x^3}$

5. Simplify: 5. ____________

$\sqrt[4]{\frac{x^2}{16y^6}}$

6. Simplify: $-\sqrt{54w^3s^9}$ 6. ____________

7. Simplify:

$$\sqrt{\frac{3a^3}{16d^5}}$$

7. ____________

8. Simplify by rationalizing the denominator

$$\frac{4x}{\sqrt[4]{x^3}}$$

8. ____________

9. Simplify by combining like radicals.

$$5\sqrt{50a^5} - 4a\sqrt{98a^3}$$

9. ____________

10. Simplify: $\dfrac{5\sqrt{20}}{\sqrt{45}} - \dfrac{8\sqrt{5}}{\sqrt{50}}$

10. ____________

11. Multiply and simplify: $(3\sqrt{x^3})(7\sqrt{8x^4})$

11. ____________

12. Multiply and simplify: $5\sqrt{14y}\,(\sqrt{2y} + 3\sqrt{21y^3})$

12. ____________

13. Multiply and simplify: $(2 - \sqrt[3]{4})(2 + \sqrt[3]{4})$ 13. ____________

14. Multiply $\sqrt{10} + 6\sqrt{8}$ by its conjugate and simplify the result. 14. ____________

15. Rationalize the denominator and simplify: $\dfrac{9 + \sqrt{m}}{3\sqrt{m} - 6}$ 15. ____________

16. Solve the radical equation: $\sqrt{4 - 3x} = \dfrac{1}{2}$ 16. ____________

17. Solve the radical equation: $\sqrt{8r} = 4\sqrt{3}$. 17. ____________

18. Solve the radical equation: $\sqrt{2x - 3} - \sqrt{x - 2} = 1$ 18. ____________

19. The cube root of the sum of a number and 4 is -3. Find the number. 19. ____________

20. Evaluate the expression: $64^{-1/3} - 9^{-1/2}$ 20. ____________

21. Use properties of exponents to simplify:

$$\left(\frac{m^{-2/3}}{w^{-1/3}}\right)^6$$

21. ______________

22. Replace radicals with rational exponents and simplify: $\sqrt[3]{\sqrt{m}}$

22. 

23. Write $-\sqrt{-150}$ as an imaginary number.

23. ______________

24. Perform the indicated operations and write the answer in the form $a + bi$.

$$3 - (6 + 2i) - (1 - 8i)$$

24. ______________

25. Perform the indicated operations and write the answer in the form $a + bi$.

$$\frac{3 + i}{6 - 2i}$$

25. ______________

Name ____________________ Chapter 8 Form D Score ______

1. Find the two square roots of 169. 1. ____________

   a. 43 and - 43
   b. $84\frac{1}{2}$ and $-84\frac{1}{2}$
   c. 13 and -13
   d. 1 and 13
   e. None of these

2. Find the value of $\sqrt[3]{-216}$ if it exists. 2. ____________

   a. -6
   b. 6
   c. -8
   d. -72
   e. None of these

3. Simplify the expression $\sqrt[3]{-m^6n^9p^{15}}$ 3. ____________

   a. $-m^3n^6p^{12}$
   b. $-m^2n^6p^5$
   c. $-m^3n^3p^5$
   d. $-m^2n^3p^5$
   e. None of these

4. Multiply and simplify: $\sqrt{6r}\ \sqrt{24r}$ 4. ____________

   a. 12r
   b. 36r
   c. 72r
   d. 24r
   e. None of these

5. Simplify: 5. ____________

$$\sqrt{\frac{6}{36x}}$$

   a. $\frac{\sqrt{6x}}{x}$
   b. $\frac{\sqrt{6x}}{6x}$
   c. 1
   d. $\frac{1}{6x}$
   e. None of these

6. Simplify: $\sqrt{162}$ 6. ____________

a. 81
b. $6\sqrt{2}$
c. $81\sqrt{2}$
d. $\frac{9\sqrt{2}}{2}$
e. None of these

7. Simplify: 7. ____________

$$\sqrt{\frac{25u^3}{5w}}$$

a. $\frac{\sqrt{5u^3w}}{w}$

b. $\frac{u\sqrt{uw}}{w}$

c. $\frac{u\sqrt{5uw}}{w}$

d. $\frac{u\sqrt{uw}}{5w}$

e. None of these

8. Simplify by rationalizing the denominator 8. ____________

$$\frac{y^3}{\sqrt{32y}}$$

a. $\frac{y}{32}$

b. $\frac{y^2\sqrt{2y}}{4}$

c. $\frac{\sqrt{2}\ y^2}{8}$

d. $\frac{y^2\sqrt{2y}}{8}$

e. None of these

9. Simplify by combining like radicals. 9. ____________

$$5\sqrt{180} - \sqrt{125} - \sqrt{245}$$

a. $5\sqrt{190}$
b. $18\sqrt{5}$
c. $53\sqrt{5}$
d. $106\sqrt{5}$
e. None of these

10. Simplify: $\dfrac{\sqrt{18}}{6} + \dfrac{\sqrt{48}}{4}$ 10. ____________

a. $\dfrac{3\sqrt{2} + 8\sqrt{3}}{2}$
b. $\dfrac{\sqrt{2} + 3\sqrt{3}}{2}$
c. $\dfrac{\sqrt{66}}{10}$
d. $\dfrac{\sqrt{2} + 2\sqrt{3}}{2}$
e. None of these

11. Multiply and simplify: $(6\sqrt{10})(5\sqrt{2})$ 11. ____________

a. $30\sqrt{20}$
b. $10\sqrt{6}$
c. $60\sqrt{5}$
d. $120\sqrt{5}$
e. None of these

12. Multiply and simplify: $7\sqrt{a}\,(\sqrt{a^5} - 3\sqrt{a})$ 12. ____________

a. $7a^3 - 3a$
b. $7a^3 - 21a$
c. $-21a^2\sqrt{a}$
d. $7a^3 - 3\sqrt{a}$
e. None of these

13. Multiply and simplify: $(\sqrt{xy} - 9)(6\sqrt{xy} + 3)$ 13. ____________

a. $6xy - 51\sqrt{xy} - 27$
b. $6xy - 27$
c. $6xy - 57\sqrt{xy} - 27$
d. $-45\sqrt{xy} - 27$
e. None of these

14. Multiply $\sqrt{12} + 4$ by its conjugate and simplify the result. 14. ____________

a. 108
b. 8
c. -4
d. 28
e. None of these

15. Rationalize the denominator and simplify: $\frac{y}{4 - \sqrt{y}}$ 15. ____________

a. $\frac{\sqrt{y}}{3}$

b. $\frac{y\sqrt{y}}{4 - y}$

c. $\frac{4y + y\sqrt{y}}{4 - y}$

d. $\frac{4y + y\sqrt{y}}{16 - y}$

e. None of these

16. Solve the radical equation: $\sqrt{y + 2} = \frac{2}{3}$ 16. ____________

a. $y = -\frac{14}{9}$

b. $y = \frac{22}{9}$

c. $y = -\frac{2}{3}$

d. $y = \frac{2}{9}$

e. None of these

17. Solve the radical equation: $13 - 2\sqrt{y} = 9$. 17. ____________

a. $y = 22$
b. $y = 4$
c. $y = 6$
d. $y = \sqrt{2}$
e. None of these

18. Solve the radical equation: $\sqrt{2x^2 + 5x} = x + 10$ 18. ____________

a. $x = 20$
b. $x = 20$ or $x = -5$
c. $x = -5$
d. $x = 5$
e. None of these

19. The sum of the square root of twice a number and 5 is 11. Find the number. 19. ____________

a. 58
b. 48
c. 18
d. 128
e. None of these

20. Evaluate the expression: 20. ____________

$$\left(\frac{25}{144}\right)^{3/2}$$

a. $\frac{125}{512}$
b. $\frac{15}{36}$
c. $\frac{125}{1728}$
d. $\frac{25}{96}$
e. None of these

21. Use properties of exponents to simplify: 21. ____________

$$(y^{3/8} \cdot y^{1/4})^4$$

a. $y^{5/4}$

b. $y^{3/8}$

c. $y^{11/8}$

d. $y^{3/2}$

e. None of these

22. Replace radicals with rational exponents and simplify: $\sqrt[6]{m^3}$

22. ____________

a. m^2

b. $m^{1/3}$

c. m^3

d. $m^{1/2}$

e. none of these

23. Write $\sqrt{-196}$ as an imaginary number.

23. ____________

a. $14i$
b. $28i$
c. -14
d. $-14i$
e. None of these

24. Perform the indicated operations and write the answer in the form $a + bi$.

24. ____________

$$7 + (2 - 8i) + (-3 + 15i)$$

a. $12 + 7i$
b. $13i$
c. $6 + 23i$
d. $6 + 7i$
e. None of these

25. Perform the indicated operations and write the answer in the form $a + bi$.

25. ____________

$$\frac{9 - 5i}{i}$$

a. $-5 + 9i$
b. $5 + 9i$
c. 4
d. $5 - 9i$
e. None of these

Name ______________________ Chapter 8 Form E Score ________

1. Find the two square roots of $\frac{25}{81}$.

1. 

a. 1 and $\frac{5}{9}$

b. 1 and $-\frac{5}{9}$

c. $\frac{12.5}{40.5}$ and $-\frac{12.5}{40.5}$

d. $\frac{5}{9}$ and $-\frac{5}{9}$

e. None of these

2. Find the value, if it exists of

2. 

$\sqrt[4]{(-3)^4}$

a. -3

b. 3

c. 9

d. -9

e. None of these

3. Simplify the expression $\sqrt{144t^4w^{16}z^{36}}$

3. ______________

a. $12t^2w^8z^{18}$

b. $72t^2w^4z^6$

c. $12t^2w^4z^6$

d. $72t^2w^8z^{18}$

e. None of these

4. Multiply and simplify: $\sqrt[3]{xy^2}\ \sqrt[3]{-27x^2y}$

4. 

a. $-3xy^2$

b. $-3xy$

c. $-3\sqrt[3]{x^2y^2}$

d. $-9xy$

e. None of these

5. Simplify: 5. ____________

$$\sqrt[4]{\frac{8}{256}}$$

a. 1/32

b. $\frac{\sqrt{2}}{4}$

c. $\frac{\sqrt[4]{8}}{4}$

d. 1/2

e. None of these

6. Simplify: $\sqrt[3]{24w^8}$ 6. ____________

a. $2w^2\sqrt[3]{3w^2}$

b. $2w^4\sqrt[3]{3}$

c. $8w^2\sqrt[3]{w^2}$

d. $2w^3\sqrt[3]{3w^2}$

e. None of these

7. Simplify: 7. ____________

$$\sqrt[3]{\frac{16x}{9y^5}}$$

a. $\frac{4\sqrt{xy}}{3y^3}$

b. $\frac{2\sqrt[3]{2xy}}{3y^2}$

c. $\frac{2\sqrt[3]{18xy^2}}{9y^3}$

d. $\frac{2\sqrt[3]{6xy}}{3y^2}$

e. None of these

8. Simplify by rationalizing the denominator

$$\frac{5}{\sqrt[3]{w^5}}$$

8. ______________

a. $\frac{5\sqrt{w}}{w^3}$

b. $\frac{5}{w}$

c. $\frac{5\sqrt{w}}{w^2}$

d. $\frac{5\sqrt[3]{w^2}}{w^3}$

e. None of these

9. Simplify by combining like radicals.

$$4\sqrt[3]{32} - 3\sqrt[3]{108} + 4\sqrt[3]{256}$$

9. ______________

a. $11\sqrt[3]{4}$

b. $5\sqrt[3]{4}$

c. $15\sqrt[3]{4}$

d. $16\sqrt[3]{2} - 18\sqrt[3]{3} + 64$

e. None of these

10. Simplify: $$\frac{2w^4\sqrt{x}}{4\sqrt{w^2x}} - \frac{w\sqrt{x^3}}{4\sqrt{wx^2}}$$

10. ______________

a. $\frac{2w^3 - \sqrt{xw}}{4}$

b. $\frac{2w^3 - w\sqrt{x}}{4w}$

c. $\frac{2w^4 - \sqrt{w}}{4w}$

d. $\frac{w^3 - \sqrt{xw}}{2}$

e. None of these

11. Multiply and simplify: $(-9\sqrt{y})(6\sqrt{y})$ 11. ____________

a. $-54y^2$

b. $-3\sqrt{y}$

c. $-54\sqrt{2y}$

d. $-54y$

e. None of these

12. Multiply and simplify: $12\sqrt[3]{m^4}\,(3\sqrt[3]{m^2} - 4)$ 12. ____________

a. $36m^2 - 48\sqrt[3]{m^4}$

b. $36m^3 - 48m\sqrt[3]{m}$

c. $36m^2 - 48m\sqrt[3]{m}$

d. $36m^2 - 4$

e. None of these

13. Multiply and simplify: $(6\sqrt{2x} + 3\sqrt{6y})^2$ 13. ____________

a. $72x + 54y$

b. $72x + 36\sqrt{3xy} + 54y$

c. $72x + 72\sqrt{3xy} + 54y$

d. $72x + 18\sqrt{12xy} + 54y$

e. None of these

14. Multiply $7\sqrt{wx} + 5\sqrt{y}$ by its conjugate and simplify. 14. ____________

a. $49wx + 70\sqrt{wxy} + 25y$
b. $7wx - 5y$
c. $49wx + 70\sqrt{wxy} + 25y$
d. $49wx - 25y$
e. None of these

15. Rationalize the denominator and simplify: $\frac{8\sqrt{6}}{\sqrt{6} - \sqrt{8}}$ 15. ____________

a. $-24 + 16\sqrt{3}$

b. $-24 - 16\sqrt{3}$

c. $-24 - 12\sqrt{3}$

d. $-8\sqrt{3}$

e. None of these

16. Solve the radical equation: $\sqrt{4x - 6} = -3$ 16. ____________

a. $x = \frac{15}{4}$

b. $x = \frac{3}{4}$

c. $x = \frac{4}{15}$

d. $x = \frac{4}{3}$

e. None of these

17. Solve the radical equation: $4\sqrt{6x} - 1 = 11$. 17. ____________

a. $x = \frac{2}{3}$

b. $x = \frac{5}{4}$

c. $x = \frac{3}{2}$

d. $x = \frac{25}{24}$

e. None of these

18. Solve the radical equation: $\sqrt{5x + 4} - x = -2$ 18. ____________

a. $x = 0$, or $x = -5$
b. $x = 0$
c. $x = 9$
d. $x = 0$, or $x = 9$
e. None of these

19. The product of the square root of a number and the square root of the difference of the number and 3 is 2. Find the number. 19. ____________

a. -1
b. 1 or 2
c. 4 or -1
d. 4
e. None of these

20. Evaluate the expression: 20. ____________

$$\left(\frac{256}{16}\right)^{-1/4}$$

a. 2

b. -2

c. $\frac{1}{11}$

d. $\frac{1}{2}$

e. None of these

21. Use properties of exponents to simplify: 21. ____________

$$(-2x^{3/4}y^{-1/2})^8$$

a. $\frac{256x^6}{y^4}$

b. $\frac{x^6}{256y^4}$

c. $-256x^6y^4$

d. $\frac{-2x^6}{y^4}$

e. None of these

22. Replace radicals with rational exponents and simplify: $\dfrac{\sqrt[4]{m^3}}{\sqrt[6]{m^5}}$ 22. ____________

a. $m^{9/10}$

b. $\dfrac{1}{m}$

c. $m^{-1/12}$

d. $m^{19/12}$

e. None of these

23. Write $-\sqrt{-324}$ as an imaginary number. 23. ____________

a. $18i$
b. $-18i$
c. 18
d. -18
e. None of these

24. Perform the indicated operations and write the answer in the form $a + bi$. 24. ____________

$$21i - (-4 - 6i) + (7 + i)$$

a. $11 + 28i$
b. $3 + 28i$
c. $11 + 16i$
d. $3 + 16i$
e. None of these

25. Perform the indicated operations and write the answer in the form $a + bi$. 25. ____________

$$\frac{9 + 15i}{3i}$$

a. $9 + 5i$
b. $3 + 5i$
c. $5 - 3i$
d. $-5 + 3i$
e. None of these

Name ______________________ Chapter 8 Form F Score ________

1. Find the two square roots of 0.64. 1. ____________

a. 0.08 and -0.08
b. 0.8 and -0.8
c. 2 and 0.32
d. 0.32 and -0.32
e. None of these

2. Find the value, if it exists of 2. ____________

$$\sqrt[5]{-\frac{1}{16}}$$

a. $-\frac{1}{80}$

b. $-\frac{3}{10}$

c. $-\frac{1}{2}$

d. $\frac{1}{2}$

e. None of these

3. Simplify the expression: 3. ____________

$$\sqrt[4]{81p^{16}q^{8}t^{4}}$$

a. $20\frac{1}{4}p^4q^2t$

b. $3p^4q^2t$

c. $9p^4q^2t$

d. $3p^4q^4t$

e. None of these

4. Multiply and simplify:

$\sqrt[4]{128x^2}\ \sqrt[4]{8x^6}$

a. $4x\ \sqrt[4]{4x^2}$

b. $32x^2$

c. $4x^2\sqrt[4]{4}$

d. $4x^3\sqrt[4]{4}$

e. None of these

4. ____________

5. Simplify:

$\sqrt[3]{\frac{-m^2}{16n^{12}}}$

a. $-\frac{\sqrt[3]{4m^2}}{4n^4}$

b. $-\frac{\sqrt[3]{2m^2}}{4n^4}$

c. $-\frac{\sqrt[3]{m^2}}{n^4}$

d. $-\frac{\sqrt[3]{m^2}}{4n^4}$

e. None of these

5. ____________

6. Simplify: $-\sqrt{48x^9y^7}$

6. ____________

a. $-24x^4y^3\sqrt{xy}$

b. $-16x^4y^3\sqrt{3xy}$

c. $-4x^3y^3\sqrt{3y}$

d. $-4x^4y^3\sqrt{3xy}$

e. None of these

7. Simplify: 7. ____________

$$\sqrt{\frac{10w^3}{25y^7}}$$

a. $\frac{w\sqrt{10wy}}{5y^4}$

b. $\frac{w\sqrt{2w}}{y^3}$

c. $\frac{w\sqrt{10wy}}{5y^3}$

d. $\frac{w\sqrt{10wy}}{5y^5}$

e. None of these

8. Simplify by rationalizing the denominator 8. ____________

$$\frac{6y}{\sqrt[4]{y^7}}$$

a. $\frac{6\sqrt[4]{y}}{y^3}$

b. $\frac{6\sqrt[4]{y}}{y}$

c. $\frac{6\sqrt[4]{y^3}}{y^3}$

d. $\frac{6\sqrt[4]{y^3}}{y^5}$

e. None of these

9. Simplify by combining like terms: 9. ____________

$$2\sqrt{108x^7} - 3x\sqrt{4x^5}$$

a. $6x^3\sqrt{x}$

b. $6x^3\sqrt{2x}$

c. $12x^3\sqrt{3x} - 6x^5\sqrt{x}$

d. $72x^3\sqrt{3x} - 12x^3\sqrt{x}$

e. None of these

10. Simplify: $\dfrac{2\sqrt{72}}{\sqrt{98}} - \dfrac{3\sqrt{8}}{\sqrt{12}}$ 10. ____________

a. $36 - \sqrt{6}$

b. $\dfrac{9\sqrt{6}}{4}$

c. $\dfrac{12 - 7\sqrt{6}}{7}$

d. $\dfrac{12 - 3\sqrt{2}}{7}$

e. None of these

11. Multiply and simplify: $(12\sqrt{a^5})(-4\sqrt{27a^6})$ 11. ____________

a. $-144a^5\sqrt{3a}$

b. $-45a^5\sqrt{3a}$

c. $-432a^5\sqrt{3a}$

d. $-144a^{15}\sqrt{3}$

e. None of these

12. Multiply and simplify: $3\sqrt{18z}\,(\sqrt{2z} - 6\sqrt{8z^3})$ 12. ____________

a. $18z - 12z\sqrt{2z}$

b. $18z - 30z^2$

c. $12z^3$

d. $18z - 216z^2$

e. None of these

13. Multiply and simplify: $(6 - \sqrt[3]{9})(6 + \sqrt[3]{9})$ 13. ____________

a. $33\sqrt[3]{3}$

b. $36 - 12\sqrt[3]{9} - 3\sqrt[3]{3}$

c. $36 - 3\sqrt[3]{3}$

d. 27

e. None of these

14. Multiply $\sqrt{14} - 7\sqrt{12}$ by its conjugate and simplify.

14. ______________

a. $14 - 98\sqrt{3}$
b. -420
c. $-84\sqrt{3}$
d. $602 - 28\sqrt{42}$
e. None of these

15. Rationalize the denominator and simplify: $\dfrac{10 - \sqrt{y}}{2 + \sqrt{y}}$

15. ______________

a. $\dfrac{20 - 10\sqrt{y} + y}{4 - y}$
b. 4
c. $\dfrac{20 - y}{4 - y}$
d. $4 - 12\sqrt{y}$
e. None of these

16. Solve the radical equation: $\sqrt{9 - 5x} = \dfrac{3}{4}$

16. ______________

a. $x = \dfrac{3}{2}$
b. $x = -\dfrac{153}{8}$
c. $x = \dfrac{27}{16}$
d. $x = \dfrac{18 - \sqrt{3}}{10}$
e. None of these

17. Solve the radical equation: $\sqrt{12t} = 6\sqrt{2}$.

17. ______________

a. $t = 1$
b. $t = 12$
c. $t = \dfrac{1}{6}$
d. $t = 6$
e. None of these

18. Solve the radical equation: $\sqrt{7-n} + \sqrt{n+11} = 6$ 18. ____________

a. $n = -9$
b. $n = 9$
c. $n = 2$
d. $n = -2$
e. None of these

19. The cube root of the sum of twice a number and 3 is 3. Find the number. 19. ____________

a. $x = 3$
b. $x = 12$
c. $x = 15$
d. $x = \frac{15}{2}$
e. None of these

20. Evaluate the expression: $(-27)^{-1/3} - 36^{-1/2}$ 20. ____________

a. $-\frac{1}{2}$
b. 9
c. $-\frac{1}{6}$
d. $-\frac{1}{3}$
e. None of these

21. Use properties of exponents to simplify: 21. ____________

$$\left(\frac{a^{-5/6}}{b^{-2/3}}\right)^{12}$$

a. $\frac{a^{10}}{b^8}$

b. $\frac{b^8}{a^{10}}$

c. $-\frac{a^{10}}{b^8}$

d. $-\frac{b^8}{a^{10}}$

e. None of these

22. Replace radicals with rational exponents and simplify: $\sqrt[5]{\sqrt[4]{m^3}}$

22. ____________

a. $m^{20/3}$

b. $m^{3/20}$

c. $m^{15/4}$

d. $m^{19/20}$

e. None of these

23. Write $-\sqrt{-98}$ as an imaginary number.

23. ____________

a. $7i\sqrt{2}$
b. $7\sqrt{2}$
c. $-7\sqrt{2}$
d. $-7i\sqrt{2}$
e. None of these

24. Perform the indicated operations and write the answer in the form $a + bi$.

$$8 - (5 + 11i) - (2 - 4i)$$

24. ____________

a. $1 - 3i$
b. $1 - 15i$
c. $1 - 7i$
d. $1 + 7i$
e. None of these

25. Perform the indicated operations and write the answer in the form $a + bi$.

$$\frac{6 + 3i}{9 - 6i}$$

25. ____________

a. $\frac{4}{13} + \frac{7}{13}i$

b. $\frac{2}{3} - \frac{1}{2}i$

c. $\frac{8}{13} + \frac{7}{13}i$

d. $\frac{6}{13} + \frac{2}{13}i$

e. None of these

CHAPTER # 8 TEST KEYS

Form A

1. 9 and -9
2. -5
3. $2a^4b^2c^5$
4. 16
5. $\frac{\sqrt{2}}{4}$
6. $6\sqrt{3}$
7. $\frac{3t^2\sqrt{2rt}}{2r}$
8. $\frac{x\sqrt{2x}}{4}$
9. $7\sqrt{2}$
10. $\frac{9\sqrt{2} + 8\sqrt{3}}{12}$
11. $24\sqrt{3}$
12. $3h^2 + 12h$
13. $3wt - 5\sqrt{wt} - 12$
14. -28
15. $\frac{x(\sqrt{x} - 3)}{x - 9}$
16. $z = \frac{5}{4}$
17. $x = 4$

Form B

1. $\frac{6}{11}$ and $-\frac{6}{11}$
2. 4
3. $6w^6x^4y^2$
4. $6\sqrt[3]{9}$
5. $\frac{\sqrt[3]{9}}{3}$
6. $2a^5\sqrt[3]{2a}$
7. $\frac{\sqrt[3]{12mn^2}}{2n^2}$
8. $\frac{3\sqrt[3]{y^2}}{y^2}$
9. $-3\sqrt[3]{2}$
10. $\frac{m^3 - \sqrt{pm}}{4}$
11. 32w
12. $30x\sqrt[3]{x} - 60\sqrt[3]{x^2}$
13. $25r - 40\sqrt{rt} + 16t$
14. $16mn - 64p$
15. $-5 + 5\sqrt{2}$
16. No solution
17. $w = \frac{9}{5}$

18. $w = \frac{5}{3}$

19. 36

20. $\frac{512}{729}$

21. $\frac{1}{x^{3/4}}$

22. $t^{7/4}$

23. $7i$

24. $9 - 5i$

25. $-4 - 6i$

18. $x = 2$

19. 9

20. not a Real number

21. $799x^4y^9$

22. $y^{16/15}$

23. $-11i$

24. $2 + 16i$

25. $4 - 2i$

CHAPTER # 8 TEST KEYS

Form C

1. 0.2

2. $\frac{3}{4}$

3. $2x^3y^4z^2$

4. $2x^2$

5. Answer:

$$\frac{\sqrt[4]{x^2y^2}}{2y^2}$$

6. $-3ws^4\sqrt{6ws}$

7. $\frac{a\sqrt{3ad}}{4d^3}$

8. Answer:

$4\sqrt[4]{x}$

9. $-3a^2\sqrt{2a}$

10. $\frac{50 - 12\sqrt{10}}{15}$

11. $42x^3\sqrt{2x}$

12. $10y\sqrt{7} + 105y^2\sqrt{6}$

13. $4 - 2\sqrt[3]{2}$

14. -277

15. $\frac{m + 11\sqrt{m} + 18}{3m - 12}$

Form D

1. c) 13 and -13

2. a) -6

3. d) $-m^2n^3p^5$

4. a) $12r$

5. b) $\frac{\sqrt{6x}}{6x}$

6. e) None of these

7. c) $\frac{u\sqrt{5uw}}{w}$

8. d)

$$\frac{y^2\sqrt{2y}}{8}$$

9. b) $18\sqrt{5}$

10. d) $\frac{\sqrt{2} + 2\sqrt{3}}{2}$

11. c) $60\sqrt{5}$

12. b) $7a^3 - 21a$

13. a) $6xy - 51\sqrt{xy} - 27$

14. c) -4

15. d) $\frac{4y + y\sqrt{y}}{16 - y}$

16. $x = \frac{5}{4}$

17. $r = 6$

18. $x = 2$

19. -31

20. $-\frac{1}{12}$

21. $\frac{w^2}{m^4}$

22. $m^{1/6}$

23. $-5i\sqrt{6}$

24. $-4 + 6i$

25. $\frac{2}{5} + \frac{1}{20}i$

16. a) $y = -\frac{14}{9}$

17. b) $y = 4$

18. b) $x = 20$ or $x = -5$

19. c) 18

20. c) $\frac{125}{1728}$

21. e) None of these

22. d) $m^{1/2}$

23. a) $14i$

24. d) $6 + 7i$

25. b) $5 + 9i$

CHAPTER # 8 TEST KEYS

Form E

1. d) $\frac{5}{9}$ and $-\frac{5}{9}$
2. b) 3
3. a) $12t^2w^8z^{18}$
4. b) $-3xy$
5. c) $\frac{\sqrt[4]{8}}{4}$
6. a) $2w^2\sqrt[3]{3w^2}$
7. d) $\frac{2\sqrt[3]{6xy}}{3y^2}$
8. e) None of these
9. c) $15\sqrt[3]{4}$
10. a) $\frac{2w^3 - \sqrt{xw}}{4}$
11. d) $-54y$
12. c) $36m^2 - 48m\sqrt[3]{m}$
13. b) $72x + 18\sqrt{12xy} + 54y$
14. d) $49wx - 25y$

Form F

1. b) 0.8 and -0.8
2. c) $-\frac{1}{2}$
3. b) $3p^4q^2t$
4. c) $4x^2\sqrt[4]{4x^2}$
5. a) $-\frac{\sqrt[3]{4m^2}}{4n^2}$
6. d) $-4x^4y^3\sqrt{3xy}$
7. a) $\frac{w\sqrt{10wy}}{5y^4}$
8. b) $\frac{6\sqrt[4]{y}}{y}$
9. e) None of these
10. c) $\frac{12 - 7\sqrt{6}}{7}$
11. a) $-144a^5\sqrt{3a}$
12. d) $18z - 216z^2$
13. c) $36 - 3\sqrt[3]{3}$
14. e) None of these

15. b) $-24 - 12\sqrt{3}$

16. e) None of these

17. c) $x = \frac{3}{2}$

18. c) $x = 9$

19. d) 4

20. d) $\frac{1}{2}$

21. a) $\frac{256x^6}{y^4}$

22. c) $m^{-1/12}$

23. b) $-18i$

24. a) $11 + 28i$

25. c) $5 - 3i$

15. a) $\frac{20 - 10\sqrt{y} + y}{4 - y}$

16. c) $x = \frac{27}{16}$

17. d) $t = 6$

18. d) $n = -2$

19. b) $x = 12$

20. a) $-\frac{1}{2}$

21. b) $\frac{b^8}{a^{10}}$

22. b) $m^{3/20}$

23. d) $-7i\sqrt{2}$

24. c) $1 - 7i$

25. a) $\frac{4}{13} + \frac{7}{13}i$

Name ______________________ Chapter 9 Form A Score ______

1. Solve the equation: $x^2 = 144$ 1. ____________

2. Solve the equation: $(x + 3)^2 = 81$ 2. ____________

3. From the given right triangle, express s in terms of c. 3. ____________

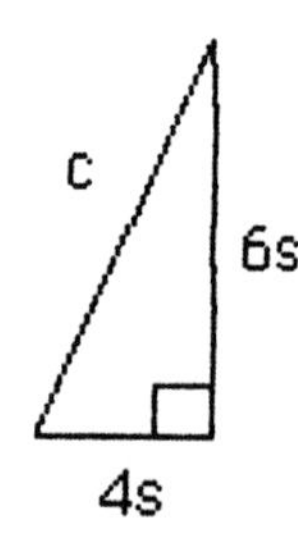

4. The volume of a rectangular solid with a square base is given by $V = hs^2$. If the volume is 324 cubic inches and the height is 9 inches, what is the length of a side of the square base? 4. ____________

5. What constant must be added to $x^2 - 12x$ to make a perfect square trinomial? 5. ____________

6. Solve the equation by completing the square: 6. ____________

$$x^2 - 6x = 12$$

7. Solve the equation by completing the square: 7. ____________

$$4t^2 + 8t = 1$$

8. Use the quadratic formula to solve:

$$2x^2 + 4x - 3 = 0$$

8. ______________

9. Use the quadratic formula to solve:

$$-30 = x^2 - 11x$$

9. ______________

10. Solve using the quadratic formula. Then approximate the solutions to the nearest tenth.

$$2x^2 - x - 2 = 0$$

10. ______________

11. Solve the quadratic equation $x(3x - 4) = 6$

11. ______________

12. Solve: $n + 3 = \frac{4}{n}$

12. ______________

13. Solve the quadratic equation. Write all solutions that are complex numbers in standard form.

$$x^2 + 16 = 0$$

13. ______________

14. Solve the quadratic equation. Write all solutions that are complex numbers in standard form.

$$x^2 + 2x - 2 = 0$$

14. ______________

15. Solve the quadratic equation. Write all solutions that are complex numbers in standard form. 15. ____________

$$(t - 3)^2 = 2t$$

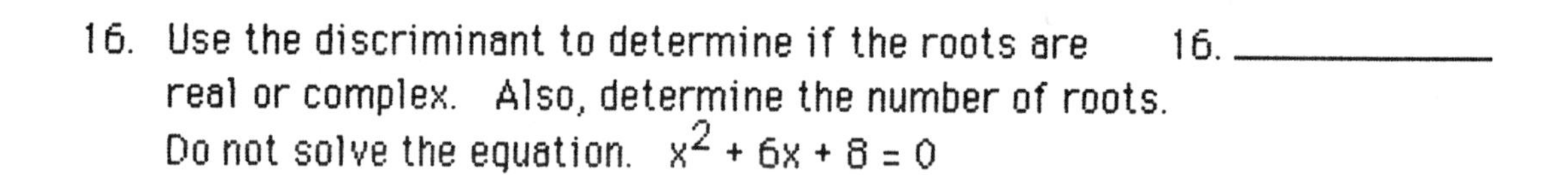

16. Use the discriminant to determine if the roots are real or complex. Also, determine the number of roots. Do not solve the equation. $x^2 + 6x + 8 = 0$ 16. ____________

17. A skier accelerates as he travels downhill. The distance s traveled in t seconds is given by $s = 10t^2 + 10t$ (feet). How long does it take him to go 560 feet downhill? 17. ____________

18. One number is three times another number. If their product is 18, find the two numbers. 18. ____________

19. A city lot in the shape of a rectangle has an area of 1000 square meters. If its length is 10 meters more than two times its width, what are its dimensions? 19. ____________

20. Big Heel Company makes and sells x dozen pair of boots per day. The daily cost C is given by $C = 3x^2 + 11x + 8$, and the daily revenue R is given by $R = 25x$. Because of the time needed to make each pair, the company can produce no more than 1 dozen pair per day. Find the break-even point for this company. 20. ____________

21. Graph the equation $y = 2x^2$

21. 

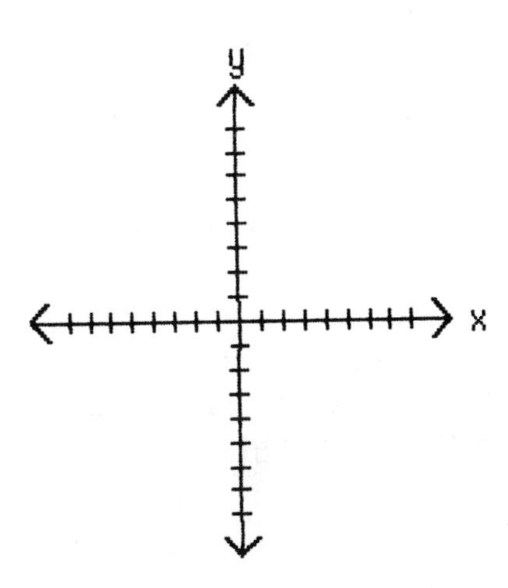

22. Graph the equation $y = -x^2 + 2$

22. 

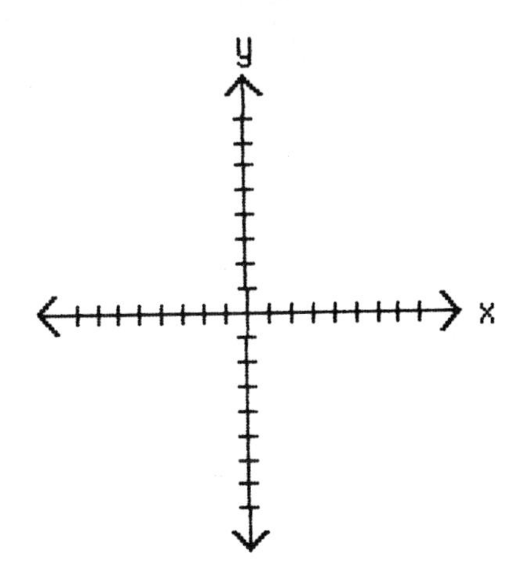

23. Complete the square to put the equation in the form $y = a(x - h)^2 + k$ and graph: $y = x^2 + 6x - 1$

23. _______________

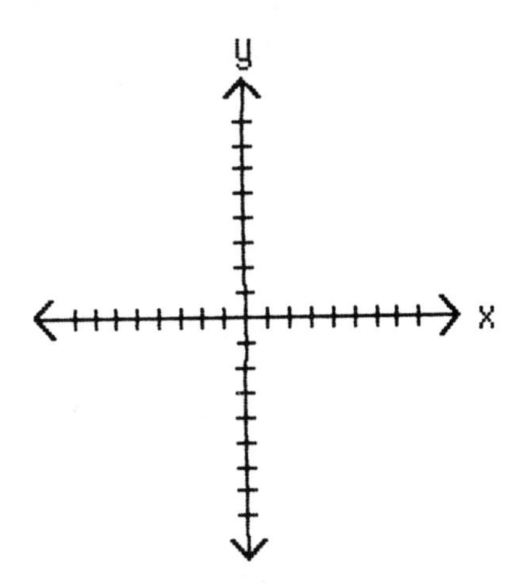

24. Find the value of any real numbers that are x-intercepts of the graph of $y = 2x^2 - 7x + 3$.

24. ____________

25. Determine if the graph of $y = 4x^2 - 20x + 96$ has a highest point or a lowest point and find the coordinates of this point.

25. ____________

Name ______________________ Chapter 9 Form B Score ________

1. Solve the equation: $y^2 = 48$ 1. ____________

2. Solve the equation: $(2x - 5)^2 = 12$ 2. ____________

3. From the given right triangle, express s in terms of c. 3. 

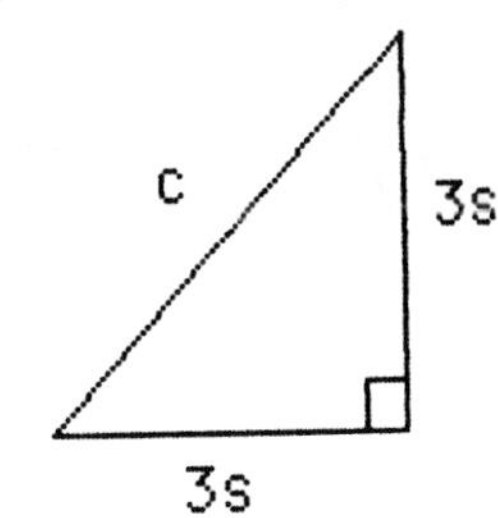

4. Four is added to twice a positive number. The result when squared is equal to 24. Find the number. 4. ____________

5. What constant must be added to $a^2 - 3a$ to make a perfect square trinomial? 5. ____________

6. Solve the equation by completing the square: 6. ____________

$$z^2 + 9z = -9$$

7. Solve the equation by completing the square: 7. ____________

$$2x^2 - 3x - 9 = 0$$

8. Use the quadratic formula to solve:

$$3x^2 - 8x + 2 = 0$$

8. ____________

9. Use the quadratic formula to solve:

$$2x - 8 = -x^2$$

9. 

10. Solve using the quadratic formula. Then approximate the solutions to the nearest tenth.

$$3w^2 + 3w - 1 = 0$$

10. 

11. Solve the quadratic equation $(2z + 5)(z - 3) = 8$

11. ____________

12. Solve: $\dfrac{2}{2x + 3} + \dfrac{2}{2x - 3} = 1$

12. ____________

13. Solve the quadratic equation. Write all solutions that are complex numbers in standard form.

$$(m + 3)^2 = -9$$

13. ____________

14. Solve the quadratic equation. Write all solutions that are complex numbers in standard form.

$$w^2 - 6 = 2w$$

14. 

15. Solve the quadratic equation. Write all solutions 15. ____________
that are complex numbers in standard form.

$$(q - 1)(q + 5) = 9$$

16. Use the discriminant to determine if the roots are 16. ____________
real or complex. Also, determine the number of roots.
Do not solve the equation. $3x^2 + 10x - 1 = 0$

17. The number of diagonals N of a polygon of n sides 17. ____________
is given by $N = \frac{n^2 - 3n}{2}$. If a polygon has 54 diagonals,

how many sides does it have?

18. The base of a triangle is 2 centimeters more than 18. ____________
its height. If the area is 9.18 square centimeters,
find the length of the base and height.

19. An ice-skating rink is 30 meters long by, 20 meters 19. ____________
wide. Plans are made to double the rinks area,
retaining the rectangular shape. A strip will be
added at one end, and a strip of the same width will
be added along one side. Find the width of the strips.

20. Acme Manufacturing makes and sells x dozen pair of mittens per day. The daily cost C is given by $C = 2x^2 + 72$, and the daily revenue R is given by $R = 26x$. Because of the time needed to make a pair of mittens, the company can produce no more than 7 dozen pair per day. Find the break-even point for this company.

20. 

21. Graph the equation $y = \frac{2}{3}x^2$

21. 

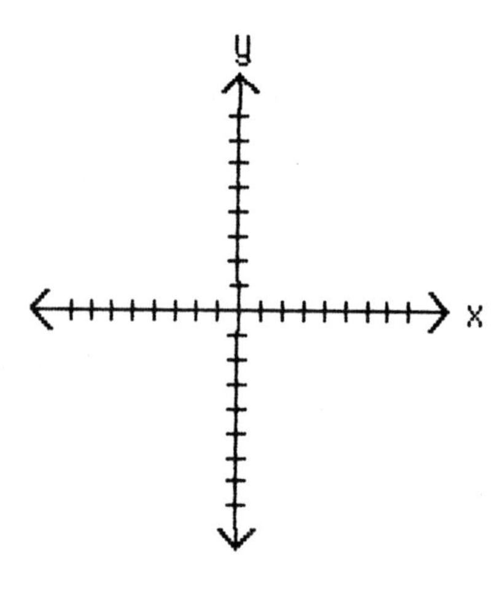

22. Graph the equation $y = (x + 2)^2$

22. 

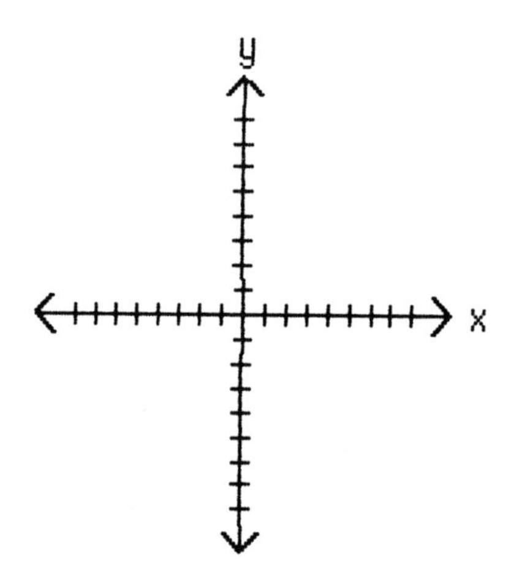

23. Complete the square to put the equation in the form $y = a(x - h)^2 + k$ and graph: $y = -x^2 + 2x - 1$

23. ____________

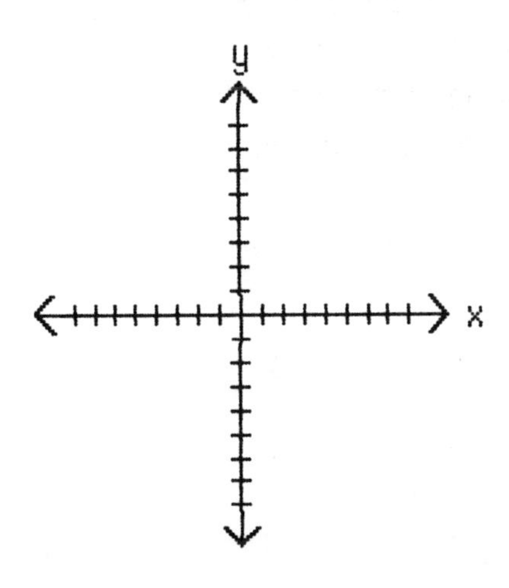

24. Find the values of any real numbers that are x-intercepts of the graph of $y = x^2 - 6x + 9$.

24. ____________

25. Determine if the graph of $y = -6x^2 + 12x - 18$ has a highest point or a lowest point and find the coordinates of this point.

25. ____________

Name ____________________ Chapter 9 Form C Score ______

1. Solve the equation: $8x^2 = 96$ 1. __________

2. Solve the equation: $\left(\frac{2}{3} - w\right)^2 = \frac{25}{36}$ 2. 

3. From the given right triangle, express s in terms of c. 3. __________

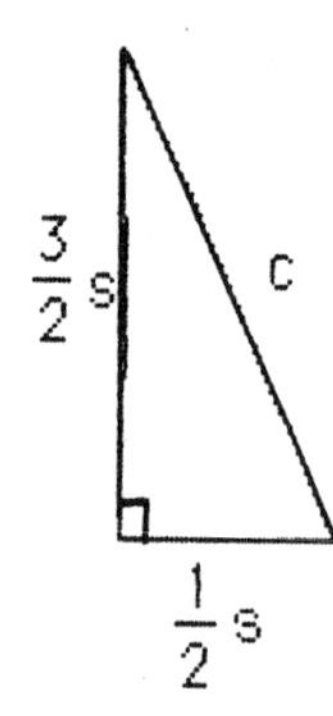

4. The braking distance d of a car depends upon its speed V. For one particular model, the braking distance is given by $d = \frac{4}{50}V^2$, where d is measured in feet and V in mph. Solve this equation for V. 4. 

5. What constant must be added to $w^2 + \frac{4}{7}w$ to make a perfect square trinomial? 5. __________

6. Solve the equation by completing the square: 6. __________

$$y^2 - \frac{8}{15}y = -\frac{1}{15}$$

7. Solve the equation by completing the square: 7. ______________

$$8x^2 + 16x + 20 = 14$$

8. Use the quadratic formula to solve: 8. ______________

$$-3x^2 + 4x + 2 = 0$$

9. Use the quadratic formula to solve: 9. ______________

$$x^2 - \frac{2}{3} = \frac{1}{3}x$$

10. Solve using the quadratic formula. Then approximate the solutions to the nearest tenth. 10. ______________

$$4y^2 + 9y + 3 = 0$$

11. Solve the quadratic equation 11. ______________

$$(6u + 1)(u - 3) = 3u - 1$$

12. Solve: $\dfrac{6}{w - 1} + \dfrac{3}{w} = 3$ 12. ______________

13. Solve the quadratic equation. Write all solutions that are complex numbers in standard form. 13. ______________

$$(3y + 2)^2 - 8 = 0$$

14. Solve the quadratic equation. Write all solutions that are complex numbers in standard form.

$$y^2 - 6y = -12$$

14. ____________

15. Solve the quadratic equation. Write all solutions that are complex numbers in standard form.

$$(3y - 1)(y + 5) = 12y - 7$$

15. ____________

16. Use the discriminant to determine if the roots are real or complex. Also, determine the number of roots. Do not solve the equation. $4x^2 - 20x + 25 = 0$

16. ____________

17. The Sum S of the first n positive integers is given by $S = \frac{n(n+1)}{2}$. Find n if the sum S is 276.

17. ____________

18. The difference of a number and its reciprocal is $\frac{7}{12}$. Find the number.

18. ____________

19. An open box is to be made from a square sheet of cardboard by cutting squares measuring 4 inches on a side from each corner and folding up the sides. If the required volume is 1024 cubic inches, what size piece of cardboard is needed to make the box?

19. ____________

20. The Pack-It-Up Company packs and sells x gross of cans of peaches each day. The daily cost C is given by $C = 8x^2 + 768$, and the daily revenue R is given by $R = 160x$. Because of the time needed to pack a gross of cans of peaches, the company can pack no more than 10 gross each day. Find the break-even point for this company.

20. ____________

21. Graph the equation $y = -3x^2$

21. ____________

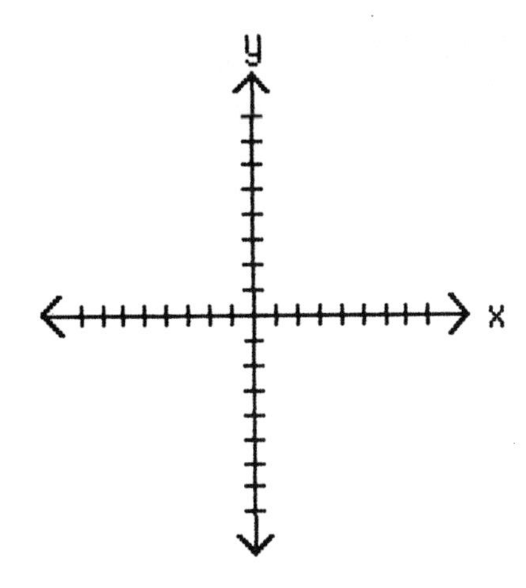

22. Graph the equation $y = -\frac{1}{2}(x + 1)^2 - 2$

22. ____________

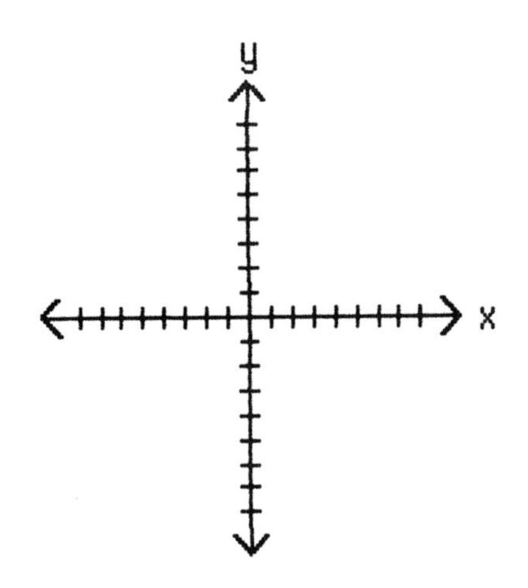

23. Complete the square to put the equation in the form $y = a(x - h)^2 + k$ and graph: $y = 3x^2 + 6x - 1$

23. ______________

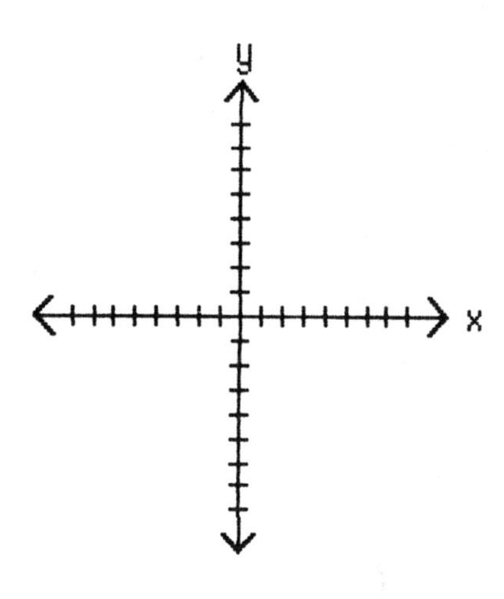

24. Find the value of any real numbers that are x-intercepts of the graph of $y = 2x^2 - 3x - 5$

24. 

25. Determine if the graph of $y = x^2 - 2x + 3$ has a highest point or a lowest point and find the coordinates of this point.

25. ______________

Name ______________________ Chapter 9 Form D Score ________

1. Solve the equation: $x^2 = 196$ 1. ____________
   a. $x = 14$
   b. $x = \pm 16$
   c. $x = \pm 98$
   d. $x = \pm 14$
   e. None of these

2. Solve the equation: $(x - 4)^2 = 16$ 2. ____________
   a. $x = 0$ or $x = 8$
   b. $x = 8$
   c. $x = 12$ or $x = -4$
   d. $x = -12$ or $x = 20$
   e. None of these

3. From the given right triangle, express s in terms of c. 3. 

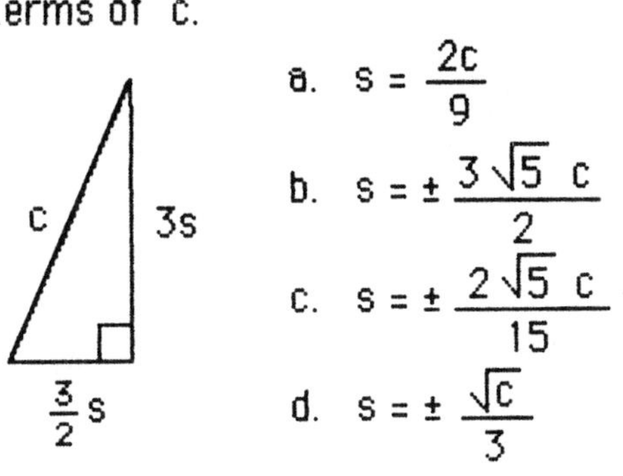

   a. $s = \frac{2c}{9}$
   b. $s = \pm \frac{3\sqrt{5}\ c}{2}$
   c. $s = \pm \frac{2\sqrt{5}\ c}{15}$
   d. $s = \pm \frac{\sqrt{c}}{3}$
   e. None of these

4. The volume of a rectangular solid with a square base is given by $V = hs^2$. If the volume is 392 cubic feet and the height is 8 inches, what is the length of a side of the square base? 4. 
   a. 7 inches
   b. $\pm$ 7 inches
   c. $24\frac{1}{2}$ inches
   d. 6.125 inches
   e. None of these

5. What constant must be added to $x^2 - 16x$ to make a perfect square trinomial? 5. ____________
   a. 16
   b. -64
   c. -16
   d. 64
   e. None of these

6. Solve the equation by completing the square: 6. ______________

$m^2 - 8m = 16$

a. $m = -4 \pm 4\sqrt{2}$

b. $m = 4 \pm 4\sqrt{2}$

c. $m = -8 \pm 4\sqrt{5}$

d. $m = 8 \pm 4\sqrt{5}$

e. None of these

7. Solve the equation by completing the square: 7. ______________

$2t^2 - 6t = -1$

a. $t = \frac{3 \pm 2\sqrt{2}}{2}$

b. $t = -\frac{3 \pm 2\sqrt{2}}{2}$

c. $t = \frac{3 \pm \sqrt{7}}{2}$

d. $t = \frac{-3 \pm \sqrt{7}}{2}$

e. None of these

8. Use the quadratic formula to solve: 8. ______________

$5x^2 + 10x + 3 = 0$

a. $x = \frac{-5 \pm 2\sqrt{10}}{10}$

b. $x = \frac{-5 \pm \sqrt{10}}{5}$

c. $x = -1 \pm 2\sqrt{10}$

d. $x = \frac{5 \pm \sqrt{10}}{5}$

e. None of these

9. Use the quadratic formula to solve: 9. ______________

$3x^2 + 9 = 2x^2$

a. $x = -3$ or $x = \frac{3}{2}$

b. $x = \frac{1 \pm \sqrt{26}}{3}$

c. $x = \pm 3$

d. $x = \frac{-3 \pm 3\sqrt{7}}{4}$

e. None of these

10. Solve using the quadratic formula. Then approximate the solutions to the nearest tenth.

$2a^2 - 7a - 3 = 0$

a. $a = 3$ or $a = 0.5$
b. $a = -2.2$ or $a = 3.9$
c. $a = 3.9$ or $a = -3.9$
d. $a = 3.9$ or $a = -0.4$
e. None of these

10. ____________

11. Solve the quadratic equation

$y(4 - 2y) = -3$

a. $y = -\frac{3}{2}$
b. $y = \pm 2\sqrt{10}$
c. $y = \frac{2 \pm \sqrt{2}}{3}$
d. $y = \frac{2 \pm \sqrt{10}}{2}$
e. None of these

11. ____________

12. Solve: $p - 8 = \frac{6}{p}$

a. $p = 4 \pm 2\sqrt{22}$
b. $p = 4 \pm \sqrt{10}$
c. $p = 4 \pm \sqrt{22}$
d. $p = \pm\sqrt{14}$
e. None of these

12. ____________

13. Solve the quadratic equation. Write all solutions that are complex numbers in standard form.

$m^2 + 64 = 0$

a. $m = \pm 8i$
b. $m = \pm 8$
c. $m = \pm 32i$
d. $m = \pm 32$
e. None of these

13. ____________

14. Solve the quadratic equation. Write all solutions that are complex numbers in standard form.

$y^2 + 4y + 2 = 0$

a. $y = -2 \pm 2\sqrt{2}$
b. $y = -2 \pm \sqrt{2}$
c. $y = -2 \pm 2\sqrt{6}$
d. $y = 2 \pm \sqrt{2}$
e. None of these

14. ____________

15. Solve the quadratic equation. Write all solutions that are complex numbers in standard form. 15. ______________

$(x - 4)^2 = 4x$

a. $x = 6 \pm 2\sqrt{13}$
b. $x = 2 \pm 2\sqrt{3}\,i$
c. $x = 12 \pm 8\sqrt{2}$
d. $x = 6 \pm 2\sqrt{5}$
e. None of these

16. Use the discriminant to determine if the roots are real or complex. Also, determine the number of roots. Do not solve the equation. $2x^2 + 4x = -3$ 16. ______________

a. two complex roots
b. one real root
c. two real roots
d. one complex root
e. None of these

17. A skier accelerates as he travels downhill. The distance s traveled in t seconds is given by $s = 10t^2 + 10t$ (feet). How long does it take him to go 1320 feet downhill? 17. ______________

a. 12 seconds
b. 11 seconds
c. 10 seconds
d. 13 seconds
e. None of these

18. One positive number is four times another number. If their product is 8, find the two numbers. 18. ______________

a. 2 and 4
b. $-\sqrt{2}$ and $-4\sqrt{2}$
c. $\sqrt{2}$ and $4\sqrt{2}$
d. $\pm\sqrt{2}$
e. None of these

19. A rectangular picture is 4 inches longer than twice its width. Its area is 96 square inches. Find its length. 19. ______________

a. 6 inches
b. 16 inches
c. $4 + 4\sqrt{3}$ inches
d. $-1 + 5\sqrt{2}$ inches
e. None of these

20. The Vipco Company makes and sells x lawn mowers each day. The daily cost C is given by $C = 9x^2 + 90$, and the daily revenue R is given by $R = 63x$. The company can make no more than 4 mowers each day. Find the break-even point for this company. 20. ____________

a. 2 mowers
b. 5 mowers
c. 1 mower
d. 4 mowers
e. None of these

21. Graph the equation $y = 5x^2$ 21. 
The coordinates of the vertex are

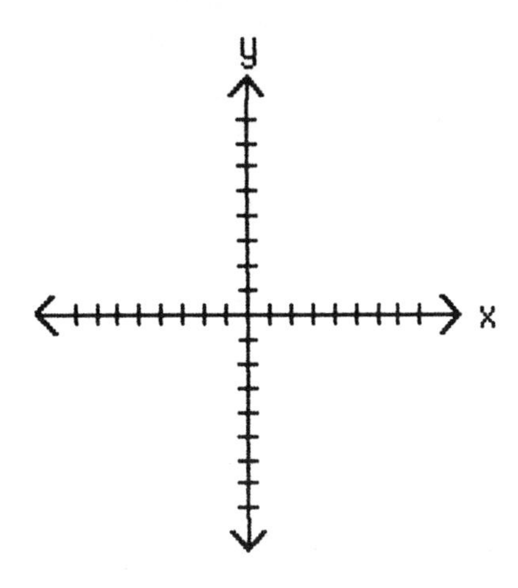

a. (1, 5)
b. (-1, 5)
c. (0, 0)
d. (2, 20)
e. None of these

22. Graph the equation $y = x^2 - 4$ 22. 
The coordinates of the vertex are

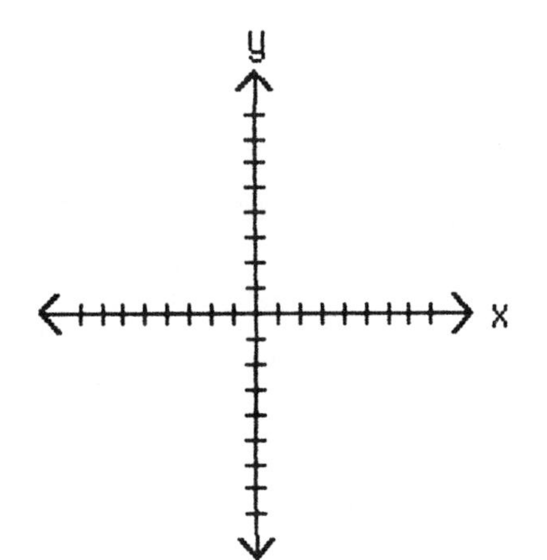

a. (-4, 0)
b. (2, 0)
c. (-2, 0)
d. (0, -4)
e. None of these

23. Complete the square to put the equation in the form $y = a(x - h)^2 + k$ and graph: 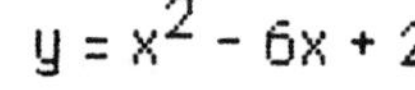 $y = x^2 - 6x + 2$
The coordinates of the vertex are

23. ____________

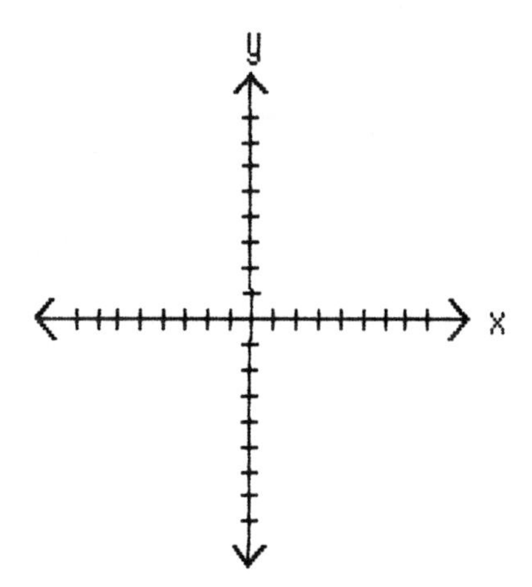

a. (-3, 11)
b. (3, -7)
c. (3, 11)
d. (-3, -7)
e. None of these

24. Find the value of any real numbers that are x-intercepts of the graph of $y = x^2 - 4x + 7$

24. ____________

a. $x = 2 + \sqrt{3}$ and $x = 2 - \sqrt{3}$
b. $x = 0$
c. $x = 2$ and $x = 3$
d. $x = -1$ and $x = 7$
e. None of these

25. Determine if the graph of $y = -3x^2 + 24x - 36$ has a highest point or a lowest point and find the coordinates of this point.

25. ____________

a. highest point (-4, 12)
b. lowest point (-4, 12)
c. highest point (4, 12)
d. lowest point (4, 12)
e. None of these

Name ______________________ Chapter 9 Form E Score ________

1. Solve the equation: $y^2 = 27$ 1. ____________

   a. $y = \pm 13.5$
   b. $y = \pm 9\sqrt{3}$
   c. $y = \pm 3\sqrt{3}$
   d. $y = \pm 3$
   e. None of these

2. Solve the equation: $(4w - 9)^2 = 144$ 2. ____________

   a. $w = \frac{3}{4}$ or $w = -\frac{21}{4}$
   b. $w = -\frac{3}{4}$ or $w = \frac{21}{4}$
   c. $w = \pm\frac{21}{4}$
   d. $w = \pm\frac{3}{4}$
   e. None of these

3. From the given right triangle, express s in terms of c. 3. 

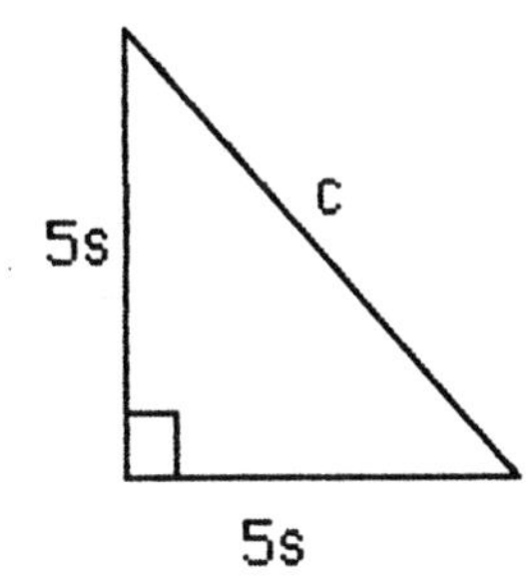

   a. $s = \frac{c}{10}$
   b. $s = \pm\frac{c}{25}$
   c. $s = \pm\frac{\sqrt{2}\,c}{5}$
   d. $s = \pm\frac{c\sqrt{2}}{10}$
   e. None of these

4. Eight is added to four times a positive number. The result, when squared is equal to 96. Find the number. 4. ____________

   a. $-2 \pm \sqrt{6}$
   b. $-2 + \sqrt{6}$
   c. $\frac{\sqrt{22}}{2}$
   d. $\sqrt{2}$
   e. None of these

5. What constant must be added to $d^2 - 9d$ to make a perfect square trinomial? 5. ______________

a. 81

b. $-\frac{81}{4}$

c. $\frac{81}{4}$

d. $\frac{9}{2}$

e. None of these

6. Solve the equation by completing the square: 6. ______________

$p^2 - 5p = 6$

a. $p = 6$ or $p = -1$

b. $p = \frac{5}{2} \pm \frac{1}{2}i$

c. $p = \frac{5 \pm \sqrt{31}}{2}$

d. $p = 1$ or $p = -6$

e. None of these

7. Solve the equation by completing the square: 7. ______________

$16x^2 - 24x + 5 = 0$

a. $x = \frac{9 \pm \sqrt{139}}{3}$

b. $x = \frac{3 \pm \sqrt{89}}{4}$

c. $x = \pm\frac{5}{4}$

d. $x = \frac{5}{4}$ or $x = \frac{1}{4}$

e. None of these

8. Use the quadratic formula to solve: 8. ______________

$$-4x^2 + 6x + 3 = 0$$

a. $x = \dfrac{3 \pm \sqrt{21}}{4}$

b. $x = \dfrac{-3 \pm \sqrt{3}}{4}$

c. $x = -\dfrac{1}{2}$ or $x = \dfrac{3}{2}$

d. $x = \dfrac{3 \pm \sqrt{21}}{2}$

e. None of these

9. Use the quadratic formula to solve: 9. ______________

$$7x + 6 = 3x^2$$

a. $x = \pm 3$

b. $x = -3$ or $x = \dfrac{2}{3}$

c. $x = \pm \dfrac{2}{3}$

d. $x = 3$ or $x = -\dfrac{2}{3}$

e. None of these

10. Solve using the quadratic formula. Then approximate the solutions to the nearest tenth. 10. ______________

$$8z^2 + 9z + 2 = 0$$

a. $z = 0.2$ or $z = -1.3$

b. $z = \pm 0.3$

c. $z = -0.3$ or $z = -0.8$

d. $z = -0.2$ or $z = -0.9$

e. None of these

11. Solve the quadratic equation
$(3x + 4)(x - 4) = 4$

11. ____________

a. $x = \frac{4 \pm 2\sqrt{11}}{3}$

b. $x = \frac{4 \pm 2\sqrt{13}}{3}$

c. $x = \frac{4 \pm 2\sqrt{19}}{3}$

d. $x = \pm \frac{2\sqrt{15}}{3}$

e. None of these

12. Solve: $\frac{3}{4x + 1} + \frac{3}{4x - 1} = 1$

12. ____________

a. $x = \frac{1}{24}$

b. $x = \frac{3}{4}$

c. $x = 6 \pm \sqrt{10}$

d. $x = \frac{3 \pm \sqrt{10}}{4}$

e. None of these

13. Solve the quadratic equation. Write all solutions that are complex numbers in standard form.
$(z - 5)^2 = -36$

13. ____________

a. $z = \pm 11i$

b. $z = 1$ or $z = -1$

c. $z = \pm i$

d. $z = -5 \pm 6i$

e. None of these

14. Solve the quadratic equation. Write all solutions that are complex numbers in standard form. 14. ____________

$w^2 + 8 = 4w$

a. $w = 2 \pm 2i$
b. $w = -2 \pm 2i$
c. $w = -2 \pm 2\sqrt{3}$
d. $w = 2 \pm 2\sqrt{3}$
e. None of these

15. Solve the quadratic equation. Write all solutions that are complex numbers in standard form. 15. ____________

$(m - 4)(m + 2) = -10$

a. $m = \pm i\sqrt{2}$
b. $m = 1$
c. $m = 1 \pm i$
d. $m = 1 \pm 2i$
e. None of these

16. Use the discriminant to determine if the roots are real or complex. Also, determine the number of roots. Do not solve the equation. $x^2 + 3x = 6$ 16. ____________

a. one real root
b. two real roots
c. two complex roots
d. one complex root
e. None of these

17. The number of diagonals N of a polygon of n sides is given by $N = \frac{n^2 - 3n}{2}$ If a polygon has 104 diagonals, how many sides does it have? 17. ____________

a. 16 sides
b. 8 sides
c. 13 sides
d. 18 sides
e. None of these

18. The base of a triangle is 3 inches more than its height. If the area is 12.92 square inches, find the length of the base.

18. ____________

a. 3.8 inches
b. 6.8 inches
c. 7.8 inches
d. 4.8 inches
e. None of these

19. An ice-skating rink is 60 meters long by 40 meters wide. Plans are made to double the rink's area, retaining the rectangular shape. A strip will be added at one end, and a strip of the same width will be added along one side. Find the width of the strips.

19. ____________

a. 20 meters
b. $20\sqrt{6}$ meters
c. 40 meters
d. 24 meters
e. None of these

20. The Kitchen Cut Company makes and sells x gross of dish towells each day. The daily cost C is given by $C = 4x^2 + 176$, and the daily revenue R is given by $R = 60x$. The company can make no more than 8 gross of dish towells each day. Find the break-even point for this company.

20. ____________

a. 7 gross
b. 11 gross
c. 8 gross
d. 6.6 gross
e. None of these

21. Graph the equation $y = \frac{4}{3}x^2$ 21. 

The coordinates of the vertex are

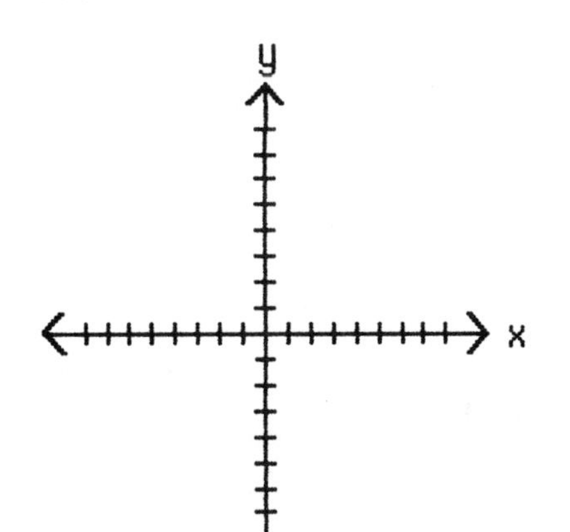

a. (3, 4)
b. (0, 0)
c. (3, 12)
d. $(1, \frac{4}{3})$
e. None of these

22. Graph the equation $y = (x - 3)^2$ 22. 

The coordinates of the vertex are

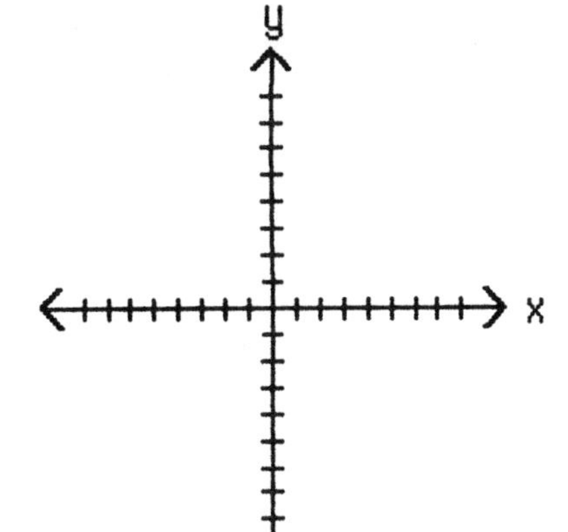

a. (-3, 0)
b. (1, 4)
c. (3, 0)
d. (0, 9)
e. None of these

23. Complete the square to put the equation in the form $y = a(x - h)^2 + k$ and graph: $y = -x^2 - 2x - 1$ 23. ____________

The coordinates of the vertex are

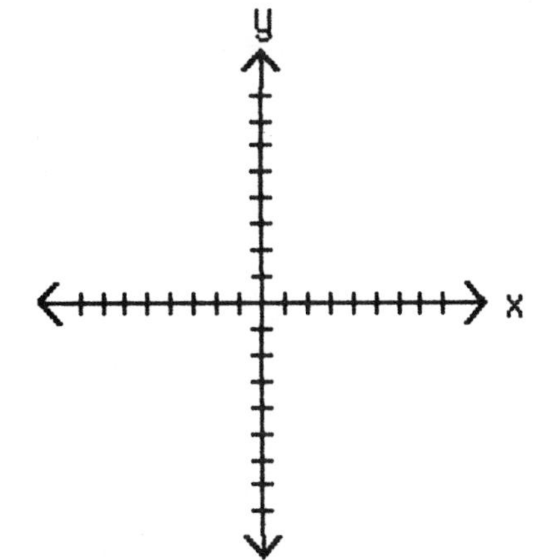

a. (-1, 0)
b. (1, 0)
c. (0, -1)
d. (-1, 2)
e. None of these

24. Find the value of any real numbers that are x-intercepts of the graph of $y = -2x^2 - 4x$

a. $x = -2$
b. $x = 0$ and $x = 2$
c. $x = 2$ and $x = -2$
d. $x = 0$ and $x = -2$
e. None of these

25. Determine if the graph of $y = -16x^2 + 80x$ has a highest point or a lowest point and find the coordinates of this point.

a. lowest point $(-\frac{5}{2}, 100)$

b. lowest point $(\frac{5}{2}, 100)$

c. highest point $(\frac{5}{2}, 100)$

d. highest point $(-\frac{5}{2}, 100)$

e. None of these

Name ______________________ Chapter 9 Form F Score ________

1. Solve the equation: $6x^2 = 72$ 1. ____________

a. $x = \pm 4\sqrt{3}$

b. $x = \pm 2\sqrt{3}$

c. $x = \pm \sqrt{2}$

d. $x = \pm \sqrt{66}$

e. None of these

2. Solve the equation: $(\frac{5}{8} - 2x)^2 = \frac{64}{100}$ 2. ____________

a. $x = -\frac{7}{80}$

b. $x = \frac{7}{80}$ or $x = -\frac{57}{80}$

c. $x = -\frac{7}{80}$ or $x = \frac{57}{80}$

d. $x = -\frac{57}{20}$ or $x = -\frac{7}{20}$

e. None of these

3. From the given right triangle, express s in terms of c. 3. ____________

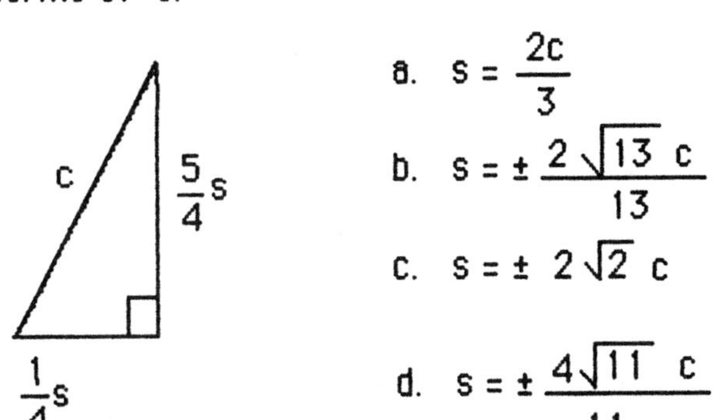

a. $s = \frac{2c}{3}$

b. $s = \pm \frac{2\sqrt{13}\,c}{13}$

c. $s = \pm 2\sqrt{2}\,c$

d. $s = \pm \frac{4\sqrt{11}\,c}{11}$

e. None of these

4. The braking distance d of a car depends upon the speed V. For one particular model, the braking distance is given by $d = \frac{5}{50}V^2$, where d is measured in feet and V in mph. Solve this equation for V. 4. ____________

a. $V = \pm \sqrt{2d}$

b. $V = \pm \frac{\sqrt{5d}}{5}$

c. $V = \pm \sqrt{10d}$

d. $V = \pm \frac{\sqrt{10d}}{10}$

e. None of these

5. What constant must be added to $w^2 - \frac{4}{9}w$ to make a perfect square trinomial? 5. ____________

a. $\frac{4}{81}$

b. $\frac{2}{9}$

c. $-\frac{2}{9}$

d. $-\frac{4}{81}$

e. None of these

6. Solve the equation by completing the square: 6. ____________

$$y^2 - \frac{8}{9}y = \frac{1}{9}$$

a. $y = \frac{-4 \pm \sqrt{7}}{9}$

b. $y = -1$ or $y = \frac{1}{9}$

c. $y = \frac{4 \pm \sqrt{7}}{9}$

d. $y = 1$ or $y = -\frac{1}{9}$

e. None of these

7. Solve the equation by completing the square: 7. ____________

$$6x^2 - 18x + 5 = 2$$

a. $x = -\frac{3 \pm \sqrt{7}}{2}$

b. $x = \frac{3 \pm \sqrt{7}}{2}$

c. $x = -\frac{3 \pm \sqrt{3}}{2}$

d. $x = \frac{3 \pm \sqrt{3}}{2}$

e. None of these

8. Use the quadratic formula to solve: 8. ____________

$$2x^2 - 8x + 4 = 0$$

a. $x = 4 \pm \sqrt{2}$
b. $x = 2 \pm \sqrt{6}$
c. $x = \dfrac{2 \pm \sqrt{2}}{2}$
d. $x = 2 \pm \sqrt{2}$
e. None of these

9. Use the quadratic formula to solve: 9. ____________

$$x^2 - \frac{1}{4} = \frac{3}{4}x$$

a. $x = -1$ or $x = \dfrac{1}{4}$
b. $x = 1$ or $x = -\dfrac{3}{4}$
c. $x = 1$ or $x = -\dfrac{1}{4}$
d. $x = -1$ or $x = \dfrac{3}{4}$
e. None of these

10. Solve using the quadratic formula. Then approximate the solutions to the nearest tenth. 10. ____________

$$6m^2 + 8m - 1 = 0$$

a. $m = -0.1$ or $m = -1.2$
b. $m = 0.1$ or $m = -1.4$
c. $m = 1.4$ or $m = -1.5$
d. $m = 0.1$ or $m = -1.5$
e. None of these

11. Solve the quadratic equation 11. ____________

$$(10x + 5)(x - 2) = 4 - 3x$$

a. $x = \dfrac{3 \pm 2\sqrt{11}}{5}$
b. $x = \dfrac{-3 \pm \sqrt{569}}{10}$
c. $x = \dfrac{-3 \pm 2\sqrt{11}}{5}$
d. $x = \dfrac{9 \pm \sqrt{141}}{10}$
e. None of these

12. Solve: $\frac{5}{t} + \frac{3}{t-1} = 4$ 12. ____________

a. $t = 2$
b. $t = -\frac{5}{2}$ or $t = -\frac{1}{2}$
c. $t = \frac{9}{8}$
d. $t = \frac{5}{2}$ or $t = \frac{1}{4}$
e. None of these

13. Solve the quadratic equation. Write all solutions that are complex numbers in standard form. 13. ____________

$$(4x - 5)^2 - 12 = 0$$

a. $x = 37.25$
b. $x = \frac{5}{4} \pm \frac{\sqrt{3}}{2}i$
c. $x = \frac{5 \pm 2\sqrt{3}}{4}$
d. $x = \frac{-5 \pm 2\sqrt{3}}{4}$
e. None of these

14. Solve the quadratic equation. Write all solutions that are complex numbers in standard form. 14. ____________

$$z^2 - 6z = -12$$

a. $z = -3 \pm \sqrt{21}$
b. $z = 3 \pm \sqrt{21}$
c. $z = -3 \pm i\sqrt{3}$
d. $z = 3 \pm i\sqrt{3}$
e. None of these

15. Solve the quadratic equation. Write all solutions that are complex numbers in standard form. 15. ____________

$$(4x - 3)(x + 2) = 11x - 10$$

a. $x = \frac{3}{4} \pm \frac{\sqrt{7}}{4}i$
b. $x = -2 \pm 2\sqrt{2}$
c. $x = \frac{11 \pm \sqrt{57}}{8}$
d. $x = -\frac{3}{4} \pm \frac{\sqrt{7}}{4}i$
e. None of these

16. Use the discriminant to determine if the roots are real or complex. Also, determine the number of roots. Do not solve the equation. $2x^2 - 8x - 8 = 0$ 16. ____________

a. one real root
b. one complex root
c. two real roots
d. two complex roots
e. None of these

17. The sum S of the first n positive integer is given by $S = \frac{n(n+1)}{2}$. Find n if the sum S is 703. 17. ____________

a. 35
b. 36
c. 38
d. 37
e. None of these

18. One more than the reciprocal of a negative number is twice that number. Find the number. 18. ____________

a. $-\frac{1}{2}$
b. 1
c. $-\frac{1}{3}$
d. $-\frac{1}{4} - \frac{\sqrt{7}\,i}{4}$
e. None of these

19. An open box is to be made from a square sheet of cardboard by cutting squares measuring 2.5 inches on a side from each corner and folding up the sides. If the required volume is 360 cubic inches, what size piece of cardboard is needed to make the box? 19. ____________

a. 7 inches by 7 inches
b. 16 inches by 16 inches
c. 15 inches by 15 inches
d. 17 inches by 17 inches
e. None of these

20. The U-DO-IT Company produces and sells x camping trailers per day. The daily cost C is given by $C = 6x^2 + 300$, and the daily revenue R is given by $R = 90x$. The company can produce no more than 9 trailers each day. Find the break-even point for this company. 20. ____________

a. 10 trailers
b. 5 trailers
c. 9 trailers
d. 6 trailers
e. None of these

21. Graph the equation $y = -2x^2$
The line of symmetry is 21. 

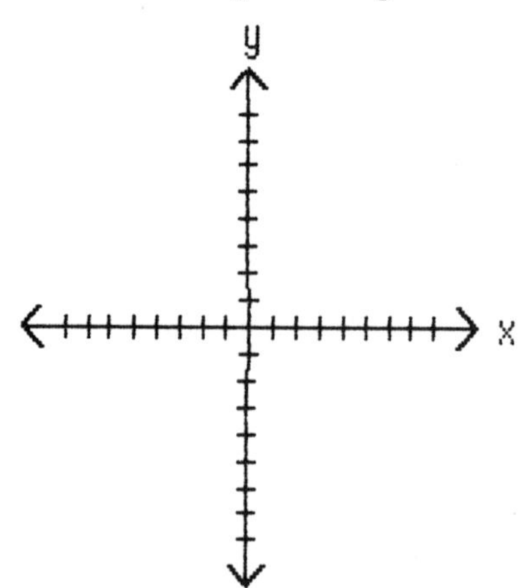

a. $x = 0$
b. $x = -2$
c. $x = 2$
d. $y = 0$
e. None of these

22. Graph the equation $y = -\frac{1}{4}(x + 3) - 2$ 22. ____________

The coordinates of the vertex are

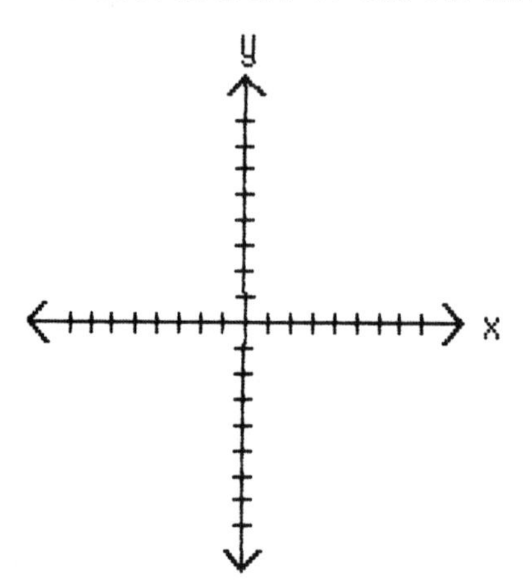

a. $(-3, 2)$
b. $(-3, -2)$
c. $(3, -2)$
d. $(3, 2)$
e. None of these

23. Complete the square to put the equation in the form $y = a(x - h)^2 + k$ and graph: $y = -3x^2 + 6x$
The coordinates of the vertex are

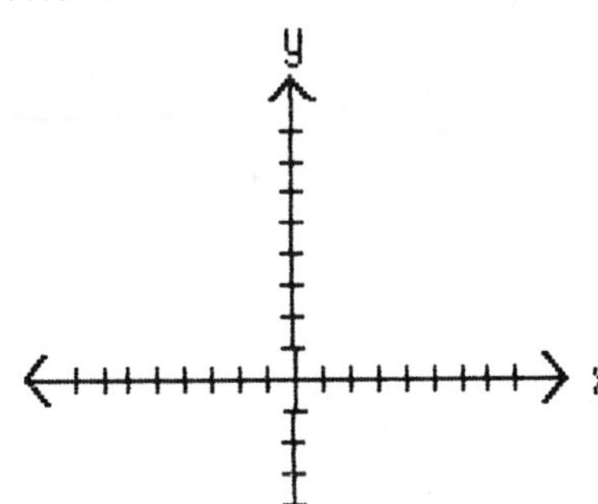

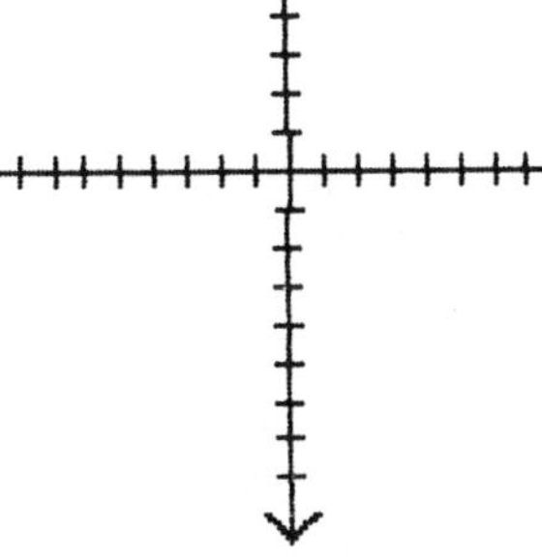

a. (1, -3)
b. (-1, 3)
c. (-1, -3)
d. (1, 3)
e. None of these

24. Find the value of any real numbers that are x-intercepts of the graph of $y = 2x^2 - 3x - 5$

24. __________

a. $x = -\frac{1}{2}$ and $x = 5$

b. $x = -\frac{5}{2}$ and $x = 1$

c. $x = \frac{5}{2}$ and $x = -1$

d. $x = \frac{5}{2}$ and $x = \frac{1}{4}$

e. None of these

25. Determine if the graph of $y = -3x^2 + 24x - 40$ has a highest point or a lowest point and find the coordinates of this point.

25. __________

a. lowest point (4, 8)
b. highest point (4, - 88)
c. lowest point (4, - 88)
d. highest point (4, 8)
e. None of these

CHAPTER 9 TEST KEYS

Form A

1. $x = \pm 12$
2. $x = 6$ or $x = -12$
3. $s = \pm \frac{\sqrt{13}\ c}{26}$
4. 6 inches
5. 36
6. $x = 3 \pm \sqrt{21}$
7. $t = -1 \pm \frac{\sqrt{5}}{2}$
8. $x = \frac{-2 \pm \sqrt{10}}{2}$
9. $x = 6$ or $x = 5$
10. $x = 1.3$ or $x = -0.8$
11. $x = \frac{2 \pm \sqrt{22}}{3}$
12. $n = 1$ or $n = -4$
13. $x = \pm 4i$
14. $x = -1 \pm i$
15. $t = 4 \pm \sqrt{7}$
16. 2 Real roots
17. 7 seconds
18. $\pm\sqrt{6}$ or $\pm 3\sqrt{6}$
19. 50 m. by 20 m.

Form B

1. $y = \pm 4\sqrt{3}$
2. $x = \frac{5}{2} \pm \sqrt{3}$
3. $s = \pm \frac{c\sqrt{2}}{6}$
4. $-2 + \sqrt{6}$
5. $\frac{9}{4}$
6. $z = \frac{-9 \pm 3\sqrt{5}}{2}$
7. $x = \frac{3}{2}$ or $x = -3$
8. $x = \frac{4 \pm \sqrt{10}}{3}$
9. $x = 2$ or $x = -4$
10. $w = 0.3$ or $w = -1.3$
11. $z = \frac{1 \pm \sqrt{185}}{4}$
12. $x = \frac{2 \pm \sqrt{13}}{2}$
13. $m = 3 \pm 3i$
14. $w = 1 \pm \sqrt{7}$
15. $q = -2 \pm 3\sqrt{2}$
16. 2 Real roots
17. 12 sides
18. base 5.4 cm, height 3.4 cm
19. 10 meters

20. $\frac{2}{3}$ dozen or 8 pair

21. Answer:

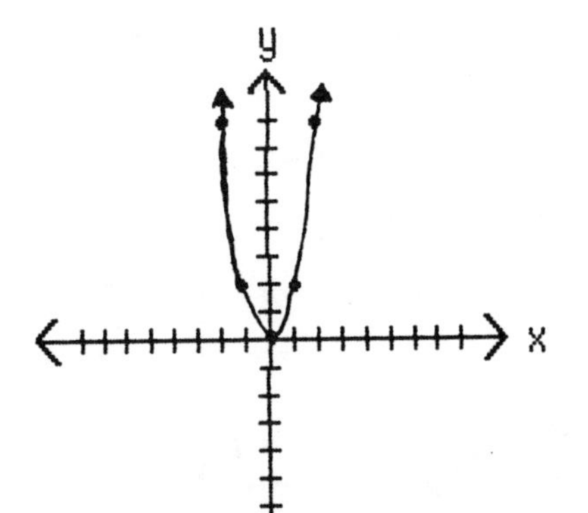

22. Answer:

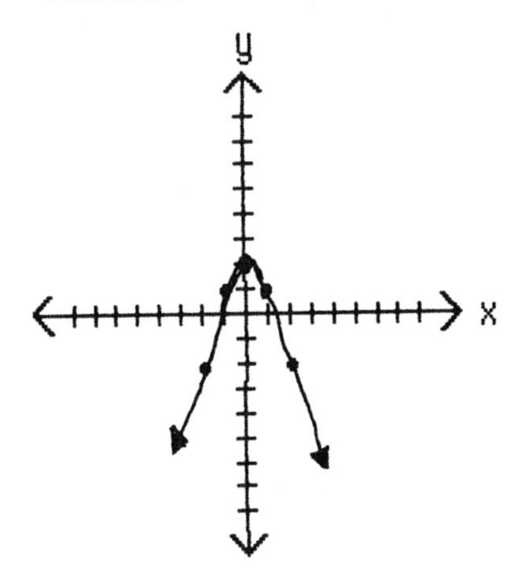

23. $y = (x + 3)^2 - 10$

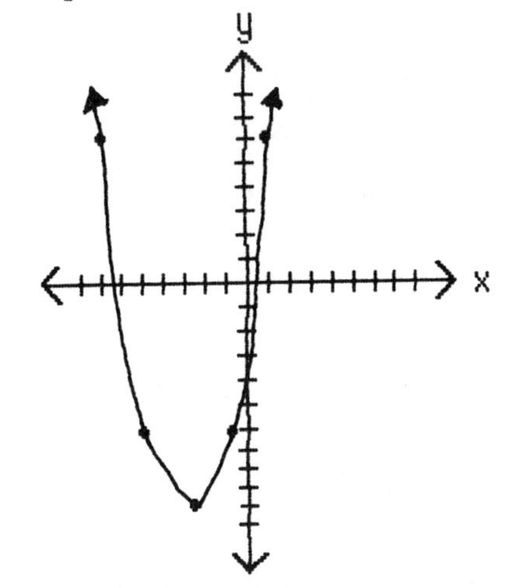

24. $x = \frac{1}{2}$ and $x = 3$

25. lowest point $(\frac{5}{2}, 7)$

20. 4 dozen

21. Answer:

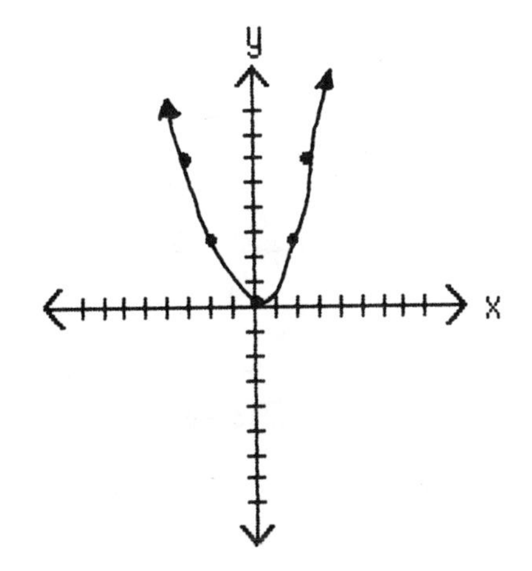

22. Answer:

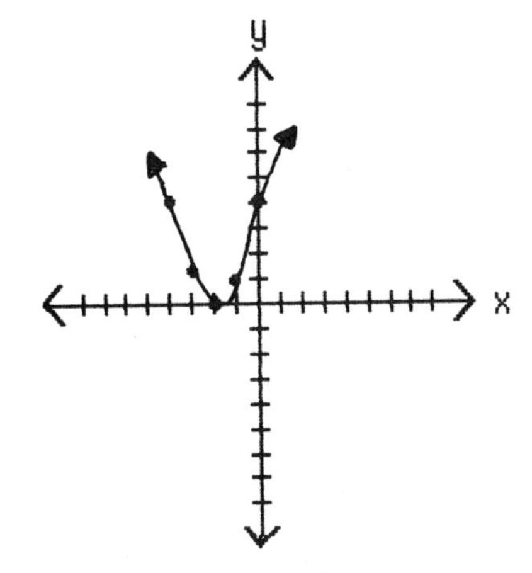

23. $y = -(x - 1)^2$

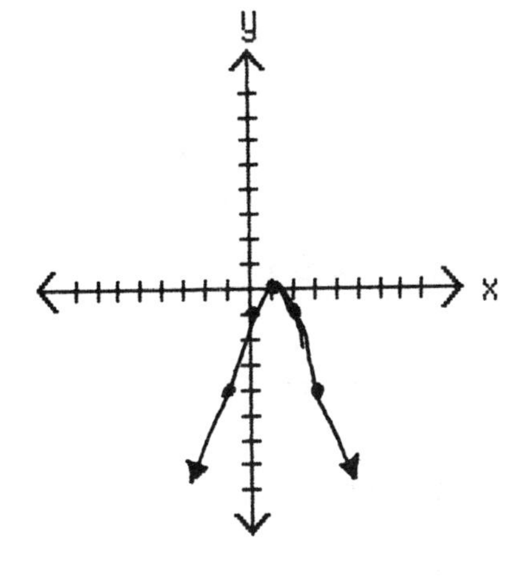

24. $x = 3$

25. highest point $(1, -12)$

Chapter 9 Test Keys

Form C

1. $x = \pm 2\sqrt{3}$
2. $x = \frac{3}{2}$ or $x = -\frac{1}{6}$
3. $s = \pm \frac{\sqrt{10}\ c}{5}$
4. $V = \pm \frac{5\sqrt{2d}}{2}$
5. $\frac{4}{49}$
6. $y = \frac{1}{3}$ or $y = \frac{1}{5}$
7. $x = 0$ or $x = -2$
8. $x = \frac{2 \pm \sqrt{10}}{3}$
9. $x = 1$ or $x = -\frac{2}{3}$
10. $y = -0.4$ or $y = -1.8$
11. $u = \frac{5 \pm 2\sqrt{7}}{3}$
12. $w = 1 \pm \sqrt{2}$
13. $y = \frac{-2 \pm 2\sqrt{2}}{3}$
14. $y = 3 \pm i\sqrt{3}$
15. $y = -\frac{1}{3} \pm \frac{\sqrt{5}}{6}i$
16. one Real root
17. $n = 23$
18. $\frac{4}{3}$ or $-\frac{3}{4}$
19. 32 inches by 32 inches

Form D

1. d) $x = \pm 14$
2. a) $x = 0$ or $x = 8$
3. c) $s = \pm \frac{2\sqrt{5}\ c}{15}$
4. a) 7 inches
5. d) 64
6. b) $m = 4 \pm 4\sqrt{2}$
7. c) $t = \frac{3 \pm \sqrt{7}}{2}$
8. b) $x = \frac{-5 \pm \sqrt{10}}{5}$
9. e) None of these
10. d) $a = 3.9$ or $a = -0.4$
11. d) $y = \frac{2 \pm \sqrt{10}}{2}$
12. c) $p = 4 \pm \sqrt{22}$
13. a) $m = \pm 8i$
14. b) $y = -2 \pm \sqrt{2}$
15. d) $x = 6 \pm 2\sqrt{5}$
16. a) two complex roots
17. b) 11 seconds
18. c) $\sqrt{2}$ and $4\sqrt{2}$
19. b) 16 inches

20. 8 gross

21. Answer:

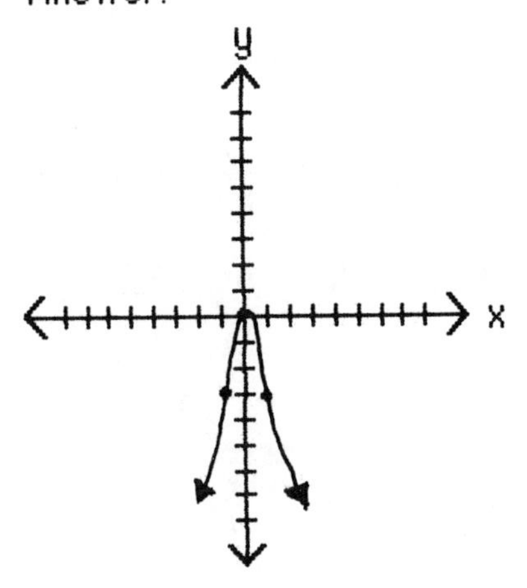

22. Answer:

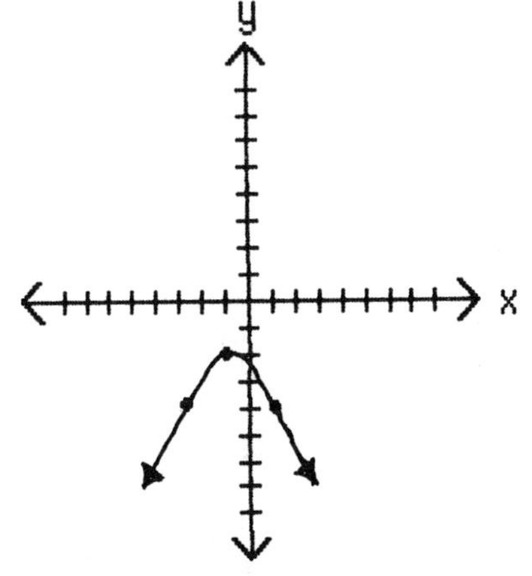

23. $y = 3(x + 1)^2 - 4$

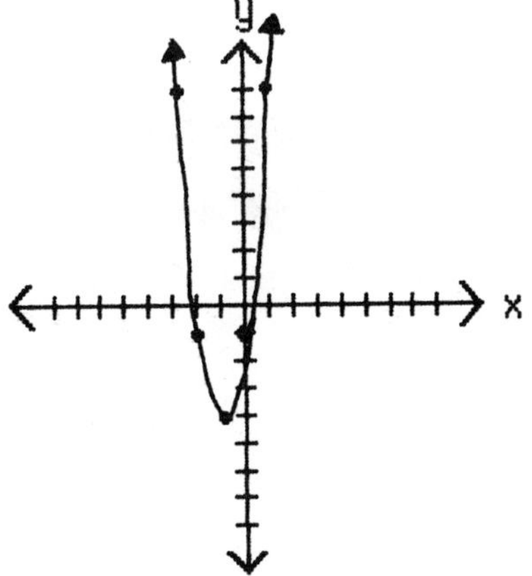

24. $x = -1$ and $x = \frac{5}{2}$

25. lowest point (1, 2)

20. a) 2 mowers

21. c) (0, 0)

22. d) (0, -4)

23. b) (3, -7)

24. e) None of these

25. c) highest point (4, 12)

Chapter 9 Test Keys

Form E

1. c) $y = \pm 3\sqrt{3}$
2. b) $w = -\frac{3}{4}$ or $w = \frac{21}{4}$
3. d) $s = \pm \frac{c\sqrt{2}}{10}$
4. b) $-2 + \sqrt{6}$
5. c) $\frac{81}{4}$
6. a) $p = 6$ or $p = -1$
7. d) $x = \frac{5}{4}$ or $x = \frac{1}{4}$
8. a) $x = \frac{3 \pm \sqrt{21}}{4}$
9. d) $x = 3$ or $x = -\frac{2}{3}$
10. c) $z = -0.3$ or $z = -0.8$
11. c) $x = \frac{4 \pm 2\sqrt{19}}{3}$
12. d) $x = \frac{3 \pm \sqrt{10}}{4}$
13. e) None of these
14. a) $w = 2 \pm 2i$
15. c) $m = 1 \pm i$
16. b) two Real roots
17. a) 16 sides
18. b) 6.8 inches
19. a) 20 meters

Form F

1. b) $x = \pm 2\sqrt{3}$
2. c) $x = -\frac{7}{80}$ or $x = \frac{57}{80}$
3. e) None of these
4. c) $V = \pm \sqrt{10d}$
5. a) $\frac{4}{81}$
6. d) $y = 1$ or $y = -\frac{1}{9}$
7. b) $x = \frac{3 \pm \sqrt{7}}{2}$
8. d) $x = 2 \pm \sqrt{2}$
9. c) $x = 1$ or $x = -\frac{1}{4}$
10. b) $m = 0.1$ or $m = -1.4$
11. a) $x = \frac{3 \pm 2\sqrt{11}}{5}$
12. e) None of these
13. c) $x = \frac{5 \pm 2\sqrt{3}}{4}$
14. d) $z = 3 \pm i\sqrt{3}$
15. a) $x = \frac{3}{4} \pm \frac{\sqrt{7}}{4}i$
16. c) two Real roots
17. d) 37
18. a) $-\frac{1}{2}$
19. d) 17 inches by 17 inches

20. e) None of these

21. b) (0, 0)

22. c) (3, 0)

23. a) (-1, 0)

24. d) $x = 0$ and $x = -2$

25. b) lowest point $(\frac{5}{2}, 100)$

20. b) 5 trailers

21. a) $x = 0$

22. b) (-3, -2)

23. d) (1, 3)

24. c) $x = \frac{5}{2}$ and $x = -1$

25. d) highest point (4, 8)

Name ____________ Appendix Form A Score ________

1. Convert 0.48 to a fraction in lowest terms. 1. ________

2. Convert 5.6 to a fraction in lowest terms. 2. ________

3. Convert $\frac{4}{5}$ to a decimal. 3. ________

4. Convert $\frac{13}{8}$ to a decimal. 4. ________

5. Round 3.6894 to two decimal places. 5. ________

6. Round 12.3864 to the nearest hundredth. 6. ________

7. Perform the indicated operations: 3.45 + 0.6 7. ________

8. Perform the indicated operations: 8. ________
   7.8 + 3.094 + 11.67

9. Perform the indicated operations: 8.3 - 2.75 9. ________

10. Perform the indicated operations: 15.31 - 9.68 10. ________

11. Perform the indicated operations: (0.02)(6.9) 11. ________

12. Perform the indicated operations: (3.4)(19.6) 12. ____________

13. Perform the indicated operations: 9.928 ÷ 0.68 13. ____________

14. Divide 567.8 by 54.3 . Round the quotient to the nearest hundredth. 14. ____________

15. Change 86% to a decimal. 15. ____________

16. Change 6.34% to a decimal. 16. ____________

17. Change 0.065 to a percent. 17. ____________

18. Find 8% of 245. 18. ____________

19. What percent of 300 is 48 ? 19. ____________

20. A person who earns $1450 every two weeks receives an 8% increase. What is the new salary? 20. ____________

Name ____________________ Appendix Form B Score __________

1. Convert 0.52 to a fraction in lowest terms. 1. __________

a. $\frac{52}{100}$

b. $\frac{21}{50}$

c. $\frac{12}{25}$

d. $\frac{13}{25}$

e. None of these

2. Convert 3.8 to a fraction in lowest terms. 2. __________

a. $\frac{19}{50}$

b. $\frac{19}{5}$

c. $\frac{12}{5}$

d. $\frac{17}{5}$

e. None of these

3. Convert $\frac{6}{15}$ to a decimal. 3. __________

a. 2.5
b. 4
c. 0.4
d. 0.53
e. None of these

4. Convert $\frac{15}{8}$ to a decimal. 4. __________

a. 1.875
b. 0.53
c. 1.85
d. 1.35
e. None of these

5. Round 7.5386 to three decimal places. 5. ____________

a. 7.54
b. 7.539
c. 7.53
d. 7.538
e. None of these

6. Round 15.3649 to the nearest hundredth. 6. ____________

a. 20
b. 15.37
c. 15.365
d. 15.36
e. None of these

7. Perform the indicated operations: 6.78 + 0.9 7. ____________

a. 7.68
b. 15.78
c. 6.68
d. 6.87
e. None of these

8. Perform the indicated operations: 8. ____________
9.2 + 6.085 + 15.28

a. 30.365
b. 30.385
c. 30.565
d. 77.05
e. None of these

9. Perform the indicated operations: 9.2 - 5.86 9. ____________

a. 4.66
b. 3.34
c. 3.44
d. 3.36
e. None of these

10. Perform the indicated operations: $16.42 - 9.76$ 10. ____________

a. 6.74
b. 3.34
c. 6.64
d. 6.76
e. None of these

11. Perform the indicated operations: $(0.07)(8.9)$ 11. ____________

a. 0.0623
b. 6.23
c. 62.3
d. 0.623
e. None of these

12. Perform the indicated operations: $(7.8)(18.9)$ 12. ____________

a. 147.52
b. 140.72
c. 147.42
d. 147.32
e. None of these

13. Perform the indicated operations: $7.224 \div 0.48$ 13. ____________

a. 15.05
b. 1.505
c. 0.1505
d. 17.5
e. None of these

14. Divide 643.9 by 28.6. Round the quotient to the nearest thousandth. 14. ____________

a. 22.513
b. 22.5139
c. 2.251
d. 22.514
e None of these

15. Change 64% to a decimal. 15. ____________

a. 64
b. 0.64
c. 6.4
d. 0.064
e. None of these

16. Change 8.45% to a decimal. 16. ____________

a. 0.0845
b. 845
c. 0.845
d. 8.45
e. None of these

17. Change 0.084 to a percent. 17. ____________

a. 0.84%
b. 84%
c. 0.084%
d. 8.4%
e. None of these

18. Find 6% of 346. 18. ____________

a. 20.76
b. 14.46
c. 2.076
d. 207.6
e. None of these

19. What percent of 400 is 52 ? 19. ____________

a. $26\frac{2}{3}\%$
b. 7%
c. 13%
d. 1.3%
e. None of these

20. A person who earns $940 every week receives a 9% increase. What is the new salary? 20. ____________

a. $924.60
b. $84.60
c. $1024.60
d. $1786
e. None of these

Appendix Keys

Form A		Form B	
1.	$\frac{12}{25}$	1.	d) $\frac{13}{25}$
2.	$\frac{28}{5}$	2.	b) $\frac{19}{5}$
3.	0.8	3.	c) 0.4
4.	1.625	4.	a) 1.875
5.	3.69	5.	b) 7.539
6.	12.39	6.	d) 15.36
7.	4.05	7.	a) 7.68
8.	22.564	8.	c) 30.565
9.	5.55	9.	b) 3.34
10.	5.63	10.	e) None of these
11.	0.138	11.	d) 0.623
12.	66.64	12.	c) 147.42
13.	14.6	13.	a) 15.05
14.	10.46	14.	d) 22.514
15.	0.86	15.	b) 0.64
16.	0.0634	16.	a) 0.0845
17.	6.5%	17.	d) 8.4%
18.	19.6	18.	a) 20.76
19.	16%	19.	c) 13%
20.	$1566	20.	c) $1024.60

Name ______________________ Form A Score ______

Midterm Chapters 1-5

1. Write as a single fraction in lowest terms. 1. ________

$$\left(\frac{21}{25} \cdot \frac{10}{18}\right) \div \left(\frac{2}{15} + \frac{2}{3}\right)$$

2. Simplify the expression: $15 - 3^2 \cdot 4 + 18 \div 3$ 2. ________

3. Simplify: $22 - [6 - \frac{2}{3}(12 - 21)]$ 3. ________

4. Evaluate: $x^2 - (6 - y) - 3$ if $x = -5$ and $y = -7$ 4. ________

5. Check for solutions of the equation $5 + |x| = 2x$ from the set $\{-5, -\frac{5}{3}, \frac{5}{3}, 5\}$ 5. ________

6. Remove parenthesis using the distributive property, then simplify: $5(3w - 4) - 2(6 + 2w)$ 6. ________

7. Solve the equation: $13 - 4(7x - 3) = 2x - 5$ 7. ________

8. James is five times as old as his daughter, Amy. Three years ago, Amy was $\frac{1}{8}$ as old as her Dad. How old is James now? 8. ________

9. Solve the inequality: $4 - 3x < 16$

9. 

10. Two trains leave a station at the same time traveling in opposite directions. One is traveling at 70 mph and the other at 80 mph. How long will it take for them to be 90 miles apart?

10. 

11. Simplify. Write your answer without negative exponents: $(2xy^2z^3)(-3xy^4)^{-1}(x^{-2}y^0z^{-5})$

11. ______________

12. Simplify. Write your answer in descending order of exponents: $(7y^3 - y - 4) - (8 - 4y + y^2) + (3y^2 - 9 - 8y^2)$

12. ______________

13. Simplify: $(x - 2y)(2x + y) - (3x - y)^2$

13. ______________

14. The difference of the square of a number and six is equal to the square of the sum of the number and three. Find the number.

14. ______________

15. Divide: $\dfrac{6 - y + y^3}{y + 2}$

15. ______________

16. Factor completely: $2x^4 + 6x^3 - 36x^2$

16. ______________

17. Factor completely: $8x^2 - 14x - 15$ 17. 

18. Factor completely by grouping: 18. 

$$xm^2 - 3m^2 - xn^2 + 3n^2$$

19. Solve the equation: $6x^2 + 3x - 18 = 0$ 19. 

20. The "Fuzzy Wuzzy Bear" company makes teddy bears. The daily cost C of making x dozen bears is given by $C = 15x^2 - 90x + 120$. On one day, the daily cost was \$945. How many bears were made that day? 20. ____________

21. Determine any values of the variable for which the rational expression $\dfrac{x}{9 - x^2}$ is undefined. 21. 

22. Divide and write the answer in lowest terms: 22. ____________

$$\frac{x^2 + x - 12}{x^2 - x - 20} \div \frac{2x^2 - 7x + 3}{x^2 - 6x + 5}$$

23. Solve the equation: $\dfrac{9}{x} - \dfrac{2}{x - 3} = \dfrac{x + 3}{x^2 - 3x}$ 23. ____________

24. Joe can plow the garden in 4 hours. Eddy can plow it in 6 hours. How long does it take them to plow the garden together?

24. ____________

25. Suppose y varies directly as x and $y = 12$ when $x = 9$. Find y when $x = 27$.

25. ____________

Name ______________________ Form B Score ______

Midterm Chapters 1-5

1. Write as a single fraction in lowest terms. 1. ____________

$$\left(\frac{16}{21} \cdot \frac{14}{24}\right) \div \left(\frac{7}{5} - \frac{1}{3}\right)$$

a. $\frac{4}{27}$

b. $\frac{5}{14}$

c. $\frac{5}{12}$

d. $\frac{10}{9}$

e. None of these

2. Simplify the expression: $12 - 4^3 \cdot 2 - 27 \div 3$ 2. ____________

a. -125

b. $332\frac{1}{3}$

c. -131

d. -21

e. None of these

3. Simplify: $23 - [8 - \frac{3}{4}(-15 - 13)]$ 3. ____________

a. 52

b. 226

c. $\frac{13}{2}$

d. -6

e. None of these

4. Evaluate: $x^2 - (9 - y) - 4$ if $x = -3$ and $y = 2$ 4. ____________

a. -20

b. -2

c. -6

d. -17

e. None of these

5. Check for solutions of the equation $3 + |x| = 3x - 1$ from the set $\{-2, -1, 1, 2\}$ 5. ____________

   a. 2
   b. 1
   c. -1
   d. -2
   e. None of these

6. Remove parenthesis using the distributive property, then simplify: $2(5x - 3) - 4(2 - 3x)$ 6. ____________

   a. $7x - 11$
   b. $-2x - 14$
   c. $22x - 14$
   d. $22x - 2$
   e. None of these

7. Solve the equation: $15 - 8(3x - 4) = 4x - 9$ 7. ____________

   a. $x = -2$
   b. $x = \frac{1}{2}$
   c. $x = \frac{5}{7}$
   d. $x = \frac{19}{17}$
   e. None of these

8. Suzette is five times as old as her niece Sally. Eight years from now, Sally will be $\frac{1}{3}$ as old as Suzette. How old is Suzette now? 8. ____________

   a. 8 years
   b. 24 years
   c. 32 years
   d. 40 years
   e. None of these

9. Solve the inequality: $5 - 6x > 17$ 9. ____________

   a. $x < -\frac{11}{3}$
   b. $x > -\frac{11}{3}$
   c. $x < -2$
   d. $x > -2$
   e. None of these

10. Two trains leave a station at the same time traveling in opposite directions. One is traveling at 75 mph and the other at 85 mph. How long will it take for them to be 80 miles apart? 10. ________

a. 2 hours
b. 30 minutes
c. 8 hours
d. 45 minutes
e. None of these

11. Simplify. Write your answer without negative exponents: $(4m^2n^3p)(-2mp^4)^{-2}(m^{-2}n^0p^{-4})$ 11. ________

a. $\frac{-16n^3}{m^2p}$
b. 0
c. $\frac{n^3p}{m^2}$
d. $\frac{n^3}{m^2p^{11}}$
e. None of these

12. Simplify. Write your answer in descending order of exponents: 12. ________

$$(9w^2 - 3w + 6) - (12 - 3w^3 + 2w) + (4w^2 - 9 - 6w)$$

a. $-3w^3 + 13w^2 - 7w - 15$
b. $3w^3 + 13w^2 - 11w - 15$
c. $3w^3 + 5w^2 + w + 3$
d. $3w^3 + 13w^2 - 7w - 15$
e. None of these

13. Simplify: $(3x - y)(x + 3y) - (2x + y)^2$ 13. ________

a. $-x^2 + 8xy - 4y^2$
b. $-x^2 + 12xy - 2y^2$
c. $-x^2 + 4xy - 4y^2$
d. $-x^2 - 4y^2$
e. None of these

14. The sum of the square of a number and sixteen is equal to the square of the difference of the number and two. Find the number.

14. ____________

a. -3
b. -7
c. -5
d. -4
e. None of these

15. Divide: $\frac{m^3 - 3m + 18}{m + 3}$

15. ____________

a. $m^2 + 3m + 6$
b. $m^2 - 3m + 6$
c. $m^2 - 3m - 6$
d. $m^2 - 6$
e. None of these

16. Factor completely: $3x^3 + 9x^2 - 30x$

16. ____________

a. $3x(x - 2)(x + 5)$
b. $(3x - 6)(x^2 + 5x)$
c. $3x(x^2 + 3x - 10)$
d. $3x(x - 5)(x + 2)$
e. None of these

17. Factor completely: $12x^2 - 8x - 15$

17. ____________

a. $(4x + 3)(3x - 5)$
b. $(6x - 5)(2x + 3)$
c. $(4x - 3)(3x + 5)$
d. $(6x + 5)(2x - 3)$
e. None of these

18. Factor completely by grouping:
$ax^2 - ay^2 - bx^2 + by^2$

18. ____________

a. $(a - b)(x^2 - y^2)$
b. $(a - b)(a + b)(x - y)$
c. $(a - b)(x + y)(x - y)$
d. $(a - b)(x - y)^2$
e. None of these

19. Solve the equation: $12x^2 - 4x - 16 = 0$ 19. ____________

a. $x = \frac{3}{4}, x = 1$

b. $x = \frac{4}{3}, x = -1$

c. $x = \frac{3}{4}, x = -1$

d. $x = -\frac{4}{3}, x = 1$

e. None of these

20. The "Little Lamb" toy company makes stuffed lambs. The daily cost C of making x dozen lambs is given by $C = 18x^2 - 108x + 144$. On one day, the daily cost was \$1440. How many lambs were made that day? 20. ____________

a. 6 dozen
b. 11 dozen
c. 8 dozen
d. 12 dozen
e None of these

21. Determine any values of the variable for which the rational expression $\frac{x}{25 - x^2}$ is undefined. 21. ____________

a. $x = 5$ or $x = -5$
b. $x = 5$ or $x = 0$
c. $x = 0$
d. $x = 5$
e. None of these

22. Divide and write the answer in lowest terms: 22. ____________

$$\frac{3x^2 + 2x - 1}{x^2 - 1} \div \frac{9x^2 - 1}{2x^2 + x - 3}$$

a. $\frac{(3 + 2x)(x - 1)}{8}$

b. $\frac{(3x - 1)^2(3x + 1)}{(2x + 3)(x - 1)^2}$

c. $\frac{2x + 3}{3x + 1}$

d. $\frac{2x + 3}{3x - 1}$

e. None of these

23. Solve the equation: $\frac{8}{x} + \frac{4}{x-2} = \frac{x+6}{x^2-2x}$

23. ____________

a. $x = \frac{8}{11}$

b. $x = \frac{6}{11}$

c. $x = \frac{-10}{13}$

d. $x = 2$

e. None of these

24. Joellen can pick a quart of strawberries in 30 minutes. Josy can pick a quart of strawberries in 45 minutes. How long does it take them together to pick 1 quart of strawberries?

24. 

a. 18 minutes

b. 37.5 minutes

c. 15 minutes

d. 20 minutes

e. None of these

25. Suppose y varies directly as x and $y = 6$ when $x = 16$. Find y when $x = 56$.

25. ____________

a. $y = 149\frac{1}{3}$

b. $y = 10$

c. $y = 56$

d. $y = 21$

e. None of these

Midterm Test Keys

Form A

1. $\frac{7}{12}$
2. -15
3. 10
4. 9
5. 5
6. $11w - 32$
7. $x = 1$
8. 35 years
9. $x > -4$
10. 36 minutes or $\frac{3}{5}$ hour
11. $\frac{-2}{3x^2y^2z^2}$
12. $7y^3 - 6y^2 + 3y - 21$
13. $-7x^2 + 3xy - 3y^2$
14. $x = -\frac{5}{2}$
15. $y^2 - 2y + 3$
16. $2x^2(x + 6)(x - 3)$
17. $(4x + 3)(2x - 5)$
18. $(x - 3)(m + n)(m - n)$
19. $x = \frac{3}{2}$ or $x = -2$
20. 11 dozen
21. $x = 3$ and $x = -3$
22. $\frac{x - 1}{2x - 1}$
23. $x = 5$
24. $2\frac{2}{5}$ hours
25. $y = 36$

Form B

1. c) $\frac{5}{12}$
2. a) -125
3. d) -6
4. b) -2
5. a) 2
6. c) $22x - 14$
7. e) None of these
8. d) 40 years
9. c) $x < -2$
10. b) 30 minutes
11. d) $\frac{n^3}{m^2p^{11}}$
12. b) $3w^3 + 13w^2 - 11w - 15$
13. c) $-x^2 + 4xy - 4y^2$
14. a) -3
15. b) $m^2 - 3m + 6$
16. a) $3x(x - 2)(x + 5)$
17. d) $(6x + 5)(2x - 3)$
18. c) $(a - b)(x + y)(x - y)$
19. b) $x = \frac{4}{3}$, $x = -1$
20. d) 12 dozen
21. a) $x = 5$ or $x = -5$
22. c) $\frac{2x + 3}{3x + 1}$
23. e) None of these
24. a) 18 minutes
25. d) $y = 21$

Name ______________________ FINAL Form A Score ________

1. Write as a single fraction in lowest terms. 1. ____________

$$\left(\frac{18}{25} + \frac{15}{24}\right) \div \left(\frac{2}{3} + \frac{3}{4}\right)$$

2. Simplify the expression: $4^3 - 3^2 \cdot 4 + 24 \div 12$ 2. ____________

3. Simplify: $35 - [9 - \frac{4}{5}(9 - 24)]$ 3. ____________

4. Evaluate: $y^2 - 2(3 - x) - 4$ if $x = -2$ and $y = -6$ 4. ____________

5. Check for solutions of the equation $\frac{|x - 5|}{3} = 4x$ from the set $\{-\frac{5}{11}, -\frac{5}{13}, \frac{5}{13}, \frac{5}{11}\}$ 5. ____________

6. Remove parenthesis using the distributive property, then simplify: $8(5 - 2x) - 3(4 + 7x)$ 6. ____________

7. Solve the equation: $9 - 5(4 - 3x) = 3x - 5$ 7. ____________

8. Joanne is paid $350 a week plus a commission of 8% on sales. Find the sales (in dollars) needed to give her a weekly total of $580. 8. ____________

9. Solve the inequality: $-8 < 4 - 2x < 6$ 9. ____________

10. How much interest is made on $2600 invested at $8\frac{1}{2}\%$ interest for two years? 10. ____________

11. Solve: $x + 3 = 2 - 5(x + 2)$ for x 11. ____________

12. Simplify the expression and write your answer without negative exponents: 12. ____________

$$\frac{(6x^2y^{-3})(-4xz^3)^{-1}}{(3xyz^2)^{-2}}$$

13. Simplify. Write your answer in descending order of exponents: $(9m^2 - m - 5) - (3m^3 - 6 + m^2) + (4m^2 - 6m^3)$ 13. ____________

14. Simplify: $25 - 3\,[4x^2 + 6 - (x^2 - 6)]$ 14. ____________

15. Simplify: $(x - 3y)(4x + y) - (x - 2y)^2$ 15. ____________

16. Find two consecutive positive integers so that the sum of their squares is 313. 16. ____________

17. Divide: $\dfrac{x^3 - 7x - 6}{x - 3}$ 17. ________

18. Factor completely: $2x^3 + 2x^2 - 84x$ 18. ________

19. Factor completely: $6x^2 + 19x + 10$ 19. ________

20. Factor completely by grouping: $4x^2 - 4y^2 - x^3 + xy^2$ 20. ________

21. Solve the equation: $5x^2 - 14x - 24 = 0$ 21. ________

22. In a sports league of n teams in which each team plays every other team once, the total number N of games to be played is given by $N = \frac{1}{2}(n^2 - n)$. A certain league plays a total of 15 games. What is the total number of teams in the league? 22. ________

23. Determine any values of the variable for which the rational expression $\dfrac{x + 1}{1 - x^2}$ is undefined. 23. ________

24. Divide and write the answer in lowest terms: 24. ________

$$\frac{x^2 - 4x - 5}{2x^2 + 5x + 3} \div \frac{x^2 - 6x + 5}{3x^2 - x - 2}$$

25. Solve the equation: $\frac{1}{x} + \frac{3}{5x} = 4$ 25. ______________

26. A swimming pool can be filled by one hose in 6 hours and by a second hose in 8 hours. How long would it take to fill the pool if both hoses were used? 26. ______________

27. Consumer specialists have determined that the amount F that a family spends on food varies directly as its income I. A family making $12480 spends $2496 on food. How much will a family making $18600 spend on food? 27. ______________

28. Determine if the line passing through the points (3, 4) and (-2, 9) is parallel to the line passing through the points (1, 3)and (-2, 6). 28. ______________

29. In a coordinate plane, plot the point (3, -1). Then plot two other points so that all three points lie on a line with a slope $-\frac{2}{3}$. 29. ______________

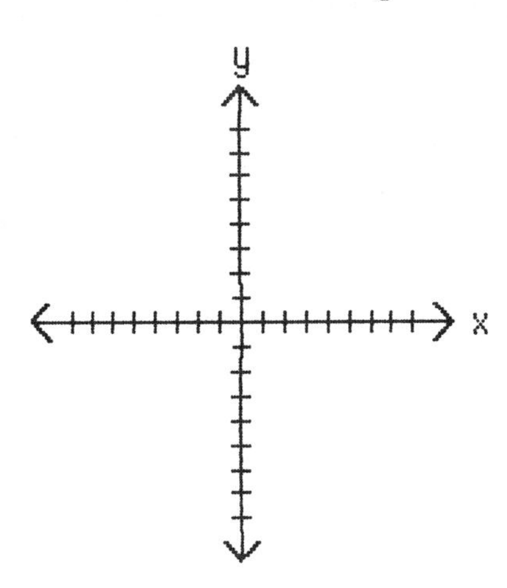

30. Find an equation of a line through the two points $P(-5, 3)$ and $Q(2, 1)$. 30. 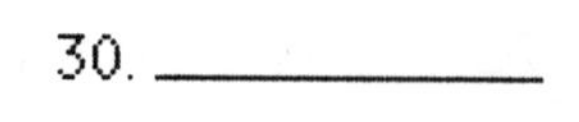

31. Graph the linear inequality given by $2x + y < 4$. 31. 

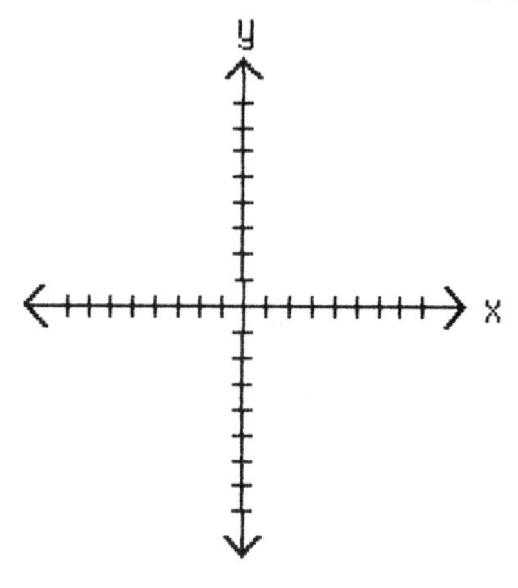

32. Alex buys a color television for \$450. The value of the television decreases with time. At the end of 3 years, the television has a resale value of \$150. Assume that the value V of the television is linearly dependent upon the number of years after purchase. Write the linear equation that expresses V in terms of t, the number of years after purchase. 32. 

33. Suppose y is a function of x defined by $y = -\dfrac{x}{9 - x}$. State the domain of the function. 33. ______________

34. Let $f(x) = \dfrac{3x^2 + 1}{3 + x}$. Find $f(4)$. 34. 

35. Solve the system of equations by the elimination method: $2x + 2y = 74$
$3x - 3y = 69$

35. ____________

36. Solve the system of equations using the substitution method: $x - y = -2$
$6x + 2y = -28$

36. ____________

37. One number is one-fifth of another. The difference between the numbers is 32. Find the two numbers.

37. ____________

38. The width of a rectangular drawing is 5 cm. less than its length. The perimeter is 95 cm. Find the length and width.

38. ____________

39. Graph the system of linear inequalities: $x + y \leq 4$
$y \geq -1$
$x \geq -2$

39. ____________

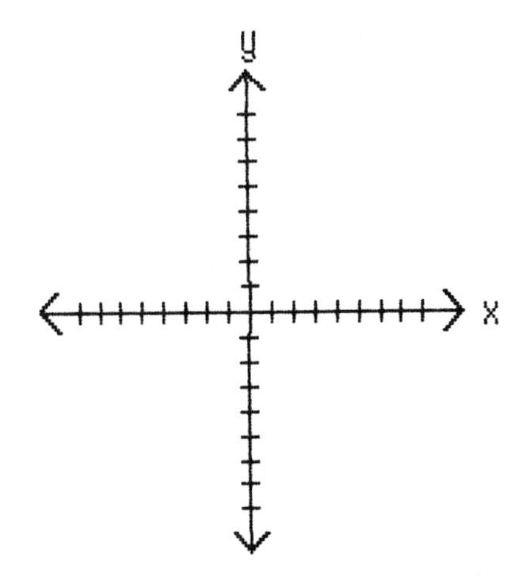

40. Simplify by combining like radicals:

$$6\sqrt{32} - 8\sqrt{50} + \sqrt{8}$$

40. ____________

41. Rationalize the denominator and simplify: $\dfrac{m}{2 - \sqrt{m}}$

41. ____________

42. Solve the radical equation: $6 + \sqrt{x - 3} = 12$

42. ____________

43. Use properties of exponents to simplify: $\left(\dfrac{2x^{1/3}}{6x^{3/4}}\right)^3$

43. ____________

44. Peform the indicated operations and write the answer in the form $a + bi$. $3 + (2 - 4i) - (1 - i)$

44. ____________

45. Peform the indicated operations and write the answer in the form $a + bi$. $\dfrac{3 - 5i}{2i}$

45. ____________

46. Solve the equation $(x - 2)^2 = 36$

46. ____________

47. Solve the quadratic equation. Write all solutions that are complex numbers in standard form.

$$4x^2 - 8x - 1 = 0$$

47. ____________

48. Use the discriminant to determine if the roots are real or complex. Also, determine the number of roots. Do not solve the equation: $x^2 - 10x - 5 = 0$ 48. ____________

49. The width of a rectangle is 5 m. less than the length. The area is 176 sq. m. Find the length and width. 49. ____________

50. Determine if the graph of $y = -2x^2 + 8x - 6$ has a highest point or a lowest point and find the coordinates of this point. 50. ____________

Name ______________________ FINAL Form B Score ______

1. Write as a single fraction in lowest terms. 1. ____________

$$\left(\frac{3}{8} + \frac{2}{3}\right) \div \left(\frac{5}{4} - \frac{5}{16}\right)$$

2. Simplify the expression: $5^2 - 2^3 \cdot 3 + 24 \div 6$ 2. ____________

3. Simplify: $42 - [16 - \frac{5}{6}(9 + 3^2)]$ 3. ____________

4. Evaluate: $2x^2 - 5(6 - y) - 2$ if $x = -4$ and $y = -5$ 4. ____________

5. Check for solutions of the equation $|2x - 1| = 3$ from the set $\{-2, -1, 1, 2\}$ 5. ____________

6. Remove parenthesis using the distributive property, then simplify: $3(8 - 3x) - 5(6 + 5x)$ 6. ____________

7. Solve the equation: $12 - 7(6 - 4x) = 12x + 2$ 7. ____________

8. Joachim is paid $475 a week plus a commission of 9% on sales. Find the sales (in dollars) needed to give him a weekly total of $655. 8. ____________

9. Solve the inequality: $-15 < 6 - 9x < 9$ 9. ____________

10. How much interest is made on \$3800 invested at $8\frac{1}{2}\%$ interest for two years? 10. ____________

11. Solve: $x + 8 = 4 - 6(x - 3)$ for x 11. ____________

12. Simplify the expression and write your answer without negative exponents: 12. ____________

$$\frac{(4x^3y^{-2})^{-2}(-3xw^4)}{(2xy^0w^{-2})^{-3}}$$

13. Simplify. Write your answer in descending order of exponents: $(13y^2 - 5y) - (9y^3 - 6y + y^2) + (22y - 14y^3)$ 13. ____________

14. Simplify: $-13 - 4[5x^2 - 12 - (7 - x^2)]$ 14. ____________

15. Simplify: $(5a - b)(a + 4b) - (2a - b)^2$ 15. ____________

16. Find two consecutive positive integers so that the difference of their squares is 63. 16. ____________

17. Divide: $\frac{x^3 - x^2 - x - 2}{x - 2}$ 17. ____________

18. Factor completely: $2x^3 - 2x^2 - 112x$ 18. ____________

19. Factor completely: $28y^2 - 15y + 2$ 19. ____________

20. Factor completely by grouping: 20. ____________

$$2m^3 - 8m - ym^2 + 4y$$

21. Solve the equation: $6x^2 + 10x - 24 = 0$ 21. ____________

22. The area of a triangle is 28 square inches. The base is 2 inches longer than three times the height. Find the length of the base. 22. ____________

23. Determine any values of the variable for which the rational expression $\frac{6}{7x - 6}$ is undefined. 23. ____________

24. Divide and write the answer in lowest terms: 24. ____________

$$\frac{a^2 - b^2}{a^2 + b^2} \div \frac{a - b}{a + b}$$

25. Solve the equation: $\frac{5x - 2}{4} - \frac{2x + 1}{6} = 3$ 25. ____________

26. The reciprocal of 4 more than a number is three times the reciprocal of the number itself. What is the number? 26. ____________

27. Consumer specialists have determined that the amount F that a family spends on food varies directly as its income I. A family making $22600 spends $4972 on food. How much will a family making $19500 spend on food? 27. ____________

28. Determine if the line passing through the points (4, 7) and (2, -1) is parallel to the line passing through the points (7, -1)and 5, -7). 28. ____________

29. In a coordinate plane, plot the point (5, -3). Then plot two other points so that all three points lie on a line with a slope $\frac{3}{4}$. 29. ____________

y

x

30. Find an equation of a line through the two points P(-4, 1) and Q(2, -4). 30. ____________

31. Graph the linear inequality given by $4x - 3y > 12$ 31. ____________

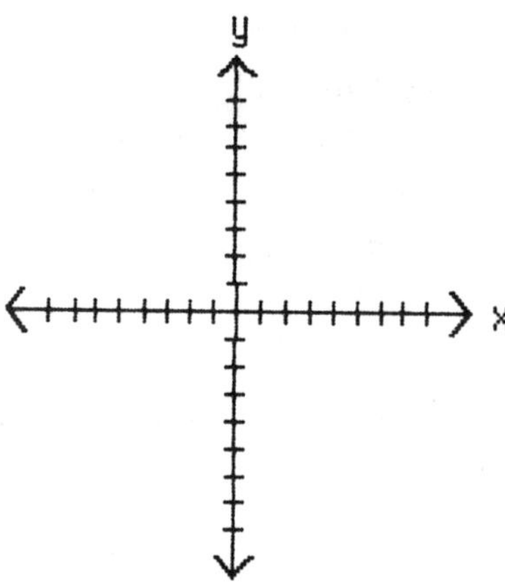

32. Jonas rents a car for an eight-day trip. If the rental agency charges $19 per day plus 25 cents per mile, express the cost of renting the car for the trip if he drove a total of x miles. 32. ____________

33. Suppose y is a function of x defined by $y = |3 - x|$. State the domain of the function. 33. ____________

34. Let $f(x) = \dfrac{|3 - x|}{x^2}$. Find $f(7)$. 34. ____________

35. Solve the system of equations by the elimination method: 35. ____________

$$3x - 5y = -1$$
$$4x + 2y = 3$$

36. Solve the system of equations using the substitution method: 36. ____________

$$4x + y = 5$$
$$x + 2y = -4$$

37. A fuel which sells for 83¢ per gallon is mixed with another fuel which sells for 92¢ per gallon. The new mixture sells for 89¢ per gallon. How many gallons of the 83¢ fuel would be used to make 12 gallons of the mixture? 37. ______

38. The perimeter of a rectangle is 83 inches. The length is 7 inches less than twice the width. Find the length. 38. ______

39. Graph the system of linear inequalities: $x + y \geq -1$ 39. ______

$$y \geq -1$$
$$x \leq 3$$

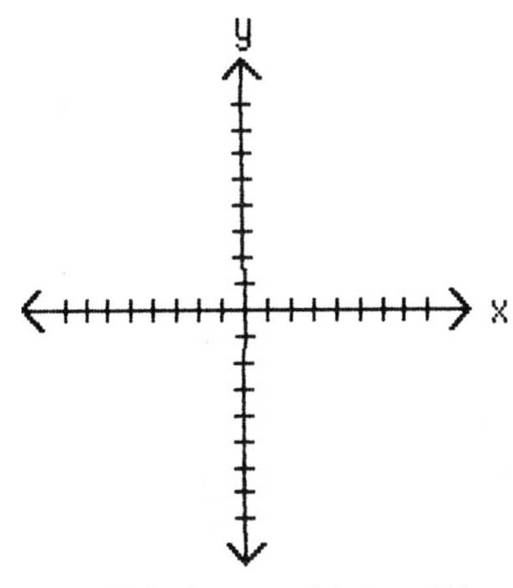

40. Simplify by combining like radicals: 40. ______

$$3\sqrt{147} - 4\sqrt{75} + 2\sqrt{27}$$

41. Rationalize the denominator and simplify: $\dfrac{3x}{2 + \sqrt{3x}}$ 41. ______

42. Solve the radical equation: $\sqrt{3x + 1} - 3 = 8$ 42. ______

43. Use properties of exponents to simplify: $\left(\frac{3y^{2/3}}{12x^{3}}\right)^{3}$ 43. ____________

44. Peform the indicated operations and write the answer in the form $a + bi$. $(6 + 3i) + (1 - 2i) - (4i)$ 44. ____________

45. Peform the indicated operations and write the answer in the form $a + bi$. $\frac{8 - 12i}{6i}$ 45. ____________

46. Solve the equation $(x + 3)^2 = 9$ 46. ____________

47. Solve the quadratic equation. Write all solutions that are complex numbers in standard form. 47. ____________

$$3x^2 - 8x + 1 = 0$$

48. Use the discriminant to determine if the roots are real or complex. Also, determine the number of roots. Do not solve the equation: $3x^2 + 5x + 2 = 0$ 48. ____________

49. The width of a rectangle is 4 meters less than the length. The area is 437 square meters. Find the width. 49. ____________

50. Determine if the graph of $y = -2x^2 + 8x + 3$ has a highest point or a lowest point and find the coordinates of this point. 50. ____________

Name ________________ FINAL Form C Score ______

1. Write as a single fraction in lowest terms. 1. ________

$$\left(\frac{15}{24}+\frac{36}{45}\right)\div\left(\frac{2}{5}+\frac{1}{2}\right)$$

2. Simplify the expression: $2^4 - 4^2 \cdot 3 + 56 \div 8$ 2. ________

3. Simplify: $54 - 2[12 - \frac{3}{5}(8 - 33)]$ 3. ________

4. Evaluate: $4a^2 - 5(4 - b) - 4$ if $a = -3$ and $b = -7$ 4. ________

5. Check for solutions of the equation $|5 - 2x| = 3x$ from the set $\{-5, -1, 1, 5\}$ 5. ________

6. Remove parenthesis using the distributive property, then simplify: $6(9 - 4x) - 4(8 - 2x)$ 6. ________

7. Solve the equation: $8 - 2(7 - 5x) = 15x - 9$ 7. ________

8. Jeremy is paid \$425 a week plus a commission of 8.5% on sales. Find the sales (in dollars) needed to give him a weekly total of \$595. 8. ________

9. Solve the inequality: $-12 < 5 - 3y < -6$ 9. ____________

10. How much interest is made on \$4500 invested at $9\frac{1}{2}\%$ interest for two years? 10. ____________

11. Solve: $m - 12 = 7 - 12(m - 4)$ for m 11. ____________

12. Simplify the expression and write your answer without negative exponents: 12. ____________

$$\frac{(6x^4y^{-3})^{-1}(-4xz^3)}{(3xy^2z^{-2})^{-4}}$$

13. Simplify. Write your answer in descending order of exponents: $(4 - x^2 + 8x) - (6x - 14x^3 + 4) + (7x^2 - 9x^3 - 1)$ 13. ____________

14. Simplify: $18 - 6\,[3x^2 - 9 - (4 - x^2)]$ 14. ____________

15. Simplify: $(4x - y)^2 - (2x + 3y)(x - y)$ 15. ____________

16. Find two consecutive odd positive integers so that the sum of their squares is 202. 16. ____________

17. Divide: $\dfrac{y^3 - 27}{y - 3}$ 17. ____________

18. Factor completely: $2w^3 + 18w^2 + 28w$ 18. ____________

19. Factor completely: $9y^2 + 9y - 10$ 19. ____________

20. Factor completely by grouping: $8 + 4y - 2m^2 - m^2y$ 20. ____________

21. Solve the equation: $4x^2 + 7x - 2 = 0$ 21. ____________

22. Two negative numbers have the property that one of them is three less than twice the other. If their product is 44, find the two numbers. 22. ____________

23. Deterimine any values of the variable for which the rational expression $\dfrac{3V + 2}{V^2 + 2V}$ is undefined. 23. ____________

24. Divide and write the answer in lowest terms: 24. ____________

$$\frac{3y + 12}{y + 4} \div \frac{y + 4}{y^2 - 16}$$

25. Solve the equation: $\frac{8}{2x} + \frac{10}{x+4} = \frac{6}{x}$

25. ____________

26. One car travels 10 mph faster than another. While one travels 75 miles, the other travels 105 miles. Find the speed of the faster car.

26. ____________

27. If m varies inversely as the square of p, and m is $\frac{1}{16}$ when p is 12, find m when p is 6.

27. ____________

28. Determine if the line passing through the points (-4, -1) and (3, 4) is parallel to the line passing through the points (6, -3)and (1, -10).

28. ____________

29. In a coordinate plane, plot the point (-3, 0). Then plot two other points so that all three points lie on a line with a slope $-\frac{5}{6}$.

29. ____________

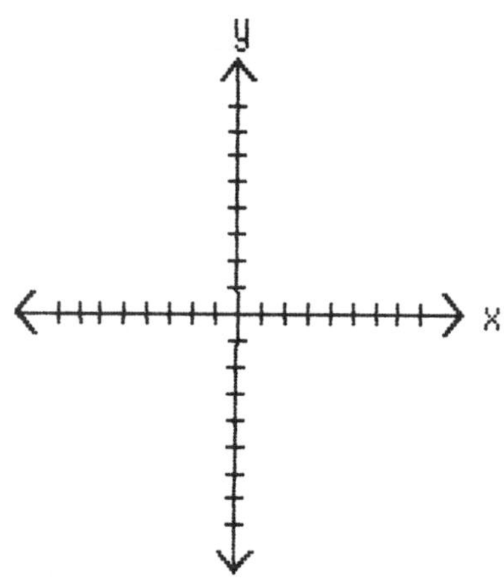

30. Find an equation of a line through the two points P(5, -1) and Q(1, 4).

30. ____________

31. Graph the linear inequality given by $5x - y \geq 6$. 31. 

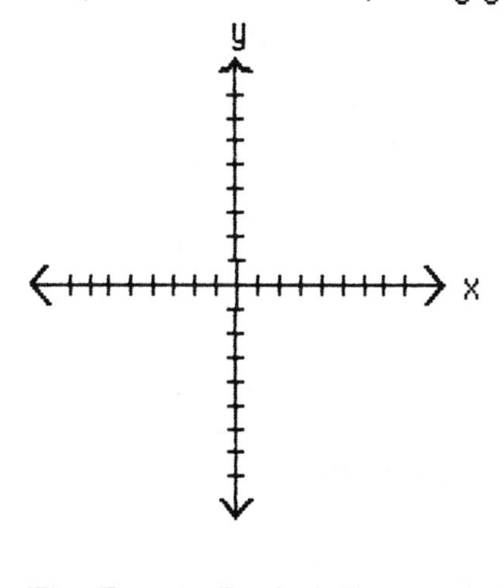

32. The Tennis Racket Company makes x tennis rackets each day with a cost per racket of \$18 and a fixed cost of \$125 per day. Express the daily cost C in terms of x. 32. ____________

33. Suppose y is a function of x defined by $y = \dfrac{4}{x^2 + 1}$. State the domain of the function. 33. ____________

34. Let $f(x) = \dfrac{6x^2 - 5}{6 + x}$. Find $f(3)$. 34. ____________

35. Solve the system of equations by the elimination method:

$$5x - 2y = 1$$
$$-x + 3y = 5$$

35. ____________

36. Solve the system of equations using the substitution method:

$$x + 2y = 6$$
$$2x + y = 7$$

36. ____________

37. Butterscotch candy worth \$1.20 per pound and peppermint candy worth \$1.45 per pound are mixed to make a 70 pound mixture which sells for \$1.30 per pound. Find the number of pounds of butterscotch candy used. 37. ____________

38. The width of a rectangular picture is 2 cm. less than its length. The perimeter is 22 cm. Find the length. 38. ____________

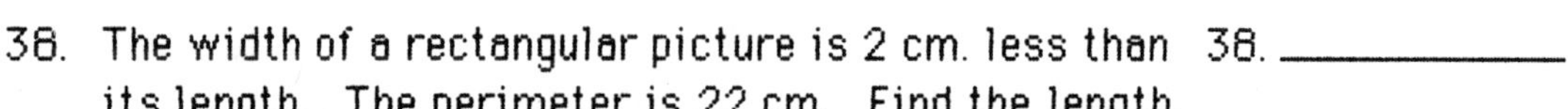

39. Graph the system of linear inequalities: 39. ____________

$$2x - y \geq 3$$
$$y < 6$$
$$x > -1$$

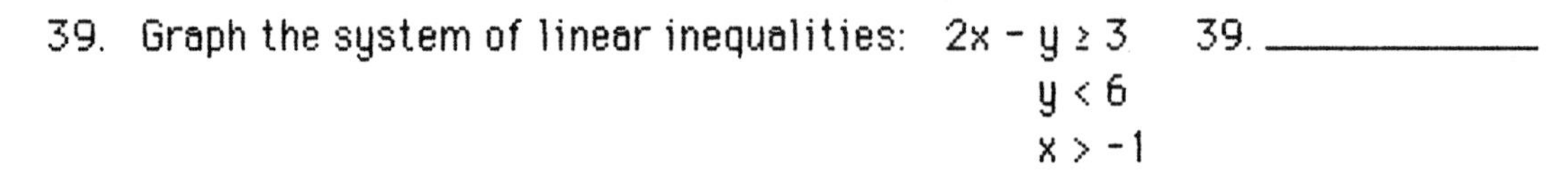

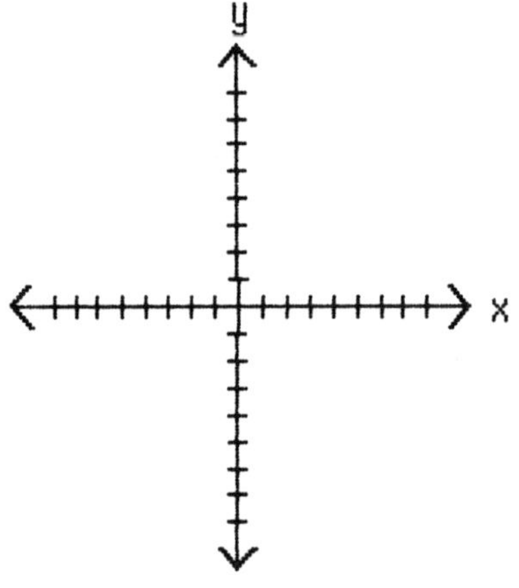

40. Simplify by combining like radicals: 40. ____________

$$4\sqrt{128} - 3\sqrt{98} + 2\sqrt{72}$$

41. Rationalize the denominator and simplify: $\dfrac{3}{6 - \sqrt{3}}$ 41. ____________

42. Solve the radical equation: $9 + \sqrt{2x - 1} = 15$ 42. ____________

43. Use properties of exponents to simplify: $\left(\frac{8m^{1/5}}{24m^{2}}\right)^{5}$ 43. ____________

44. Peform the indicated operations and write the answer in the form $a + bi$. $9 - (4 + 3i) + (2 - 3i)$ 44. ____________

45. Peform the indicated operations and write the answer in the form $a + bi$. $\frac{-9 - 6i}{3i}$ 45. ____________

46. Solve the equation $(2x - 3)^2 = 49$ 46. ____________

47. Solve the quadratic equation. Write all solutions that are complex numbers in standard form. 47. ____________

$$5x^2 + 6x + 2 = 0$$

48. Use the discriminant to determine if the roots are real or complex. Also, determine the number of roots. Do not solve the equation: $2x^2 - x + 3 = 0$ 48. ____________

49. The length of a rectangle is 3 inches less than twice the width. The area is 54 square inches. Find the length. 49. ____________

50. Determine if the graph of $y = 2x^2 + 3x - 2$ has a highest point or a lower point and find the coordinates of this point. 50. ____________

Name ______________________ FINAL Form D Score ______

1. Write as a single fraction in lowest terms. 1. ____________

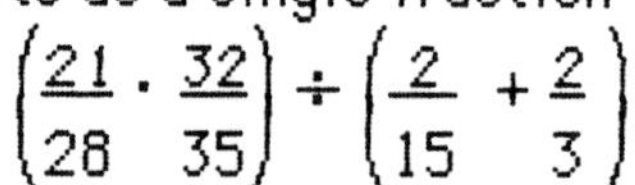

$$\left(\frac{21}{28} \cdot \frac{32}{35}\right) \div \left(\frac{2}{15} + \frac{2}{3}\right)$$

a. $\frac{3}{75}$
b. $\frac{6}{7}$
c. $\frac{5}{7}$
d. $\frac{108}{35}$
e. None of these

2. Simplify the expression: $-2^3 + 5^2 \cdot 3 - 18 \div 3^2$ 2. ____________

a. 31
b. $\frac{11}{3}$
c. 58
d. 65
e. None of these

3. Simplify: $81 - [38 - \frac{4}{5}(45 - 20)]$ 3. ____________

a. 23
b. - 849
c. 63
d. 99
e. None of these

4. Evaluate: $y^2 - 2(4 - x) - 3$ if $x = -4$ and $y = -9$ 4. ____________

a. 62
b. -37
c. 65
d. 629
e. None of these

5. Check for solutions of the equation $\frac{|x - 8|}{5} = 2x$ from the set $\{-\frac{8}{11}, -\frac{8}{9}, \frac{8}{9}, \frac{8}{11}\}$ 5. ______________

a. $x = -\frac{8}{11}, x = \frac{8}{9}$

b. $x = -\frac{8}{11}, x = -\frac{8}{9}$

c. $x = \frac{8}{9}, x = \frac{8}{11}$

d. $x = -\frac{8}{9}, x = \frac{8}{11}$

e. None of these

6. Remove parenthesis using the distributive property, then simplify: $-12(2 - 6x) - 8(9 + 4x)$ 6. ______________

a. $-104x - 96$
b. $40x - 96$
c. $76x - 96$
d. $-2x - 96$
e. None of these

7. Solve the equation: $5x + 5 = -4 - (x + 3)$ 7. ______________

a. $x = -2$
b. $x = -6$
c. $x = -1$
d. $x = -\frac{1}{2}$
e. None of these

8. Justine is paid $834 a month plus a commission of 9.5% on sales. Find the sales (in dollars) needed to give her a monthly total of $1594. 8. ______________

a. $80
b. $25557.90
c. $760
d. $80,000
e. None of these

9. Solve the inequality: $0 \le 3 - 5x \le 12$ 9. ______________

a. $-\frac{9}{5} \le x \le 0$

b. $-3 \le x \le -\frac{3}{5}$

c. $2 \le x \le 14$

d. $-\frac{9}{5} \le x \le \frac{3}{5}$

e. None of these

10. How much interest is made on \$4800 invested at $9\frac{1}{2}\%$ interest for two years? 10. ____________

a. \$9120
b. \$912
c. \$91.20
d. \$456
e. None of these

11. Solve: $2x - 21 = 8 - 17(x - 5)$ for x 11. ____________

a. $x = -6$
b. $x = 6$
c. $x = -4.8$
d. $x = \frac{24}{19}$
e. None of these

12. Simplify the expression and write your answer without negative exponents: 12. ____________

$$\frac{(8a^3b^{-1}c^{-2})^{-2}(-4a^0b^2)}{(4a^{-1}bc^3)^{-3}}$$

a. $\frac{4a^5b^2}{c^4}$
b. $\frac{4b^7c^{13}}{a^8}$
c. $\frac{4b^7c^{13}}{a^9}$
d. $\frac{4b}{a^3c^5}$
e. None of these

13. Simplify. Write your answer in descending order of exponents: 13. ____________

$$(8y^3 - 6y - 13) + (5y^3 - 9y^2 + y) - (8y + 2y^3 - 6)$$

a. $11y^3 - 9y^2 - 13y - 7$
b. $15y^3 - 22y - 7$
c. $11y^3 - 9y^2 - 14y - 7$
d. $11y^3 - 9y^2 - 15y - 7$
e. None of these

14. Simplify: $31 - 8[12 - 3x^2 - 2(x^2 - 4)]$ 14. ______

a. $460 - 115x^2$
b. $-5x^2 - 33$
c. $-5x^2 - 129$
d. $40x^2 - 129$
e. None of these

15. Simplify: $(7x - y)(x - 3y) - (2x + y)^2$ 15. ______

a. $3x^2 - 26xy + 2y^2$
b. $3x^2 - 4y^2$
c. $3x^2 - 18xy + 4y^2$
d. $3x^2 - 18xy + 2y^2$

e. None of these

16. Find two consecutive positive integers so that the sum of their squares is 685. 16. ______

a. 17 and 18
b. 19 and 20
c. 16 and 17
d. 18 and 19
e. None of these

17. Divide: $\dfrac{y^3 + 3y - 4}{y - 1}$ 17. ______

a. $y^2 + 4$
b. $y^2 - y + 4 - \dfrac{8}{y - 1}$
c. $y^2 + y + 4$
d. $y^2 + y + 4 - \dfrac{8}{y - 1}$

e. None of these

18. Factor completely: $3x^4 - 24x^3 - 144x^2$. 18. ______

a. $3x^2(x - 12)(x + 4)$
b. $3x^2(x + 16)(x - 3)$
c. $3x^2(x + 12)(x - 4)$
d. $3x^2(x - 16)(x + 3)$
e. None of these

19. Factor completely: $16x^2 + 18x - 9$ 19. ____________

a. $(8x + 3)(2x - 3)$
b. $(4x + 3)(4x - 3)$
c. $(8x - 3)(2x - 3)$
d. $(8x - 3)(2x + 3)$
e. None of these

20. Factor completely by grouping: 20. ____________

$$w^2a^2 - 9a^2 + 4w^2 - 36$$

a. $(a^2 + 4)(w^2 - 9)$
b. $(a^2 + 4)(w - 3)(w - 3)$
c. $(a + 2)^2(w - 3)(w + 3)$
d. $(a + 2)(a - 2)(w - 3)(w + 3)$
e. None of these

21. Solve the equation: $6x^2 - 15x - 36 = 0$ 21. ____________

a. $x = \frac{3}{2}, x = -4$
b. $x = \frac{3}{2}, x = 4$
c. $x = -\frac{3}{2}, x = 4$
d. $x = -\frac{2}{3}, x = 4$
e. None of these

22. The owner of a wood working shop determines that the number N of hand carved dolls sold in a month is related to the price x per doll by $N = 35x - x^2$. What is the maximum price he can charge and sell 250 dolls? 22. ____________

a. \$25
b. \$8
c. \$15
d. \$10
e. None of these

23. Determine any values of the variable for which the rational expression $\frac{x - 3}{9 - x^2}$ is undefined. 23. ____________

a. $x = 3$
b. $x = 3,\ x = -3$
c. $x = 0$
d. $x = 9$
e. None of these

24. Divide and write the answer in lowest terms: 24. ____________

$$\frac{x^2 - 4x - 5}{x^2 + 6x + 8} \div \frac{x^2 - x - 20}{x^2 + 7x + 10}$$

a. $\frac{x^2 + 6x + 5}{(x + 4)(x + 4)}$

b. $\frac{5}{16}$

c. $\frac{x + 1}{x + 5}$

d. $-\frac{x^2 - 4x - 5}{x^2 + 4x + 4}$

e. None of these

25. Solve the equation: $\frac{z + 12}{z^2 - 16} = \frac{1}{4 + z} - \frac{3}{4 - z}$ 25. ____________

a. $z = -14$

b. $z = -\frac{28}{3}$

c. $z = \frac{3}{4}$

d. $z = 4$

e. None of these

26. The speed of a freight train is 16 mph slower than the speed of a passenger train. The freight train travels 312 miles in the same time that it takes the passenger train to travel 416 miles. Find the speed of the passenger train. 26. ____________

a. 48 mph
b. 80 mph
c. 64 mph
d. 72 mph
e. None of these

27. If R varies inversely as the cube of t, and R is $\frac{1}{9}$ when t is 3, find R when t is 6.

27. ____________

a. $R = \frac{1}{12}$

b. $R = \frac{1}{72}$

c. $R = \frac{1}{216}$

d. $R = 648$

e. None of these

28. Which of the following lines is parallel to a line passing through the points (-3, 5) and (-2, -1)?

28. ____________

a. a line passing through the points (1, 2) and (-3, 4)
b. a line passing through the points (-4, 5) and (-5, -1)
c. a line passing through the points (-2, 5) and (4, -7)
d. a line passing through the points (7, 2) and (8, -4)
e. None of these

29. In a coordinate plane, plot the point (-2, 4). Then plot two other points so that all three points lie on a line with a slope $-\frac{3}{2}$.

29. ____________

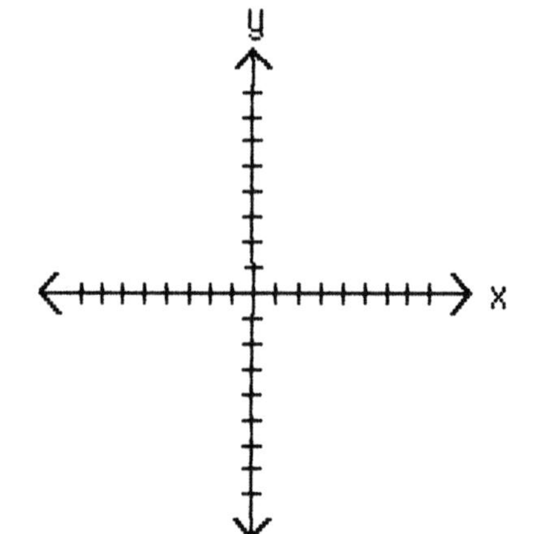

The y-intercept of the line is

a. (0, 2.5)
b. (0, -1)
c. (0, 1)
d. (0, 7)
e. None of these

30. Find an equation of a line through the two points P(-1, -1) and Q(1, 3).

30. ____________

a. $y = 2x - 5$

b. $y = 2x + 1$

c. $y = \frac{1}{2}x - \frac{1}{2}$

d. $y = x + 2$

e. None of these

31. Graph the linear inequality given by $-3x - 2y > 6$. 31. ______

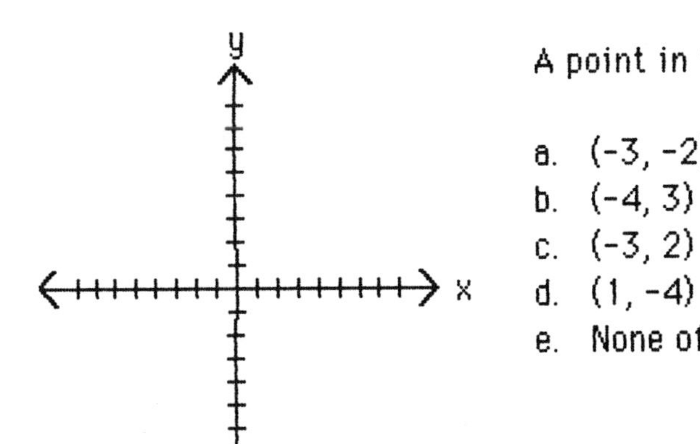

A point in the solution is

a. (-3, -2)
b. (-4, 3)
c. (-3, 2)
d. (1, -4)
e. None of these

32. Juliet buys a radio for \$89. The value of the radio decreases with time. At the end of two years, the radio has a resale value of \$50. Assume that the value V of the radio is linearly dependent upon the number of years after purchase. Write the linear equation that expresses V in terms of t, the number of years after purchase. 32. ______

a. $V = -\frac{39}{2}t + 50$

b. $V = \frac{39}{2}t + 89$

c. $V = -\frac{39}{2}t + 89$

d. $V = \frac{39}{2}t + 50$

e. None of these

33. Suppose y is a function of x defined by $y = \frac{2x}{x - 2}$. State the domain of the function. 33. ______

a. all real numbers except 2
b. all real numbers except -2
c. all real numbers except 0 and 2
d. all real numbers
e. None of these

34. Let $f(x) = \dfrac{3x-4}{3x^2 - x - 4}$. Find $f(-2)$. 34. ____________

a. $f(-2) = -\dfrac{5}{17}$

b. $f(-2) = -\dfrac{5}{9}$

c. $f(-2) = -\dfrac{5}{3}$

d. $f(-2) = -1$

e. None of these

35. Solve the system of equations by the elimination method: 35. ____________

$$4x - 7y = -1$$
$$-2x + 5y = 1$$

a. $x = -\dfrac{1}{3}, y = -\dfrac{1}{3}$

b. $x = \dfrac{1}{3}, y = \dfrac{1}{3}$

c. $x = -\dfrac{1}{4}, y = 0$

d. $x = -\dfrac{1}{2}, y = 0$

e. None of these

36. Solve the system of equations using the substitution method: 36. ____________

$$2x - y = -10$$
$$7x + 5y = -1$$

a. $x = -17,\ y = 24$

b. $x = 3,\ y = 16$

c. $x = -\dfrac{11}{17},\ y = \dfrac{12}{17}$

d. $x = -3,\ y = 4$

e. None of these

37. One positive number is one-seventh of another. The difference between the numbers is 72. Find the larger number. 37. ____________

a. 12

b. 84

c. 81

d. 9

e. None of these

38. The width of a rectangular room is 10 feet less than its length. The perimeter is 82 feet. Find the length. 38. ____________

a. 23 ft.
b. 33 ft.
c. 20.5 ft.
d. 15.5 ft.
e. None of these

39. Graph the system of linear inequalities: $3x - y > 2$ 39. ____________
$x + 2y > 3$
$-1 < x < 3$

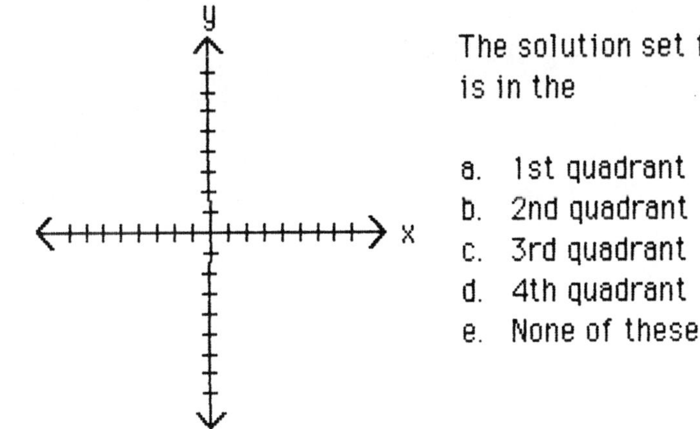

The solution set for the system is in the

a. 1st quadrant
b. 2nd quadrant
c. 3rd quadrant
d. 4th quadrant
e. None of these

40. Simplify by combining like radicals: 40. ____________
$2\sqrt{5} - 3\sqrt{125} + 4\sqrt{180}$

a. $4\sqrt{5}$
b. $6\sqrt{15}$
c. $71\sqrt{5}$
d. $11\sqrt{5}$
e. None of these

41. Rationalize the denominator and simplify: $\dfrac{5}{5 + \sqrt{y}}$ 41. ____________

a. $\dfrac{5(5 - \sqrt{y})}{5 + \sqrt{y}}$
b. $\dfrac{\sqrt{y}}{y}$
c. $\dfrac{5(5 - \sqrt{y})}{25 - y}$
d. $\dfrac{5(5 + \sqrt{y})}{25 + y}$
e. None of these

42. Solve the radical equation: $9 + \sqrt{2 - x} = 16$ 42. ______

a. $x = -5$
b. $x = -173$
c. $x = -47$
d. $x = 51$
e. None of these

43. Use properties of exponents to simplify: $\left(\frac{12x^{3/4}}{20x^{5/6}}\right)^6$ 43. ______

a. $\frac{3}{5x^{1/2}}$

b. $\frac{729}{15625x^6}$

c. $\frac{3}{5x^6}$

d. $\frac{729x^{1/2}}{15625}$

e. None of these

44. Peform the indicated operations and write the answer in the form $a + bi$. $15 - (4 - 6i) + (8 + i)$ 44. ______

a. $19 - 5i$
b. $19 + 7i$
c. $19 + 5i$
d. $3 + 5i$
e. None of these

45. Peform the indicated operations and write the answer in the form $a + bi$. $\frac{4 + 5i}{16i}$ 45. ______

a. $\frac{5}{16} + \frac{1}{4}i$

b. $-\frac{5}{16} + \frac{1}{4}i$

c. $-\frac{5}{16} - \frac{1}{4}i$

d. $\frac{5}{16} - \frac{1}{4}i$

46. Solve the equation $(x + 7)^2 = 1$ 46. ____________

a. $x = -6,\ x = -8$
b. $x = 8,\ x = 6$
c. $x = \pm 6$
d. $x = \pm 5\sqrt{2}$
e. None of these

47. Solve the quadratic equation. Write all solutions that are complex numbers in standard form. 47. ____________

$16x^2 - 24x + 7 = 0$

a. $x = \frac{-3 \pm \sqrt{2}}{4}$
b. $x = \frac{1}{4},\ x = -\frac{7}{4}$
c. $x = -\frac{1}{4},\ x = \frac{7}{4}$
d. $x = \frac{3 \pm \sqrt{2}}{4}$
e. None of these

48. Use the discriminant to determine if the roots are real or complex. Also, determine the number of roots. Do not solve the equation: $4x^2 - 12x + 9 = 0$ 48. ____________

a. one Real root
b. two Real roots
c. two complex roots
d. one complex root
e. None of these

49. The width of a rectangle is three cm. less than half the length. The area is 176 square centimeters. Find the width. 49. ____________

a. 16 cm.
b. 5 cm.
c. 8cm.
d. 22 cm.
e. None of these

50. Determine if the graph of $y = 3x^2 - 6x + 5$ has a highest point or a lowest point and find the coordinates of this point. 50. ____________

a. highest point at (1, 2)
b. highest point at (-1, 2)
c. lowest point at (1, 2)
d. lowest point at (-1, 2)
e. None of these

Name ______________________ FINAL Form E Score ________

1. Write as a single fraction in lowest terms. 1. ____________

$$\left(\frac{4}{9} - \frac{2}{3}\right) \div \left(\frac{1}{4} + \frac{2}{3}\right)$$

a. $-\frac{11}{54}$

b. $-\frac{24}{99}$

c. $-\frac{8}{33}$

d. $\frac{7}{9}$

e. None of these

2. Simplify the expression: $7^2 - 2^7 + 4 \cdot 3^2 \div 2$ 2. ____________

a. -61
b. -97
c. -7
d. 18
e. None of these

3. Simplify: $38 - [21 - \frac{5}{6}(18 + 6^2)]$ 3. ____________

a. 42
b. -28
c. -4
d. 62
e. None of these

4. Evaluate: $2x^2 - 8(11 - y) - 4$ if $x = -5$ and $y = -7$ 4. ____________

a. -48
b. -98
c. -35
d. 14
e. None of these

5. Check for solutions of the equation $|4x - 5| = 3$ from the set $\{-2, -\frac{1}{2}, \frac{1}{2}, 2\}$ 5. ______

a. $x = \frac{1}{2}$, $x = 2$

b. $x = -2$, $x = \frac{1}{2}$

c. $x = -2$, $x = -\frac{1}{2}$

d. $x = 2$, $x = -\frac{1}{2}$

e. None of these

6. Remove parenthesis using the distributive property, then simplify: $9(8 - 5m) - 7(8 - 3m)$ 6. ______

a. $16 - 66m$
b. $16 - 8m$
c. $16 - 24m$
d. $16 - 48m$
e. None of these

7. Solve the equation: $8x + 10 = -6 - (x + 11)$ 7. ______

a. $x = -18$
b. $x = -3$
c. $x = -\frac{5}{9}$
d. $x = -1$
e. None of these

8. Shanon is paid $914 a month plus a commission of 7.5% on sales. Find the sales (in dollars) needed to give her a monthly total of $1814. 8. ______

a. $12000
b. $24186
c. $13605
d. $36373
e. None of these

9. Solve the inequality: $-60 < 4 - 4x < -40$ 9. ______

a. $-16 < x < -11$
b. $-60 < x < -40$
c. $11 < x < 16$
d. $9 < x < 14$
e. None of these

10. How much interest is made on $5400 invested at 9% interest for two years? 10. ____________

a. $1200
b. $600
c. $972
d. $486
e. None of these

11. Solve: $3y - 1 = 11 - 21(4 - y)$ for y 11. ____________

a. $y = -18$
b. $y = \frac{39}{7}$
c. $y = -\frac{37}{12}$
d. $y = 4$
e. None of these

12. Simplify the expression and write your answer without negative exponents: 12. ____________

$$\frac{(9m^{-2}n^{-3}p)^3(3mp^{-1})}{(6mn^{-4}p^{-2})^{-1}}$$

a. $13122m^3n^3p^5$
b. $-\frac{729}{2m^4n^{13}}$
c. $\frac{13122p^4}{m^7n^5}$
d. $\frac{13122}{m^4n^{13}}$
e. None of these

13. Simplify. Write your answer in descending order of exponents: 13. ____________

$$(9w - 3w^3 - 7) + (8w^2 - 2w^3 - w) - (7w + 3w^3 - 21)$$

a. $-8w^3 + 8w^2 + 2w + 14$
b. $-8w^3 + 8w^2 + w + 14$
c. $w^3 + 14$
d. $w + 14$
e. None of these

14. Simplify: $-27 - 9[7x^2 - 15 - (8 - x^2)]$ 14. ________

a. $-288x^2 + 828$
b. $-54x^2 - 50$
c. $180 - 72x$
d. $180 - 54x^2$
e. None of these

15. Simplify: $(2m + 3p)(2m - p) - (3m - p)^2$ 15. ________

a. $-5m^2 - 4p^2$
b. $-5m^2 + 10mp - 4p^2$
c. $-5m^2 - 2mp - 2p^2$
d. $-9m^2 + 10mp - 2p^2$
e. None of these

16. Find two consecutive negative integers so that the difference of their squares is 31. 16. ________

a. -15 and -16
b. -16 and -17
c. -14 and -15
d. -13 and -14
e. None of these

17. Divide: $\dfrac{3x^3 - 4x - 4}{x - 2}$ 17. ________

a. $3x^2 + 2$

b. $3x^2 + 6x + 8 - \dfrac{20}{x - 2}$

c. $3x^2 - 6x + 8 - \dfrac{20}{x - 2}$

d. $3x^2 + 6x + 8 + \dfrac{12}{x - 2}$

e. None of these

18. Factor completely: $2y^2 - 38y + 96$. 18. ________

a. $2(y - 24)(y + 2)$
b. $2(y - 16)(y - 3)$
c. $2(y + 16)(y + 3)$
d. $(2y - 32)(y - 3)$
e. None of these

19. Factor completely: $8m^2 + 2m - 15$ 19. ______

a. $(4m - 5)(2m + 3)$
b. $(4m + 5)(2m - 3)$
c. $(4m + 5)(2m + 3)$
d. $(4m - 5)(2m - 3)$
e. None of these

20. Factor completely by grouping: 20. ______

$$2a^3 - 2ab^2 + a^2b - b^3$$

a. $(2a + b)(a + b)(a - b)$
b. $(2a + b)(a - b)^2$
c. $(2a + b)(a^2 - b^2)$
d. $(2a - b)(a + b)(a - b)$
e. None of these

21. Solve the equation: $8x^2 - 43x - 30 = 0$ 21. ______

a. $x = \frac{5}{8}, x = -6$
b. $x = -\frac{8}{5}, x = 6$
c. $x = -\frac{5}{8}, x = -6$
d. $x = -\frac{5}{8}, x = 6$
e. None of these

22. The width of a rectangle is three fourths its length. 22. ______
The area is 432 square inches. Find the width of the rectangle.

a. 24 inches
b. 18 inches
c. 13.5 inches
d. 16 inches
e. None of these

23. Determine any values of the variable for which the 23. ______
rational expression $\frac{12}{8x + 12}$ is undefined.

a. $x = 0$
b. $x = -\frac{2}{3}$
c. $x = -\frac{3}{2}$
d. $x = -20$
e. None of these

24. Divide and write the answer in lowest terms: 24. ________

$$\frac{x^2 - 3x}{x^2 - 9} \div \frac{6x^2 - 11x + 3}{3x^2 - 10x + 3}$$

a. $\frac{-10x^2}{6 - 33x}$

b. $\frac{x^2}{2x^2 - 9}$

c. $\frac{x}{2x - 3}$

d. $\frac{x^2 - 3x}{(x + 3)(2x - 3)}$

e. None of these

25. Solve the equation: $\frac{3x}{x - 5} + \frac{12}{x^2 - 4x - 5} = \frac{2x}{x + 1}$ 25. ________

a. $x = -12$

b. $x = -12,\ x = -1$

c. $x = 2,\ x = -\frac{3}{5}$

d. $x = \pm 3\sqrt{2}$

e. None of these

26. The reciprocal of 5 less than a number is four times the reciprocal of the number itself. What is the number? 26. ________

a. $x = \frac{5}{3}$

b. $x = 4$

c. $x = 5$

d. $x = \frac{20}{3}$

e. None of these

27. On a road map $3\frac{1}{2}$ inches represents 364 miles. If two cities are $4\frac{1}{8}$ inches apart, What is the actual distance between the two cities? 27. ________

a. 308 miles

b. 416 miles

c. 429 miles

d. 419 miles

e. None of these

28. Which of the following lines is parallel to a line passing through the points (-5, 4) and (2, -4)?

28. ____________

a. a line passing through the points (4, 2) and (-4, 9)
b. a line passing through the points (-6, 3) and (1, -3)
c. a line passing through the points (10, 9) and (-3, 1)
d. a line passing through the points (-2, -5) and (-5, -3)
e. None of these

29. In a coordinate plane, plot the point (5, -3). Then plot two other points so that all three points lie on a line with a slope $-\frac{1}{2}$.

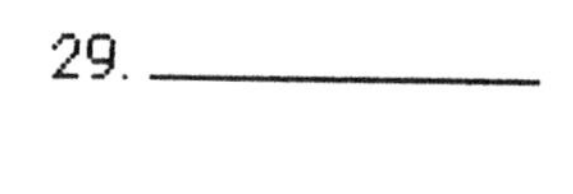

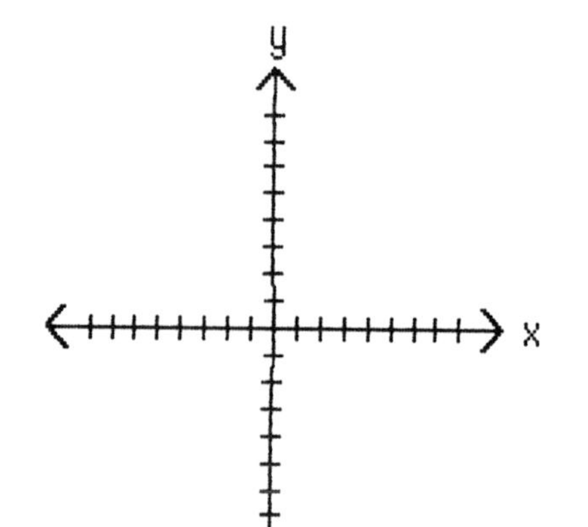

The x-intercept of the line is

a. (3.5, 0)
b. (9, 0)
c. (4, 0)
d. (-1, 0)
e. None of these

30. Find an equation of a line through the two points P(1, 3) and Q(-1, -3).

30. ____________

a. $y = 0$
b. $y = 3x + 2$
c. $y = 3x$
d. $y = 3x - 2$
e. None of these

31. Graph the linear inequality given by $4y - x < 6$.

31. ____________

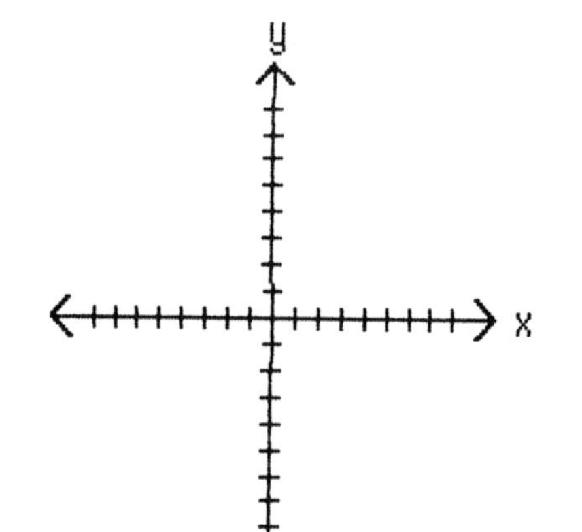

A point in the solution is

a. (2, 2)
b. (3, 2)
c. (-3, 2)
d. (4, 2)
e. None of these

32. Micky rents a car for a five-day trip. If the rental agency charges $22 per day plus 23 cents per mile, express the cost of renting the car for the trip if he drove a total of x miles.

32. ____________

a. $C = .23x + 22$
b. $C = .22x + 115$
c. $C = 5(.23x + 22)$
d. $C = .23x + 110$
e. None of these

33. Suppose y is a function of x defined by $y = 2|x - 4|$. State the domain of the function.

33. ____________

a. $\{x | x \geq 4\}$
b. all real numbers
c. $\{x | x \geq 0\}$
d. $\{x | x \neq 4\}$
e. None of these

34. Let $f(x) = \dfrac{|x + 2|}{x + 2}$. Find $f(-4)$.

34. ____________

a. $f(-4) = -3$
b. $f(-4) = 1$
c. $f(-4) = 3$
d. $f(-4) = -\dfrac{1}{4}$
e. None of these

35. Solve the system of equations by the elimination method:

$$3x - 5y = -1$$
$$4x + 2y = 3$$

35. ____________

a. $x = \dfrac{17}{14}, y = \dfrac{13}{14}$
b. $x = 3, \ y = 2$
c. $x = \dfrac{1}{2}, y = \dfrac{1}{2}$
d. $x = \dfrac{1}{13}, y = \dfrac{16}{65}$
e. None of these

36. Solve the system of equations using the substitution method: 36. ________

$$2x + 4y = 9$$
$$6x + y = 5$$

a. $x = \frac{1}{2},\ y = 2$

b. $x = -\frac{11}{26},\ y = \frac{32}{13}$

c. $x = \frac{1}{2},\ y = \frac{5}{2}$

d. $x = \frac{11}{4},\ y = \frac{-23}{2}$

e. None of these

37. One negative number is one-fourth of another. The difference between the numbers is 21. Find the larger number. 37. ________

a. -28
b. -3
c. -7
d. -24
e. None of these

38. The perimeter of a rectangle is 90 inches. The length is 3 inches more than twice the width. Find the length. 38. ________

a. 31 inches
b. 14 inches
c. 35 inches
d. 32 inches
e. None of these

39. Graph the system of linear inequalities: $x - 2y \leq 2$ 39. ________

$$y \geq 1$$
$$x < 0$$

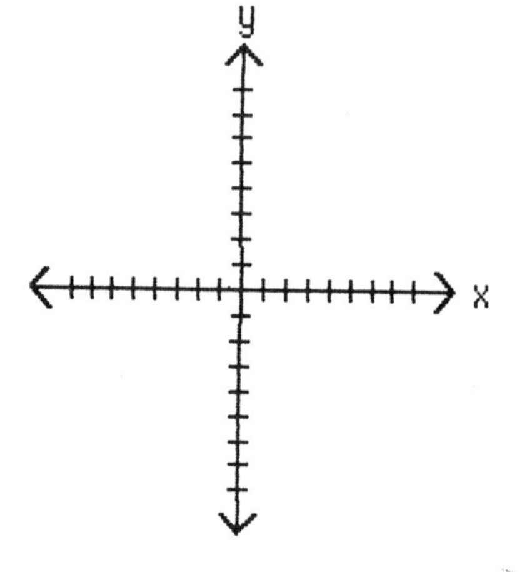

The solution set for the system is in the

a. 1st quadrant
b. 2nd quadrant
c. 3rd quadrant
d. 4th quadrant
e. None of these

40. Simplify by combining like radicals: 40. ____________

$$3\sqrt{54} + 2\sqrt{96} - 2\sqrt{108}$$

a. $5\sqrt{3}$
b. $17\sqrt{6} - 8\sqrt{3}$
c. $3\sqrt{42}$
d. $60\sqrt{6} - 12\sqrt{3}$
e. None of these

41. Rationalize the denominator and simplify: $\dfrac{4}{4 - \sqrt{2x}}$ 41. ____________

a. $\dfrac{2\sqrt{2x}}{2 - x}$
b. $-\dfrac{\sqrt{2x}}{2x}$
c. $\dfrac{2(4 + \sqrt{2x}}{7x}$
d. $\dfrac{2(4 + \sqrt{2x}}{8 - x}$
e. None of these

42. Solve the radical equation: $\sqrt{x + 4} + 8 = -4$ 42. ____________

a. $x = -2$
b. $x = 20$
c. $x = 12$
d. No real solution
e. None of these

43. Use properties of exponents to simplify: $\left(\dfrac{9y^{1/6}}{15y^{1/3}}\right)^6$ 43. ____________

a. $\dfrac{729}{15625y}$
b. $\dfrac{3}{5y}$
c. $\dfrac{729y^3}{15625}$
d. $\dfrac{729y}{15625}$
e. None of these

44. Peform the indicated operations and write the answer in the form $a + bi$. $24 - (9 - 3i) + (11 + 4i)$

44. ____________

a. $44 + 7i$
b. $26 + i$
c. $26 + 7i$
d. $33i$
e. None of these

45. Peform the indicated operations and write the answer in the form $a + bi$. $\frac{1 + 4i}{i}$

45. ____________

a. $4 - i$
b. $4 + i$
c. $-4 - i$
d. $-4 + i$
e. None of these

46. Solve the equation $(x + 8)^2 = 4$

46. ____________

a. $x = \pm 6$
b. $x = -6,\ x = -10$
c. $x = 6, x = 10$
d. $x = \pm 10$
e. None of these

47. Solve the quadratic equation. Write all solutions that are complex numbers in standard form.

$$3x^2 - 8x + 6 = 0$$

47. ____________

a. $x = -\frac{2}{3},\ x = 3$
b. $x = \frac{4 \pm 2\sqrt{2}}{3}$
c. $x = \frac{4 \pm \sqrt{34}}{3}$
d. $x = \pm \frac{5\sqrt{2}}{3} i$
e. None of these

48. Use the discriminant to determine if the roots are real or complex. Also, determine the number of roots. Do not solve the equation: $9x^2 - 6x - 1 = 0$

48. ____________

a. 1 Real root
b. 2 Real roots
c. 1 complex root
d. 2 complex roots
e. None of these

49. The length of a rectangle is 4 feet more than twice the width. The area is 126 square feet. Find the length of the rectangle.

49. ____________

a. 22 feet
b. 7 feet
c. 9 feet
d. 18 feet
e. None of these

50. Determine if the graph of $y = 4x^2 + 16x + 14$ has a highest point or a lowest point and find the coordinates of this point.

50. ____________

a. lowest point at (-2, -2)
b. lowest point at (2, -2)
c. highest point at (-2,-2)
d. highest point at (2, -2)
e. None of these

Name ____________________ FINAL Form F Score ______

1. Write as a single fraction in lowest terms.

$$\left(\frac{21}{28} \cdot \frac{42}{45}\right) \div \left(\frac{1}{4} + \frac{2}{7}\right)$$

a. $\frac{77}{30}$

b. $\frac{7}{75}$

c. $\frac{3}{8}$

d. $\frac{98}{75}$

e. None of these

2. Simplify the expression: $2^3 + 2^5 \div 4 - 16 \cdot (-1)$ 2. __________

a. 0
b. 32
c. 6
d. 26.5
e. None of these

3. Simplify: $65 - 3\,[15 - \frac{3}{5}(15 - 40)]$ 3. __________

a. 1860
b. 35
c. 167
d. 65
e. None of these

4. Evaluate: $6a^2 - 8(6 - b) - 10$ if $a = -4$ and $b = -8$ 4. __________

a. 454
b. 102
c. -26
d. -6
e. None of these

5. Check for solutions of the equation $|-9 - 4x| = 5x$ from the set $\{-9, -1, 1, 9\}$ 5. ____________

   a. $x = 1,\ x = 9$
   b. $x = -1,\ x = 9$
   c. $x = 1,\ x = -9$
   d. $x = -1, x = -9$
   e. None of these

6. Remove parenthesis using the distributive property, then simplify: $15(8 - x) - 7(9 - 5x)$ 6. ____________

   a. $57 - 50x$
   b. $57 - 6x$
   c. $57 - 20x$
   d. $20x + 57$
   e. None of these

7. Solve the equation: $6 + 14x = 2 - 6(8 + 3x)$ 7. ____________

   a. $x = -\dfrac{19}{13}$
   b. $x = -\dfrac{52}{11}$
   c. $x = -\dfrac{13}{8}$
   d. $x = 10$
   e. None of these

8. Shanon is paid \$975 a month plus a commission of 7% on sales. Find the sales (in dollars) needed to give her a monthly total of \$2305. 8. ____________

   a. \$46857
   b. \$19000
   c. \$16135
   d. \$32928
   e. None of these

9. Solve the inequality: $-38 < 7 - 9x < -20$ 9. ____________

   a. $-5 < x < -3$
   b. $\dfrac{13}{9} < x < \dfrac{31}{9}$
   c. $-\dfrac{10}{9} < x < -\dfrac{1}{9}$
   d. $3 < x < 5$
   e. None of these

10. How much interest is made on $4600 invested at 9% interest for two years? 10. ____________

a. $828
b. $1022
c. $1656
d. $414
e. None of these

11. Solve: $4y - 17 = -15 - 4(5 - 2y)$ for y 11. ____________

a. $y = \frac{13}{3}$
b. $y = \frac{39}{17}$
c. $y = -13$
d. $y = -\frac{3}{2}$
e. None of these

12. Simplify the expression and write your answer without negative exponents: 12. ____________

$$\frac{(12mn^3)^{-1}(4mp^{-3})}{(6m^2n^{-1}p^{-2})^{-2}}$$

a. $\frac{12m^4}{n^5p^7}$
b. $\frac{4m^4}{3n^5p^7}$
c. $\frac{4m^4}{n^5p^7}$
d. $\frac{12p}{m^3n}$
e. None of these

13. Simplify. Write your answer in descending order of exponents: 13. ____________

$$(15x - 12x^2 - 1) + (11x^2 - 4x^3 - x) - (7x + 2x^3 - 14)$$

a. $-2x^3 - x^2 + 7x - 15$
b. $-6x^3 - x^2 + 7x - 15$
c. $-6x^3 - x^2 + 7x + 13$
d. $-2x^3 - x^2 + 7x + 13$
e. None of these

14. Simplify: $24 - 5[7 - 5x^2 - (8 - x^2)]$ 14. ________

a. $29 + 20x^2$
b. $-95x^2$
c. $-19 - 76x^2$
d. $29 + 30x^2$
e. None of these

15. Simplify: $(5w - t)^2 - (3w + 2t)(2w - t)$ 15. ________

a. $19w^2 + t^2$
b. $19w^2 - 9wt - t^2$
c. $19w^2 - 11wt + 3t^2$
d. $19w^2 - 9wt + 3t^2$
e. None of these

16. Find two consecutive odd negative integers so that the sum of their squares is 925. 16. ________

a. -20 and -21
b. -21 and -22
c. -22 and -23
d. -19 and -20
e. None of these

17. Divide: $\frac{3x^4 - x^2 - 2}{x - 1}$ 17. ________

a. $3x^3 + 3x^2 + 2x + 2$
b. $3x^3 + 2x^2$
c. $3x^3 - x + 2$
d. $3x^3 - 3x^2 + 2x + 2$
e. None of these

18. Factor completely: $m^5 - 8m^4 + 16m^3$ 18. ________

a. $m^3(m - 4)(m + 4)$
b. $(m^3 - 4m^2)(m^2 - 4m)$
c. $m^3(m - 4)^2$
d. $m^3(m + 4)^2$
e. None of these

19. Factor completely: $20x^2 - 11x - 3$ 19. ________

a. $(4x - 1)(5x - 2)$
b. $(4x - 3)(5x + 1)$
c. $(4x + 3)(5x - 1)$
d. $(4x - 3)(5x - 1)$
e. None of these

20. Factor completely by grouping: 20. ___________

$$18a^2 - 45a - 18ab + 20b$$

a. $(9a - 4b)(9a - 5)(2a - 5b)$
b. $(9a - 4b)(2a - 5)(2a + 5)$
c. $(9a - 4b)(2a + 5)$
d. $(9a - 4b)(2a - 5)$
e. None of these

21. Solve the equation: $5x^2 - 31x - 28 = 0$ 21. ___________

a. $x = -\frac{4}{5}, x = 7$

b. $x = \frac{4}{5}, x = -7$

c. $x = -\frac{5}{4}, x = 7$

d. $x = -\frac{4}{5}, x = -7$

e. None of these

22. Two is added to a positive integer and that sum tripled. When this result is multiplied by the original integer, the product is 105. Find the number. 22. ___________

a. 6
b. 3
c. 5
d. 7
e. None of these

23. Determine any values of the variable for which the rational expression $\frac{6w - 3}{w - 2w^2}$ is undefined. 23. ___________

a. $w = 0$
b. $w = \frac{1}{2}$
c. $w = -3$
d. $w = 0, \ w = \frac{1}{2}$
e. None of these

24. Divide and write the answer in lowest terms: 24. ______

$$\frac{x^2}{x^2 + 5x} \div \frac{x^2 - 2x}{x^2 + 3x - 10}$$

a. $\frac{x^2 - 2}{x^2 - 2x}$

b. 1

c. $\frac{3x - 10}{-10x}$

d. $\frac{x^3 + 3x^2 - 10x}{x^3 + 7x^2 - 10x}$

e. None of these

25. Solve the equation: $2 + \frac{x - 3}{5} = \frac{x + 1}{3}$ 25. ______

a. $x = -6$
b. $x = 8$
c. $x = 13$
d. $x = 3$
e. None of these

26. Joseph can paint a garage in 10 hours. John can paint the same garage in 15 hours. How long would it take if they worked together? 26. ______

a. 6 hours
b. 12.5 hours
c. 5 hours
d. 8 hours
e. None of these

27. The speed S of a gear varies inversely as the number n of teeth. Gear A, which has 12 teeth, makes 400 rpm. How many revolutions per minute are made by a gear with 32 teeth that is connected to gear A? 27. ______

a. 104 rpm
b. 160 rpm
c. $106\frac{2}{3}$ rpm
d. 150 rpm
e. None of these

28. Which of the following lines is parallel to a line passing through the points (-1, 8) and (-5, 4)? 28. ____________

a. a line passing through the points (6, 5) and (8, 7)
b. a line passing through the points (1, 3) and (4, 1)
c. a line passing through the points (9, -1) and (5, -5)
d. a line passing through the points (1, -3) and (-9, -5)
e. None of these

29. In a coordinate plane, plot the point (-3, -5). Then plot two other points so that all three points lie on a line with a slope 2. 29. ____________

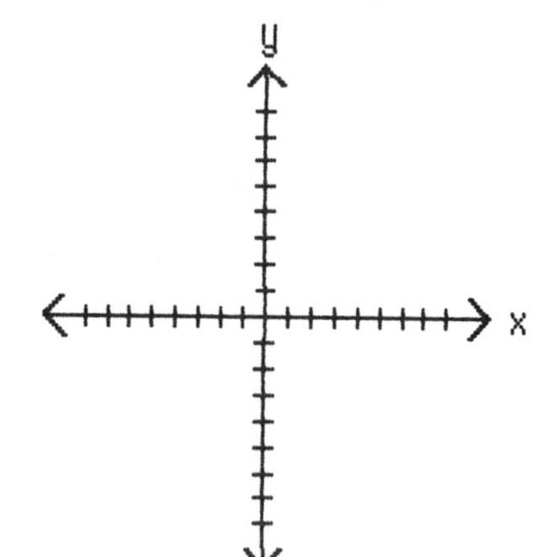

The y-intercept of the line is

a. (0, 1)
b. (0, -3.5)
c. (0, 8)
d. (0, -1)
e. None of these

30. Find an equation of a line through the two points P(2, -5) and Q(-3, -6). 30. ____________

a. $y = \frac{1}{5}x - 7$

b. $y = \frac{1}{5}x + \frac{23}{5}$

c. $y = \frac{1}{5}x + 3$

d. $y = \frac{1}{5}x - \frac{27}{5}$

e. None of these

31. Graph the linear inequality given by $7x - 3y < 4$. 31. ____________

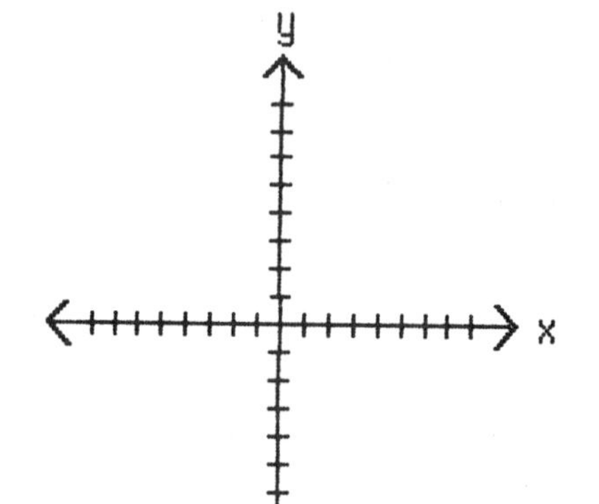

A point in the solution is

a. (-2, -6)
b. (1, 1)
c. (-3, -2)
d. (4, 7)
e. None of these

32. The U-Catch-It Company makes x gross of fishing lures each day with a cost per gross of \$16 and a fixed cost of \$142 per day. Express the daily cost C in terms of x.

32. ____________

a. $C = 16x - 142$
b. $C = 16x + 142$
c. $C = 142x + 16$
d. $C = 142x - 16$
e. None of these

33. Suppose y is a function of x defined by $y = \frac{5x}{x^2 + 3x}$. State the domain of the function.

33. ____________

a. all real numbers except 0
b. all real numbers except -3
c. all real numbers except 0 and -3
d. all real numbers
e. None of these

34. Let $f(x) = -3x^2 - 2x + 1$. Find $f(-3)$.

34. ____________

a. $f(-3) = -20$
b. $f(-3) = -32$
c. $f(-3) = 88$
d. $f(-3) = 25$
e. None of these

35. Solve the system of equations by the elimination method:

$$6x - 3y = 6$$
$$7x - 4y = -2$$

35. ____________

a. $(-10, -17)$
b. $\left(-\frac{4}{3}, -\frac{14}{3}\right)$
c. $(6, 10)$
d. $(10, 18)$
e. None of these

36. Solve the system of equations using the substitution method:

$$2x - y = -1$$
$$5x + 2y = 29$$

36. ____________

a. $(3, -7)$
b. $(3, 7)$
c. $\left(\frac{28}{9}, \frac{65}{9}\right)$
d. $(4, 9)$
e. None of these

37. Butterscotch candy worth \$1.55 per pound and peppermint candy worth \$1.35 per pound are mixed to make a 15 pound mixture which sells for \$1.47 per pound. Find the number of pounds of butterscotch candy used?

37. ____________

a. 12 pounds
b. 11 pounds
c. 6 pounds
d. 9 pounds
e. None of these

38. The length of a rectangular painting is two inches more than three times the width of the painting. The perimeter is 68 inches. Find the length.

38. ____________

a. 8 inches
b. 26 inches
c. 9 inches
d. 29 inches
e. None of these

39. Graph the system of linear inequalities:

$$3x - 2y > 6$$
$$1 < x < 4$$
$$y < 0$$

39. ____________

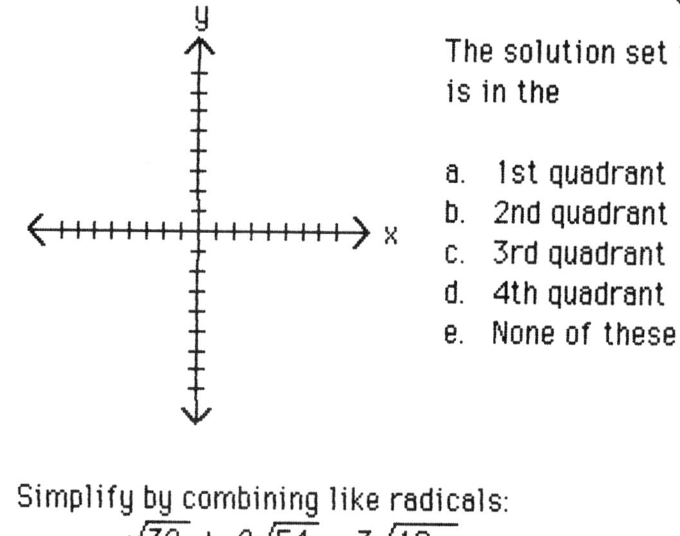

The solution set for the system is in the

a. 1st quadrant
b. 2nd quadrant
c. 3rd quadrant
d. 4th quadrant
e. None of these

40. Simplify by combining like radicals:

$$\sqrt{32} + 2\sqrt{54} - 3\sqrt{18}$$

40. ____________

a. $6\sqrt{6} - 5\sqrt{2}$
b. $-2\sqrt{17}$
c. $-2\sqrt{2} + 5\sqrt{6}$
d. $-11\sqrt{2} + 18\sqrt{6}$
e. None of these

41. Rationalize the denominator and simplify: $\dfrac{6}{9 - \sqrt{3}}$ 41. ________

a. $\dfrac{9 + \sqrt{3}}{13}$
b. $9 + \sqrt{3}$
c. $\sqrt{3}$
d. $\dfrac{9 - \sqrt{3}}{13}$
e. None of these

42. Solve the radical equation: $\sqrt{m + 5} - 5 = 20$ 42. ________

a. $m = 20$
b. $m = 620$
c. $m = 630$
d. $m = 0$
e. None of these

43. Use properties of exponents to simplify: $\left(\dfrac{18m^{3/4}}{27m^{1/3}}\right)^6$ 43. ________

a. $\dfrac{2m^{5/2}}{3}$
b. $\dfrac{64m^{5/2}}{729}$
c. $\dfrac{2m^{11/2}}{3}$
d. $\dfrac{64m^3}{729}$
e. None of these

44. Peform the indicated operations and write the answer in the form $a + bi$. $9 + (15 + 6i) - (6 - 3i)$ 44. ________

a. $18 + 3i$
b. $30 + 9i$
c. $21i$
d. $18 + 9i$
e. None of these

45. Peform the indicated operations and write the answer in the form $a + bi$. $\frac{4 - 2i}{8i}$ 45. ____________

a. $-\frac{1}{4} + \frac{1}{2}i$

b. $\frac{1}{4}$

c. $-\frac{1}{4} - \frac{1}{4}i$

d. $-\frac{1}{2} - \frac{1}{4}i$

e. None of these

46. Solve the equation $(x + 12)^2 = 25$ 46. ____________

a. $x = \pm 60$
b. $x = \pm 7$
c. $x = -7,\ x = -17$
d. $x = 37,\ x = -13$
e. None of these

47. Solve the quadratic equation. Write all solutions that are complex numbers in standard form. 47. ____________

$5x^2 + 6x - 8 = 0$

a. $x = -2,\ x = \frac{4}{5}$

b. $x = 2,\ x = -\frac{4}{5}$

c. $x = \pm\frac{4}{5}$

d. $x = \frac{-3}{5} \pm \frac{\sqrt{31}}{5}i$

e. None of these

48. Use the discriminant to determine if the roots are real or complex. Also, determine the number of roots. Do not solve the equation: $-2x^2 - x + 5 = 0$ 48. ____________

a. one Real root
b. one complex root
c. two Real roots
d. two complex roots
e. None of these

49. The width of a rectangle is three-fourths of its length. The area is 432 square inches. Find the width of the rectangle.

49. ____________

a. 18 inches
b. 24 inches
c. 13.5 inches
d. 16 inches
e. None of these

50. Determine if the graph of $y = -3x^2 - 18x$ has a highest point or a lowest point and find the coordinates of this point.

50. ____________

a. highest point at (-3, 0)
b. lowest point at (3, 0)
c. lowest point at (3, 27)
d. highest point at (-3, 27)
e. None of these

Final Test Keys

Form A

1. $\frac{27}{85}$
2. 30
3. 14
4. 22
5. $x = -\frac{5}{11}$ or $x = \frac{5}{13}$
6. $28 - 37x$
7. $x = \frac{1}{2}$
8. $2875
9. $-1 < x < 6$
10. $442
11. $x = -\frac{11}{6}$
12. $\frac{27x^3z}{2y}$
13. $-9m^3 + 12m^2 - m + 1$
14. $-9x^2 - 11$
15. $3x^2 - 7xy - 7y^2$
16. 12 and 13
17. $x^2 + 3x + 2$
18. $2x(x + 7)(x - 6)$
19. $(2x + 5)(3x + 2)$
20. $(4 - x)(x + y)(x - y)$
21. $x = 4$ or $x = -\frac{6}{5}$
22. 6 teams
23. $x = 1$ or $x = -1$
24. $\frac{3x + 2}{2x + 3}$
25. $x = \frac{2}{5}$
26. $3\frac{3}{7}$ hours
27. $3720
28. Yes

Form B

1. $\frac{10}{9}$
2. 5
3. 41
4. -25
5. $x = -1, x = 2$
6. $-6 - 34x$
7. $x = 2$
8. $2000
9. $-\frac{1}{3} < x < \frac{7}{3}$
10. $646
11. $x = 2$
12. $\frac{-3y^4}{2x^2w^2}$
13. $-23y^3 + 12y^2 + 23y$
14. $-24x^2 + 63$
15. $a^2 + 15ab - 5b^2$
16. 31 and 32
17. $x^2 + x + 1$
18. $2x(x - 8)(x + 7)$
19. $(7y - 2)(4y - 1)$
20. $(2m - y)(m + 2)(m - 2)$
21. $x = \frac{4}{3}$ or $x = -3$
22. 14 inches
23. $x = \frac{6}{7}$
24. $\frac{(a + b)^2}{a^2 + b^2}$
25. $x = 4$
26. -6
27. $4290
28. No

29. Answer:

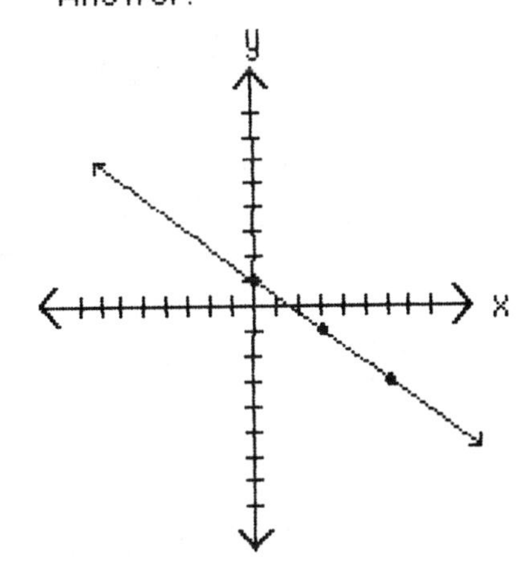

30. $y = -\frac{2}{7}x + \frac{11}{7}$

31. Answer:

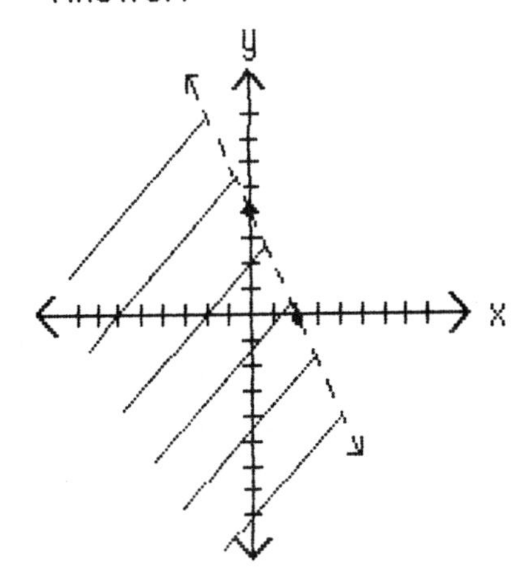

32. V = −100t + 450

33. All Real numbers except 9

34. f(4) = 7

35. x = 30, y = 7

36. x = −4, y = −2

37. 8 and 40

38. length = 26.25 cm
width = 21.25 cm

29. Answer:

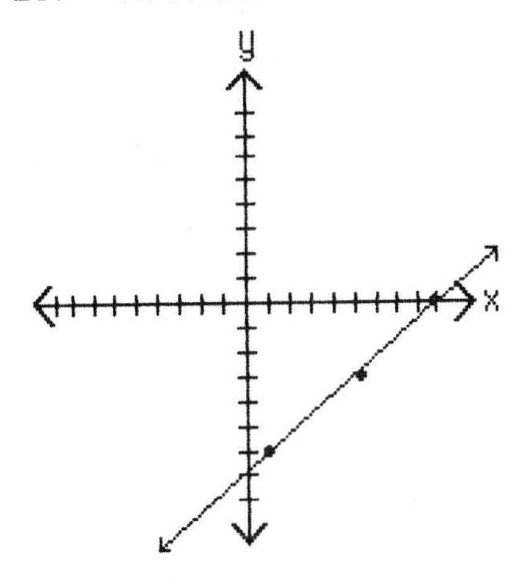

30. $y = -\frac{5}{6}x - \frac{14}{6}$

31. Answer:

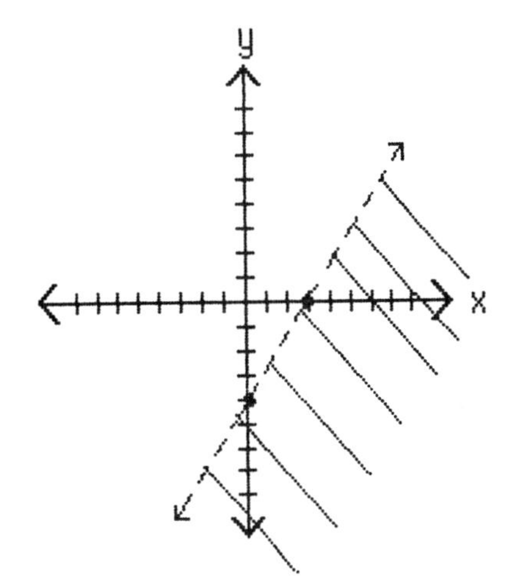

32. C = .25x + 152

33. All Real numbers

34. $f(7) = -\frac{4}{49}$

35. $x = \frac{1}{2}$, $y = \frac{1}{2}$

36. x = 2, y = −3

37. 4 gallons

38. $25\frac{1}{3}$ inches

39. Answer:

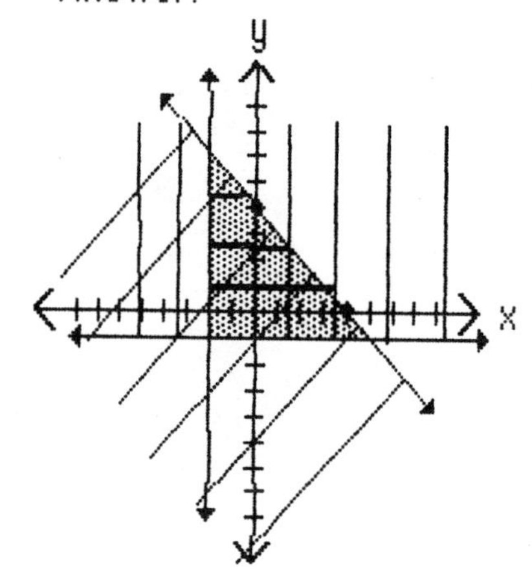

40. $-14\sqrt{2}$

41. $\dfrac{m(2+\sqrt{m})}{4-m}$

42. $x = 39$

43. $\dfrac{1}{27x^{5/4}}$

44. $4 - 3i$

45. $-\dfrac{5}{2} - \dfrac{3}{2}i$

46. $x = 8,\ x = -4$

47. $x = \dfrac{2 \pm \sqrt{5}}{2}$

48. 2 Real roots

49. length = 16m, width = 11m.

50. Highest point (2, 2)

39. Answer:

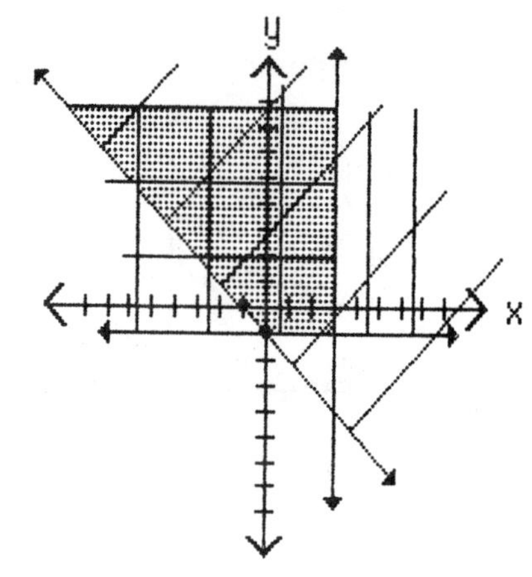

40. $7\sqrt{3}$

41. $\dfrac{3x(2-\sqrt{3x})}{4-3x}$

42. $x = 40$

43. $\dfrac{y^2}{64x^9}$

44. $7 - 5i$

45. $-2 - \dfrac{4}{3}i$

46. $x = 0,\ x = -6$

47. $x = \dfrac{4 \pm \sqrt{13}}{3}$

48. 2 Real roots

49. 19 meters

50. Highest point (2, 11)

Final Test Keys

Form C

1. $\frac{5}{9}$
2. -25
3. 0
4. -19
5. $x = 1,\ x = -5$
6. $22 - 16x$
7. $x = \frac{3}{5}$
8. $2000
9. $\frac{11}{3} < y < \frac{17}{3}$
10. $855
11. $m = \frac{67}{13}$
12. $\frac{-54xy^{11}}{z^5}$
13. $5x^3 + 6x^2 + 2x - 1$
14. $96 - 24x^2$
15. $14x^2 - 9xy + 4y^2$
16. 9 and 11
17. $x^2 + 3x + 9$
18. $2w(w + 7)(w + 2)$
19. $(3y + 5)(3y - 2)$
20. $(2 + y)(2 + m)(2 - m)$
21. $x = \frac{1}{4},\ x = -2$
22. -4 and -11
23. $v = 0,\ v = -2$
24. $3y - 12$
25. $x = 1$
26. 35 mph
27. $m = \frac{2}{3}$
28. No

Form D

1. b) $\frac{6}{7}$
2. d) 65
3. c) 63
4. a) 62
5. d) $x = -\frac{8}{9},\ x = \frac{8}{11}$
6. b) $40x - 96$
7. a) $x = -2$
8. e) None of these
9. d) $-\frac{9}{5} \le x \le \frac{3}{5}$
10. b) $912
11. b) $x = 6$
12. c) $\frac{4b^7c^{13}}{a^9}$
13. a) $11y^3 - 9y^2 - 13y - 7$
14. d) $40x^2 - 129$
15. a) $3x^2 - 26xy + 2y^2$
16. d) 18 and 19
17. c) $y^2 + y + 4$
18. a) $3x^2(x - 12)(x + 4)$
19. d) $(8x - 3)(2x + 3)$
20. e) None of these
21. c) $x = -\frac{3}{2},\ x = 4$
22. a) $25
23. b) $x = 3,\ x = -3$
24. a) $\frac{x^2 + 6x + 5}{(x + 4)(x + 4)}$
25. e) None of these
26. c) 64 mph
27. b) $R = \frac{1}{72}$
28. d) a line passing through the points (7, 2) and (8, -4)

29. Answer:

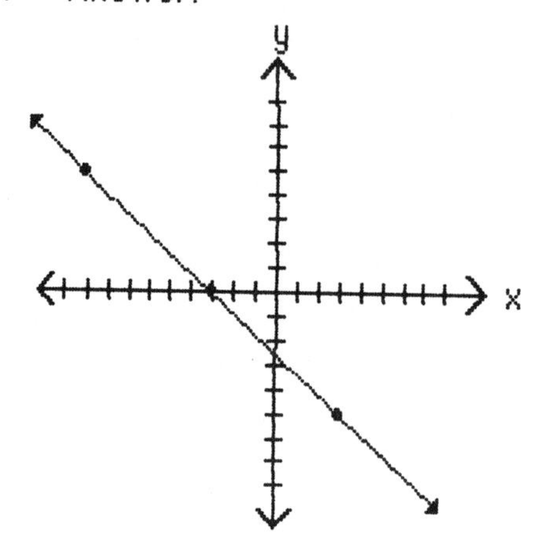

29. c) (0, 1)

30. $y = -\frac{5}{4}x + \frac{21}{4}$

30. b) $y = 2x + 1$

31. Answer:

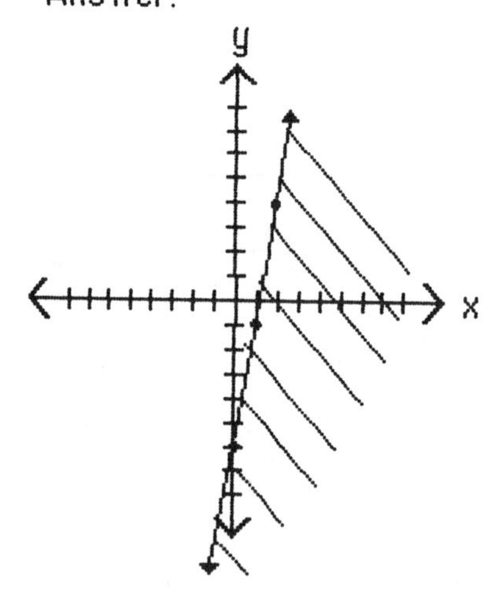

31. a) (-3, -2)

32. $C = 18x + 125$

32. c) $V = -\frac{39}{2}t + 89$

33. all Real numbers

33. a) all Real numbers except 2

34. $f(3) = \frac{49}{9}$

34. d) $f(-2) = -1$

35. $x = 1,\ y = 2$

35. b) $x = \frac{1}{3},\ y = \frac{1}{3}$

36. $x = \frac{8}{3},\ y = \frac{5}{3}$

36. d) $x = -3,\ y = 4$

37. 42 pounds

37. b) 84

38. 6.5 inches

38. e) None of these

39. Answer:

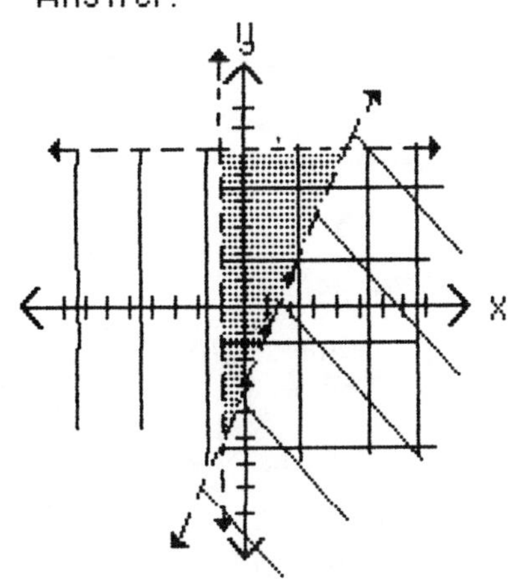

39. a) 1st quadrant

40. $23\sqrt{2}$

40. d) $11\sqrt{5}$

41. $\frac{6 + \sqrt{3}}{11}$

41. c) $\frac{5(5 - \sqrt{y})}{25 - y}$

42. $x = \frac{37}{2}$

42. c) $x = -47$

43. $\frac{1}{243m^9}$

43. e) None of these

44. $7 - 6i$

44. b) $19 + 7i$

45. $-2 + 3i$

45. d) $\frac{5}{16} - \frac{1}{4}i$

46. $x = -2,\ x = 5$

46. a) $x = -6,\ x = -8$

47. $x = -\frac{3}{5} \pm \frac{1}{5}i$

47. d) $x = \frac{3 \pm \sqrt{2}}{4}$

48. two Complex roots

48. a) one Real root

49. 9 inches

49. c) 8 cm.

50. lowest point $(-\frac{3}{4}, -\frac{25}{8})$

50. c) lowest point at (1, 2)

Final Test Keys

Form E

1. c) $-\frac{8}{11}$
2. a) -61
3. d) 62
4. b) -98
5. a) $x = \frac{1}{2},\ x = 2$
6. c) $16 - 24m$
7. b) $x = -3$
8. a) \$12000
9. c) $11 < x < 16$
10. c) \$972
11. d) $y = 4$
12. d) $\frac{13122}{m^4n^{13}}$
13. b) $-8w^3 + 8w^2 + w + 14$
14. c) $180 - 72x$
15. b) $-5m^2 + 10mp - 4p^2$
16. a) -15 and -16
17. d) $3x^2 + 6x + 8 + \frac{12}{x - 2}$
18. b) $2(y - 16)(y - 3)$
19. a) $(4m - 5)(2m + 3)$
20. a) $(2a + b)(a + b)(a - b)$
21. d) $x = -\frac{5}{8},\ x = 6$
22. b) 18 inches
23. c) $x = -\frac{3}{2}$
24. d) $\frac{x^2 - 3x}{(x + 3)(2x - 3)}$
25. a) $x = -12$
26. d) $\frac{20}{3}$
27. c) 429 miles
28. e) None of these
29. d) $(-1, 0)$
30. c) $y = 3x$

Form F

1. d) $\frac{98}{75}$
2. b) 32
3. e) None of these
4. c) -26
5. b) $x = -1,\ x = 9$
6. d) $20x + 57$
7. c) $x = -\frac{13}{8}$
8. b) \$19000
9. d) $3 < x < 5$
10. a) \$828
11. e) None of these
12. a) $\frac{12m^4}{n^5p^7}$
13. c) $-6x^3 - x^2 + 7x + 13$
14. a) $29 + 20x^2$
15. c) $19w^2 - 11wt + 3t^2$
16. b) -21 and -22
17. a) $3x^3 + 3x^2 + 2x + 2$
18. c) $m^3(m - 4)^2$
19. b) $(4x - 3)(5x + 1)$
20. d) $(9a - 4b)(2a - 5)$
21. a) $x = -\frac{4}{5},\ x = 7$
22. c) 5
23. d) $w = 0,\ w = \frac{1}{2}$
24. e) None of these
25. b) $x = 8$
26. a) 6 hours
27. d) 150 rpm
28. a) a line passing through the points $(6, 5)$ and $(8, 7)$
29. a) $(0, 1)$
30. d) $y = \frac{1}{5}x - \frac{27}{5}$

31. b) (3, 2)
32. d) $C = .23x + 110$
33. b) all Real numbers
34. e) None of these
35. c) $x = \frac{1}{2}$, $y = \frac{1}{2}$
36. a) $x = \frac{1}{2}$, $y = 2$
37. c) -7
38. a) 31 inches
39. b) the 2nd quadrant
40. e) None of these
41. d) $\frac{2(4 + \sqrt{2x})}{8 - x}$
42. d) No real solution
43. a) $\frac{729}{15625y}$
44. c) $26 + 7i$
45. a) $4 - i$
46. b) $x = -6$, $x = -10$
47. e) None of these
48. b) 2 Real roots
49. d) 18 feet
50. a) lowest point at (-2, -2)

31. c) (-3, -2)
32. b) $C = 16x + 142$
33. c) all Real numbers except 0 and -3
34. a) $f(-3) = -20$
35. d) (10, 18)
36. b) (3, 7)
37. d) 9 pounds
38. b) 26 inches
39. d) the 4th quadrant
40. a) $6\sqrt{6} - 5\sqrt{2}$
41. a) $\frac{9 + \sqrt{3}}{13}$
42. b) $m = 620$
43. b) $\frac{64m^{5/2}}{729}$
44. d) $18 + 9i$
45. e) None of these
46. c) $x = -7$, $x = -17$
47. a) $x = -2$, $x = \frac{4}{5}$
48. c) 2 Real roots
49. a) 18 inches
50. d) highest point at (-3, 27)

SUGGESTIONS ON HOW TO USE THE DIAGNOSTIC TEST

The questions on this test cover basic skills and concepts, as well as applications of those skills and concepts. The questions cover topics introduced throughout the text. The total score provides evidence of a student's overall mastery of course objectives. Below is a listing of the number of questions for each chapter of Mugridge's ELEMENTARY ALGEBRA:

Chapter 1	Operations and Variables	5
Chapter 2	Linear Equations and Inequalities	6
Chapter 3	Exponents and Polynomials	5
Chapter 4	Factoring	5
Chapter 5	Rational Expressions	6
Chapter 6	Linear Equations and their Graphs	6
Chapter 7	Systems of Equations	4
Chapter 8	Roots and Radicals	4
Chapter 9	Quadratic Equations	4

Although the questions relating to each of these chapters are insufficient to provide detailed diagnostic information, a student's performance in each area pinpoints strengths and weaknesses, and can facilitate student placement at the appropriate point in the text in an individually paced course. A high score (36 or better) on this test would suggest that the student be placed in the next course, depending on the distribution of incorrect answers. It is generally recommended that students work through topics in which they answered more than one question incorrectly.

The test can also be administered as a pre-test before the course begins and as a post-test at the end of the course to measure growth. By analyzing group performance at the end of the course, instructors can evaluate the extent to which the group has learned particular concepts.

ELEMENTARY ALGEBRA TEST

45 Questions

Directions: Solve each question and select the best of the answer choices provided.

1. For what value of k is $-3k = 12$?

(A) -9
(B) -4
(C) 4
(D) 9

2. Kathy ate $\frac{1}{6}$ of a pizza and Jan ate $\frac{1}{3}$ of it. What fraction of the pizza was left?

(A) $\frac{1}{9}$

(B) $\frac{1}{4}$

(C) $\frac{1}{3}$

(D) $\frac{1}{2}$

3. Each of the following is a factor of 24 EXCEPT

(A) 18
(B) 12
(C) 8
(D) 4

4. $\sqrt{64 + 36} =$

(A) 6
(B) 8
(C) 10
(D) 14

5. Based on the figure above, approximately what is the value of $x + y$?

(A) -1

(B) $-\frac{1}{2}$

(C) $\frac{1}{2}$

(D) 1

6. $2^3 \times 2^5 =$

(A) 2^8
(B) 2^{15}
(C) 4^8
(D) 4^{15}

7. Which of the following is equal to five times the sum of x and 3 ?

(A) $5x + 3$
(B) $5x + 8$
(C) $5x + 15$
(D) $15x$

8. $|-5| - |-2| =$

(A) -7
(B) -3
(C) 3
(D) 7

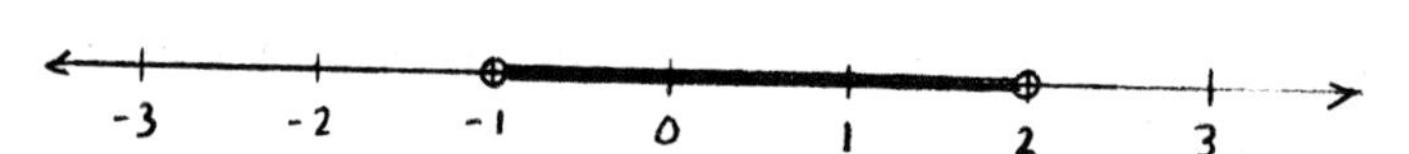

9. The graph above represents the solution of which of the following inequalities?

(A) $-1 < x < 2$
(B) $-1 > x > 2$
(C) $x > -1$ or $x > 2$
(D) $x < -1$ and $x > 2$

10. $(2x^3)^0 =$

(A) 0
(B) 1
(C) 2
(D) 6

11. Each of the following is true EXCEPT

(A) $\frac{-8}{-2} = -4$

(B) $\frac{8}{-2} = -4$

(C) $8(-2) = -16$

(D) $(-8)(-2) = 16$

12. $(2x - 5)^2 =$

(A) $4x^2 - 25$
(B) $4x^2 + 25$
(C) $4x^2 - 20x + 25$
(D) $4x^2 - 10x + 25$

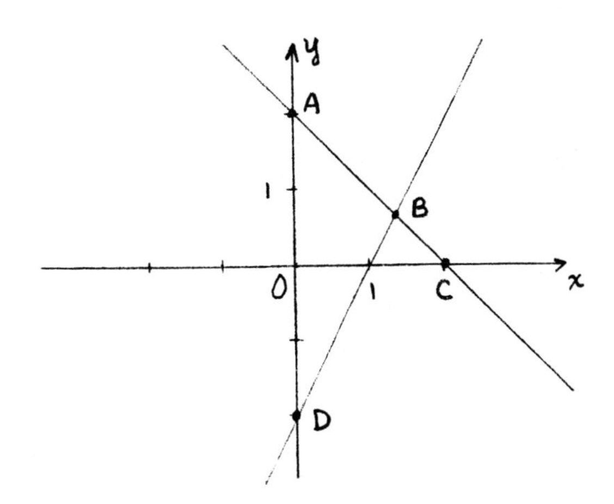

13. Which lettered point represents the solution of the equations graphed above?

(A) A
(B) B
(C) C
(D) D

14. What is the simplified form of $3x - 7(x - 2)$?

(A) $4x - 9$
(B) $-4x - 14$
(C) $-4x - 2$
(D) $-4x + 14$

15. What is the value of $x^2 - 3x + 1$ when $x = 5$?

(A) -4
(B) 11
(C) 13
(D) 27

16. Two more than three-fourths of a number is three. What is the number?

(A) $\frac{4}{3}$

(B) $\frac{3}{2}$

(C) $\frac{2}{3}$

(D) $\frac{3}{4}$

17. For what value of t is the expression $\frac{t}{2t - 1}$ undefined?

(A) $-\frac{1}{2}$

(B) 0

(C) $\frac{1}{2}$

(D) 1

18. A store is selling a shirt at a 20 percent discount. The discounted price is what fraction of the original price?

(A) $\frac{1}{5}$

(B) $\frac{1}{4}$

(C) $\frac{3}{4}$

(D) $\frac{4}{5}$

19. Which of the following is a factor of $2k^2 - 11k - 21$?

(A) $2k - 3$
(B) $k + 7$
(C) $2k + 3$
(D) $2k - 7$

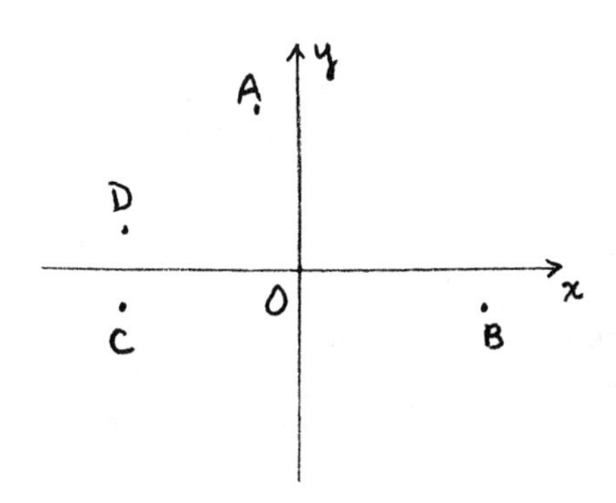

20. Which letterd point above could have coordinates $(4, -1)$?

(A) A
(B) B
(C) C
(D) D

21. If $f(x) = x(x - 1)(x - 3)$, what is the value of $f(0) + f(1)$?

(A) 0
(B) 1
(C) 2
(D) 3

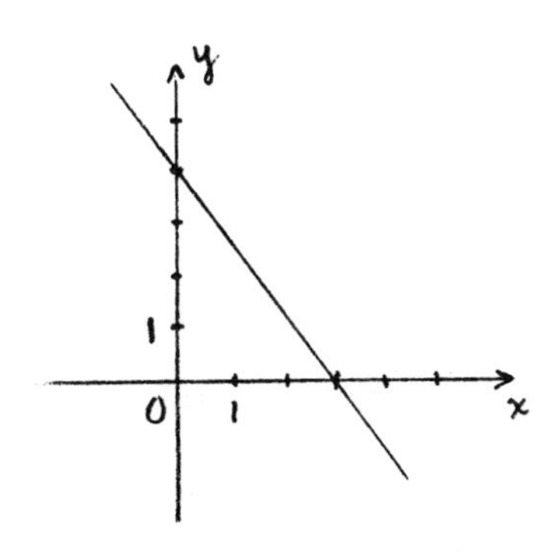

22. Which is an equation of the line graphed above?

(A) $4x + 3y = 12$
(B) $3x + 4y = 12$
(C) $3x + 4y = 7$
(D) $x + y = 7$

23. For any number n, which of the following is equal to the product of the number that is 2 less than n and the number that is 2 more than n ?

(A) $n^2 - 2$
(B) $n^2 - 4$
(C) $n^2 - 4n + 4$
(D) $n^2 - 4n - 4$

24. What are the coordinates of the point where the graph of $y = (x - 2)^2$ crosses the y-axis?

(A) (0, 2)
(B) (0, 4)
(C) (0, −2)
(D) (0, −4)

25. $\left(\frac{2}{3}\right)^{-2} =$

(A) $-\frac{4}{3}$

(B) $-\frac{4}{9}$

(C) $\frac{4}{9}$

(D) $\frac{9}{4}$

26. The sides of a triangle are consecutive integers. If the perimeter of the triangle is 72, what is the length of the longest side?

(A) 23

(B) 24

(C) 25

(D) 26

27. $\frac{2x}{y} \div \frac{8x^2}{y^3} =$

(A) $\frac{y^2}{4x}$

(B) $\frac{y^2}{4}$

(C) $\frac{4x}{y^2}$

(D) $\frac{16x^2}{y^4}$

28. Which of the following ordered pairs (x,y) satisfies the equation $2x - y = 0$?

(A) (2, −4)

(B) (3, 6)

(C) (4, 2)

(D) (4, −2)

29. Which of the following is NOT a factor of $3x^2 + 15x + 18$?

(A) 3

(B) $x + 1$

(C) $x + 2$

(D) $x + 3$

30. $\sqrt{32} - \sqrt{2} =$

(A) 4

(B) 8

(C) $3\sqrt{2}$

(D) $5\sqrt{2}$

31. $$\begin{cases} 2x - y = 6 \\ x + 3y = -3 \end{cases}$$

In the solution of the system of equations above, what is the value of x ?

(A) $\frac{2}{3}$

(B) 1

(C) $\frac{9}{5}$

(D) $\frac{15}{7}$

32. The product of two positive numbers is 20 and the difference between them is 8. What is the sum of these two numbers?

(A) 9

(B) 12

(C) 14

(D) 28

33. Which of the following is a root of the equation $(x - 5)^2 = 16$?

(A) 1

(B) 3

(C) 8

(D) 11

34. If $x = -\frac{1}{2}$, what is the value of 64^x ?

(A) −32

(B) −8

(C) $\frac{1}{32}$

(D) $\frac{1}{8}$

35. If $y = 3x$ and $y = x - 8$, what must be the value of x ?

(A) −4

(B) −2

(C) 2

(D) 4

36. $\frac{5}{3k} - \frac{7}{6k}$

(A) $-\frac{2}{3k}$

(B) $\frac{1}{2k}$

(C) $\frac{1}{3k}$

(D) $\frac{1}{6k}$

37. $\frac{9x^2 + 3x}{3x} =$

(A) $6x$

(B) $9x^2$

(C) $9x^2 + 1$

(D) $3x + 1$

38. What are the solutions of the equation $m^3 - m = 0$?

(A) 0 only

(B) 0 and 1 only

(C) 0 and −1 only

(D) 0, −1, and 1

39. What is the y-intercept of the graph of $x - 2y = 12$?

(A) 12

(B) 6

(C) −6

(D) −12

40. For what value of t does

$\frac{1}{t} + \frac{1}{6} = \frac{1}{4}$?

(A) 12

(B) 2

(C) $\frac{1}{2}$

(D) $\frac{1}{12}$

41. The variable T varies directly as the square of r. When $r = 2$ the value of T is 2. If $r = 8$, what is the value of T ?

(A) 4

(B) 8

(C) 16

(D) 32

42. What is the value of k if the graph of $y = kx - 3$ passes through the point (1,2) ?

(A) −1

(B) 1

(C) 5

(D) 7

43. $\sqrt[3]{-27x^6} =$

(A) $-9x^3$

(B) $-9x^2$

(C) $-3x^3$

(D) $-3x^2$

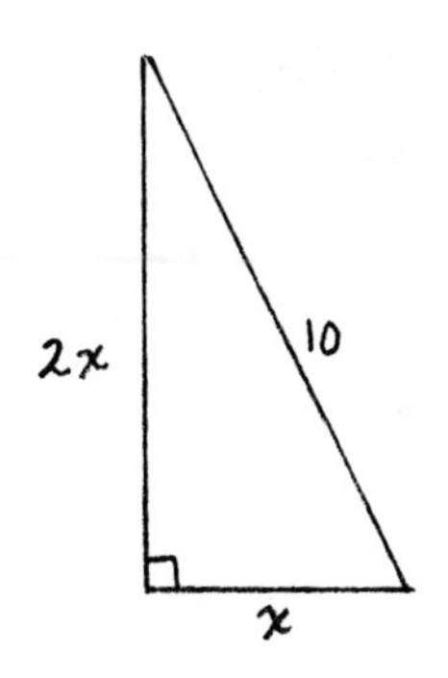

44. For the right triangle above, what is the value of x

(A) $\sqrt{10}$

(B) $\sqrt{20}$

(C) $\sqrt{30}$

(D) $\sqrt{50}$

45. Which of the following is one root of the equation $z^2 - 4z + 5 = 0$?

(A) $4 + i$

(B) $4 - i$

(C) $2 + i$

(D) $1 + i$

END OF TEST

DIAGNOSTIC TEST

ANSWER KEY

1. B (2.3)	16. A (2.4)	31. D (7.2)
2. D (1.1)	17. C (5.1)	32. B (7.4)
3. A (4.1)	18. D (2.6)	33. A (9.1)
4. C (8.1)	19. C (4.3)	34. D (8.6)
5. D (1.4)	20. B (6.1)	35. A (7.3)
6. A (3.1)	21. A (6.7)	36. B (5.4)
7. C (2.1)	22. A (6.4)	37. D (5.1)
8. C (1.3)	23. B (3.7)	38. D (4.6)
9. A (2.7)	24. B (9.6)	39. C (6.2)
10. B (3.1)	25. D (3.2)	40. A (5.6)
11. A (1.5)	26. C (4.7)	41. D (5.8)
12. C (3.6)	27. A (5.2)	42. C (6.2)
13. B (7.1)	28. B (6.2)	43. D (8.2)
14. D (2.1)	29. B (4.2)	44. B (9.1)
15. B (1.6)	30. C (8.3)	45. C (9.4)

Note: Numbers in parentheses are chapter and subheading references.